NASA Engineers and the Age of Apollo

NASA SP-4104

JUN 0 5 1992

NASA Engineers and the Age of Apollo

Sylvia Doughty Fries

The NASA History Series

National Aeronautics and Space Administration
Scientific and Technical Information Program
Washington, DC   1992

Library of Congress Cataloging-in-Publication Data

NASA engineers and the age of Apollo / [compiled by] Sylvia
Doughty Fries.
      p.   cm. -- (NASA SP ; 4104)
    Includes bibliographical references.
    1. United States. National Aeronautics and Space Administration--
Officials and employees--Biography.   2. Aeronautical engineers--United
States--Biography.   3. Project Apollo (U.S.)   I. Fries, Sylvia Doughty.
II. United States. National Aeronautics and Space Administration.
III. Series.
TL521.312.N365   1991
629.1'092'273--dc20
[B]   90-39761
                                            CIP

For sale by the U.S. Government Printing Office
Superintendent of Documents, Mail Stop: SSOP, Washington, DC 20402-9328
ISBN 0-16-036174-5

Contents

Preface

The twentieth anniversary of the landing of an American on the surface of the Moon occasioned many bittersweet reflections. Sweet was the celebration of the historic event itself, and sweet to space enthusiasts was President George Bush's call for a new era of human space exploration — back to the Moon and on to Mars. Bitter, for those same enthusiasts, was the knowledge that during the twenty intervening years much of the national consensus that launched this country on its first lunar adventure had evaporated, and foraging for funds to keep going seemed to have become a major preoccupation of the old guard that had watched over that adventure.

Less apparent was the fact that the final act in another human drama was taking place: a generation of men and women who had defined their lives to a large extent in terms of this nation's epochal departure from Earth's surface was taking its leave of the program they had built. Would they, or their work, be remembered? Would anyone care? As the historian for the National Aeronautics and Space Administration, I had the responsibility of attempting — attempting, because the task could never be fully done — to capture the essence of their lives and careers. Those who worked "on the front lines" of what I have called, after William James, a "moral equivalent of war," have had their quirks and genius memorialized in the agency's lore. Many have had their organizational and technical trials recorded in the narrative histories produced by NASA. More recently, and with great success, Charles Murray and Catherine Bly Cox, in *Apollo: The Race to the Moon* (Simon and Schuster, 1989), have combined the human and technical sagas of the designers, flight operators, and project managers who made Apollo happen to weave an arresting tale of a unique moment in our history.

But history also gathers up in its sweep many ordinary people, not only those who give orders and do combat at the front lines, but those who slug it out and otherwise endure in the trenches. If our memory of the Apollo era neglected those ordinary people, that memory would be incomplete, and we would have done an injustice to the true nature of life over time. Thus, the lives and careers laid out on the pages that follow have been drawn from hours of conversation with a variety of people: they are my best approximation of the "average" NASA engineer of the Apollo age; some did remarkable things, while others just filled in the pieces. It soon became apparent, however, that even the most "average" of them were part of a story that was larger than the Apollo story itself, much less NASA's story. What happened to them over the course of their careers was part of the undertow of what happened to this country during the post-World War II era and the 1960s.

This book would not have been possible without the willing and good-natured participation of fifty-one NASA engineers who gave freely and openly of themselves during my extensive interviews. It is to them that this book owes its first and greatest debt. Not all have had their stories fully retold here, simply because several had similar stories to tell. Nathaniel B. Cohen, my supervisor at NASA when this project was conceived, supported it enthusiastically. A veteran of one of NASA's original aeronautical research laboratories, Nat Cohen has been a firm believer (to my benefit) that to manage a scientific or scholarly program well, one must continue to be an active researcher. Nat also patiently read the first draft of the manuscript, trying to save me from embarrassing errors here, taking issue with me there, but always in an encouraging way. A. Michal McMahon, who served as associate historian in the NASA History Division for two years during the early phase of this project, did half of the interviewing and contributed much through his insightful and well-informed observations on the engineering profession, interview topics, and how the interviews might best be interpreted. Lee D. Saegesser, NASA archivist, to whom virtually every researcher of space history owes a debt, tirelessly found and delivered to my desk mountains of folders and publications without which I would have been unable to fill in the details that are typically lost in interviews. Marion Davis prepared many of the transcripts, edited them, and provided bibliographic support. Patricia Shephard, administrative assistant for the NASA History Division, stood watch over my time in a way that would be the envy of any corporate executive.

Gil Roth, Carl Praktish, David Williamson (all NASA veterans) and Richard P. Hallion read the manuscript and returned detailed and stimulating comments and criticisms, as did Howard E. McCurdy. Howard's own study of NASA's evolving organizational culture led him into some of the same thickets through which I was traveling; he has shared hours of conversations on the subject of NASA, federal bureaucracies, American politics, and American society in the postwar world. Many other colleagues responded cheerfully to questions over the telephone, or reviewed portions of the manuscript. If, notwithstanding their help, errors remain, only I am to blame.

Sylvia D. Fries

Acknowledgments

My most heartfelt acknowledgement I have reserved for the last: this is to the fifty-one men and women of NASA's Apollo era engineers who gave generously of their time and something of themselves so that their experiences might be shared with others. It is to them that this book, with deep appreciation, is dedicated.

One is never satisfied with a portrait of a person one knows.

Johann Wolfgang von Goethe
Elective Affinities,
Book II, Chapter 2

Introduction

On July 20, 1969 millions of television screens captured a new image in the iconography of American history. To the familar icons that stirred patriotic sentiment — the fiercely protective American eagle, the elegantly scripted parchment of the Declaration of Independence, the solemn countenance of George Washington, and a majestically waving Stars and Stripes lofted over outstretched hands on the island of Iwo Jima — a generation of Americans added a truly new world image: a speckled black and white television picture of a man clothed in flexible tubes of white, with a reflective sphere over his head, springing over the alien, gray surface of our nearest planetary neighbor, thereon to plant a small, vacuum-stilled American flag.

As with all icons, what brought this image into being was somewhat less than the associated rhetoric claimed for it. The rhetoric with which John F. Kennedy introduced his challenge to the nation — "before this decade is out, of landing a man on the moon and returning him safely to the earth" — is unmistakable in the meaning intended for the event: the United States was "engaged in a world-wide struggle in which we bear a heavy burden to preserve and promote the ideals that we share with all mankind, or have alien ideals forced upon them." However, for the ordinary engineers who toiled for two decades so that Neil Armstrong could one day step onto the Moon — the culmination of the nation's Apollo program — the event turned out to mean something different than rhetoric promised it would be.

The text of Kennedy's May 25, 1961 "Special Message to the Congress on Urgent National Needs" is replete with allusions to the Cold War and the Communist bloc's putative campaign to prevail in "a contest of will and purpose as well as force and violence — a battle for minds and souls as well as lives and territory." The "great battleground for the defense and expansion of freedom today is the whole southern half of the globe — Asia, Latin America, Africa and the Middle East — the lands of the rising peoples." The notion — which appears toward the end of Kennedy's Special Message — of landing an American on the Moon before the end of the decade, was offered as the winning climax of an epochal struggle against "the adversaries of freedom [who] plan to consolidate their territory — to exploit, to control, and finally to destroy the hopes of the world's newest nations; and *they have ambition to do it before the end of this decade*" [emphasis added]. As the 1960s drew to a close, the nation that stood for freedom (that, said Kennedy, was what the United States was) would be called to account.[1] The Apollo program was John F. Kennedy's "moral equivalent of war." Sharing so much else with Theodore Roosevelt, Kennedy found in the Apollo program what the earlier president had found in the Panama Canal.[2]

To be sure, the sight of Neil Armstrong taking his "giant leap for mankind" was a dramatic affirmation of the power of modern technology over nature, as well as the more timeless qualities of human questing and courage. In retrospect it was also an epiphenomenon, a shadow cast by a more fundamental transition in American life. This is the story less of heroes than of a generation of engineers who made Apollo possible. It is thus the story of the men and women who stood where the shadow was deepest. Their story is told largely in their own words, and it tells of the unraveling of the simpler notions of personal success and national purpose that had given common meaning to the lives of their parents.

When the Soviet Union successfully launched the first man-made orbiting satellite, Sputnik I, in October 1957, the Eisenhower administration and Congress promptly created the National Aeronautics and Space Administration (NASA) to orchestrate the United States' peaceful response to the Soviet challenge. NASA officially opened for business on October 1, 1958 with a complement of nearly eight thousand paid employees transferred from the National Advisory Committee for Aeronautics (the NACA). Established in 1915 by a rider attached to that year's congressional Naval Appropriations Act, the NACA had conducted research in aerodynamics and aircraft structures and propulsion systems for both industrial and military clients for forty-three years.[3] The NACA was informally structured and overseen by its main committee and various technical subcommittees; its engineering research was done largely by civil servants at Langley Aeronautical Laboratory, Hampton, Va. (established 1917), Ames Aeronautical Laboratory, Moffett Field, Calif. (established 1939), the Flight Research Center, Muroc Dry Lake, Calif. (established 1946; renamed Dryden Flight Research Center in 1976), and the Lewis Flight Propulsion Laboratory, Cleveland, Ohio (established 1940).

The NACA's closest precursors were the research laboratories of the Department of Agriculture (established 1862), the National Bureau of Standards (established 1901), and the Marine Hospital and Public Health Service (established 1902). Not until the end of World War II would Congress create a comparable institution, the Atomic Energy Commission (established 1946), which, however, relied not on civil servants but on contracts with private organizations created to carry out its research programs.

What distinguished the NACA was the ethos that came to permeate its laboratories. With its emphasis on technical competence for engineering research, evaluation of work by technical peers, and an intimate, free-wheeling working environment thought conducive to engineering innovation, the NACA's research culture was poorly equipped to adjust to the bureaucratic controls of federal administration that began to coalesce in the 1940s. Centralized administrative procedures, hierarchical organizations, standardized job classifications, and tenure as a determinant of place and influence — such mechanisms of public administrative control were resisted by the NACA, which found itself in intense competition with the powerful Department of Defense (established 1947) and threatened by the intrusive politics that accompanied expanded congressional oversight.[4]

The NACA was thus transformed in 1958 into the federal civilian space establishment with a renewed and much enlarged mission. It began with the 7966 paid employees transferred from the NACA's headquarters in Washington, D.C. and its four research centers; by the end of 1960 its personnel rolls had nearly doubled to over 16,000. The principal increases occurred largely at NASA Headquarters (where personnel more than tripled), and with the addition to the agency of the Army Ballistic Missile Agency (renamed the George C. Marshall Space Flight Center) and the new Goddard Space Flight Center in Beltsville, Md. and Wallops Station on Wallops Island, Va. The Jet Propulsion Laboratory of the California Institute of Technology, a contractor-owned and -operated facility involved in rocket research since 1936, was transferred from the U.S. Army to NASA in 1958. By the end of 1960 the old NACA laboratories and Marshall Space Flight Center accounted for 49 percent and 33 percent, respectively, of NASA's employees. (The Manned Spacecraft Center in Houston, Tex. was added in 1961 and the John F. Kennedy Space Center at Cape Canaveral, Fla. in 1962.)[5]

Thus a little over 80 percent of NASA's technical core — its engineers and scientists — during its first quarter century was acquired during the flush first days of the space program. A significant portion of that cohort held within its corporate memory the experience of working with the NACA, the Army Ballistic Missile Agency (ABMA), and the organizations from which Goddard Space Flight Center had drawn much of its personnel [the Naval Research Laboratory (NRL) and the Naval Ordnance Laboratory (NOL)].[6] Each group would bring with it a well-established culture — the NACA and NRL groups, the culture of in-house engineering research and science, and the ABMA group, the in-house technical development culture of the Army's arsenal system. (Engineers who worked on NASA's unpiloted interplanetary science programs at the Jet Propulsion Laboratory have not been included in this study because their careers are as likely to have been the consequence of working for the California Institute of Technology as for NASA.)

In time the engineers from these communities would experience the gradual erosion of the institutional discretion and the ethos of in-house technical competence that had characterized their previous careers, ultimately and inexorably defeated by the new organization and policies Congress imposed on them. First, in the future they would work for a centrally and hierarchically managed organization, split into two tiers to accommodate functionally disparate research centers and program offices. Second, their executive leadership would be chosen for them on the strength of political connections and managerial, as well as technical, experience. As experienced public administrators, that leadership would, and did, yield to the scrutiny and controls imposed by the Bureau of the Budget, the Civil Service Commission,[7] and the congressional authorization process. Third, the encroachments of managerial competence and political salesmanship on technical competence as standards for the new organization's success would reach down into the very heart and soul of the agency's work.

The ideology of the Republican presidential administration under which NASA first took form militated against the creation of a large government establishment, requiring instead that as much work as possible be contracted out to the private sector. The notion of contracting out was, of course, not new with the Eisenhower administration. Since the early nineteenth century the military services had procured goods and services from private suppliers. What the military had not wholly relied on commercial suppliers for was ordnance — hence the U.S. Army's scattered armories, or "arsenal system." The experience of World War II suggested that effective innovation in weapons technology can make the difference between victory and defeat. In the twentieth century innovation in weapons technology was no mere Edisonian enterprise; it required systematic, institutionalized research and development programs.

Lacking a general research and development or production capacity of its own, the federal government has thus, throughout the nineteenth and early twentieth centuries, periodically commandeered facilities in place in the private sector, but it commandeered them in such a way that the corporate integrity of private enterprises and chances for legitimate profit would not be compromised. So it was with NASA when it was given Kennedy's challenge to land a man on the Moon and return him safely: NASA would buy the know-how and the hardware it needed from industry; to ensure the flow of scientific knowledge into space technology, it would prime the pumps of university science and engineering departments around the country.[8]

The effectiveness of the operating structure the government chose for NASA, as well as its elaborate research and development procurement machinery (borrowed from the Department of Defense) would depend on the ease with which NASA's technical staff adapted to them. But that staff had been accustomed to working in the relatively autonomous, decentralized in-house research laboratories of the NACA, the NRL, or the ABMA "arsenal" that would produce the Saturn launch vehicle. The potential for cultural resistance among the NACA and ABMA engineers was not mitigated by the expansion of NASA's personnel during the next five years, for the "new men" would take their cues from those who had helped to establish the agency and, in the process, were establishing themselves. To have forged such a heterogenous cluster of research and development communities, sharing only a strong in-house culture, should have daunted the greatest administrative genius.

The NASA Apollo era engineers interviewed for this profile were selected by two methods, peer selection and random selection.[9] Both were used in order to verify whether the "typical" Apollo era engineer, as recognized by the agency's leadership, was in fact typical — as measured by a random sampling. To develop a candidate interviewee list by peer selection, NASA's second highest ranking executive[10] asked the agency's leadership in 1984 to nominate for our profile those individuals they believed were the most "representative" of the Apollo generation of NASA engineers. In all probability, those whom NASA's current leadership regarded as "representative" would embody those personal and professional traits which were most important to recognition and success within the agency. The 621 nominations received provided a small subgroup — the "nominee" group — which contained a higher preponderance of older men, top-ranking managers, individuals whose highest degrees were in engineering, and men who had entered NASA before 1960 (see Appendix B). Since almost 95 percent of NASA personnel when the agency opened its doors in 1958 came from the research centers of the NACA, engineers who shared the NACA experience contributed significantly to the composition of NASA's leadership in the 1980s.

A second, much larger population consisted of the 9875 engineers who entered the agency between 1958 and 1970 and were still with NASA in 1984 when this study was begun. Absent reliable or comprehensive data about engineers who left NASA during the period, we had to limit that demographic population to those who, because they were still with the agency in 1984, could be identified and located.[11] Our demographic analysis of NASA's Apollo era engineers was also designed to identify three lesser cohorts: (1) those who entered NASA between 1958 and 1960, the eve of President Kennedy's manned lunar landing challenge; (2) those who entered between 1961 and 1965, when the agency underwent the massive expansion necessary to carry out the Apollo program; and (3) those who entered between 1966 and the end of 1970, a five-year period that opened as NASA's peak employment year and ended with a precipitous decline in agency resources (see Appendix B; NASA's annual budget plummeted from $5 billion in 1967 to slightly over $3 billion in 1974, not accounting for inflation.)

This profile is thus necessarily restricted to those engineers who, for whatever reason, preferred to work for NASA. Fifty-one engineers from NASA Headquarters and its seven principal installations[12] were selected for interviews at random from each of four groups: the "nominee" group and the three cohorts that comprised the "total population" of engineers who came to work for NASA between 1958 and 1970.[13] None declined what was most often received as an opportunity to tell one's own story and thus surface from the depths of anonymity to which bureaucracy consigns most of its workers. The interviews clearly suggested that the career experiences of the "nominee" group were substantially similar to those of the "total population" *other than* what I have noted above, which is indicated by a fairly straightforward demographic analysis (see Appendix B).

NASA personnel classifications have not and do not distinguish between scientists and engineers; however, secondary breakdowns of our total population of 9875 by highest degree fields and occupational categories *were* possible. These revealed that, of the aggregate numbers of scientists and engineers, an average of 60 to 75 percent have been working in occupations classified as engineering (although increasingly their actual work would be engineering contract monitors). Management, and a miscellany of non-aerospace technical occupations, claimed the rest. The interviews strongly suggested that engineers who drifted into management or non-technical jobs nevertheless began their NASA careers as engineers.

The historian or journalist who wants to convey the experiences of others in their own words acquires the task of composing a coherent narrative out of the often broken and disorganized utterances of persons not always accustomed to talking about themselves. Only after many hours of listening can one begin to glean with any confidence the "truth" of a personal experience, distinguishing the perspectives of the subject and the observer. This is especially true of many of these engineers who, often by their own admission, are uncomfortable in a universe of words and feelings. Any solution to this problem must be faithful to the nature of the material itself, as well as the need to convey in an intelligible textual form the composite lives of numerous individuals whose aggregate experiences may not necessarily lend themselves to generalization.

My own solution has been to follow a few principles in attempting to convey the substance of these interviews. First, and above all else, I have attempted to let these engineers speak for themselves as much as possible. Second, I as writer have intervened only as necessary to sustain the narrative, establish an historical setting, or insert clarifications such as names, places, or dates. In some cases an engineer's own clarifications, drawn from the interview itself, have been interspersed among his or her own words. Every effort has been made to convey through punctuation the rhythms of the original speech. Ellipses have been used liberally to indicate when the actual sequence of a subject's speech has been broken or reordered. Finally, the text that unfolds from an engineer's own words has been "cleaned up" only to the extent of removing the "ums" and "ands" and rhetorical "buts" that litter the speech of all of us. Strict grammarians might have rewritten the original more than I have chosen to.

The chapters that follow do not necessarily incorporate the observations or reflections of every person interviewed on every single subject. Predictably, some engineers told good stories and others had few stories that they could or wanted to tell. Some simply had more interesting lives than others. Those whose comments were selected for inclusion were chosen because the experiences they related were relatively typical — that is, other engineers could have told of similar experiences. Occasionally an engineer's observations were selected precisely because they were atypical; in those instances the reader is alerted to the exceptional nature of what follows. All of the engineers we asked to interview not only agreed to talk with us, but were as open about their experiences as their apparent individual levels of personal reticence seemed to allow. Although none requested anonymity, pseudonyms have been used throughout the text that follows (however, actual place names are used).

While the sequence of the following personal accounts follows the paths of various technological problems that were overcome during the emergence of the space program in the 1960s, these chapters do not pretend to provide an historical survey of aerospace technology in NASA during the period. Moreover, the chapters rely on recollections, which can be imprecise or incorrect. For example, in the early years of NASA, competition was rife among the engineers of the old NACA centers for priority in the solution of previously intractable engineering problems. This competition among the NACA (and after 1958, NASA) centers has remained an important ingredient in the organizational life of NASA. At the research level the competition has been considered salutary; it kept the engineers "on their toes." Thus any claims to priority in these chapters should be held suspect; such claims are difficult to prove or disprove. Modern institutionalized research is often an anonymous process. For the scientist or engineer, "who discovered it first" may be the most pressing historical question — the priority of discovery normally documented in dates of publications or patent awards. For the historian, how the discovery occurred, and its significance, may be the more salient question.

A final caution about what follows: I have tried to translate much of the engineering work into terms that could be readily followed by readers whose prior knowledge lies elsewhere than engineering. Thus certain technological puzzles and developments have been simplified — perhaps too much for more technically inclined readers.

The explosion of the Space Shuttle Challenger over Cape Canaveral on the crisp, blue morning of January 29, 1986 almost devastated NASA. Subject to seemingly relentless critical press comment, numerous studies, and the unflattering scrutiny of the Presidential Commission on the Space Shuttle Challenger Accident headed by former New York State prosecuting attorney and Secretary of State William P. Rogers, the agency struggled through the two plus years it took to return the Shuttle to flight. Did this event color our interviews, which spanned the Challenger accident? Interviews at NASA Headquarters, Ames Research Center, and Johnson Space Center were conducted before January 1986. Engineers at Kennedy Space Center, Goddard Space Flight Center, Langley Research Center, Lewis Research Center, and Marshall Space Flight Center were interviewed through 1987. We took some care in the post-January 1986 interviews not to focus on the accident. Its role as a variable affecting the content of these interviews remains an imponderable, since most of the subjects explored in the interviews appear to be largely independent of the immediate issues raised by the accident. Readers may, however, want to keep in mind the time period during which interviews at particular NASA locations took place as they reflect on the observations that appear in the following chapters.

---

[1] The bi-polar world that had dominated American foreign policy since 1945 persisted in Kennedy's rhetoric, the "free world's" side under the young Democratic president to be shored up by an ambitious liberal agenda: increased spending for economic recovery at home, "prudent fiscal standards," increased economic and military assistance abroad and especially in the Third World, increased funding for NATO's conventional forces and "our own military and intelligence shield," added funding for civil defense, nuclear disarmament, and then the trip to the Moon — all "to win the battle that is now going on around the world between freedom and tyranny." See John F. Kennedy, "Special Message to the Congress on Urgent National Needs," May 25, 1961, in *Public Papers of the Presidents of the United States: John F. Kennedy, 1961* (Washington, D.C.: U.S. Government Printing Office, 1962), p. 396-406.

[2] The phrase "moral equivalent of war" was used by the American philosopher William James, who argued that mankind had evolved into a creature whose pugnacious instinct was so deeply ingrained that he required formidable obstacles to channel his energies into socially useful purposes (William James, "The Moral Equivalent of War," in *Essays on Faith and Morals* (New York, 1947). Theodore Roosevelt was a student of James's at Harvard College. See David McCullough, *The Path Between the Seas: The Creation of the Panama Canal, 1870-1914* (New York, 1977).

[3] For a history of the NACA, see Alex Roland, *Model Research: The National Advisory Committee for Aeronautics, 1915-1958*, NASA SP-4103 (Washington, D.C.: U.S. Government Printing Office, 1985), and James R. Hansen, *Engineer in Charge: A History of the Langley Aeronautical Laboratory, 1917-1958*, NASA SP-4305 (Washington, D.C.: U.S. Government Printing Office, 1987).

[4] For a detailed account of the NACA's (and later NASA's) struggles with the growth of centralized federal administrative policies and organizations (e.g., the Bureau of the Budget, the Civil Service Commission, and congressional authorization and appropriations procedures), see Roland, loc. cit., and Nancy Jane Petrovic, "Design for Decline: Executive Management and the Eclipse of NASA," Ph.D. Dissertation, University of Maryland, 1982 (Ann Arbor, Michigan: University Microfilms International, 1982).

[5] The 157 personnel who had been working on the Navy's Project Vanguard, which became the nucleus of the Goddard Space Flight Center (established 1959), were transferred to NASA in 1958 from one of the Navy's own in-house research laboratories, the Naval Research Laboratory. They were soon joined by 63 more who had been working for the Naval Research Laboratory's Space Sciences and Theoretical divisions. The next large group to transfer to NASA was the 5367 civil servants from the U.S. Army's Ballistic Missile Agency (ABMA) at Redstone Arsenal,

Huntsville, Ala. The ABMA had been essentially an in-house operation. The youngest NASA installations, the Manned Spacecraft Center (established 1961 and renamed Johnson Space Center in 1973) and Kennedy Space Center (established 1962), were initially staffed by personnel from Langley Research Center and the ABMA.

[6] Robert L. Rosholt, *An Administrative History of NASA, 1958-1963*, NASA SP-4101 (Washington, D.C.: U.S. Government Printing Office, 1966). Source for personnel data: *NASA Historical Data Book, 1958-1968. Vol. I: NASA Resources*, NASA SP-4012 (Washington, D.C.: U.S. Government Printing Office, 1976); NASA Pocket Statistics (Washington, D.C.: U.S. Government Printing Office, January 1971); Personnel Analysis and Evaluation Office, NASA Headquarters, Washington, D.C., May 1986. Personnel data analysis available in the NASA History Office.

[7] The Bureau of the Budget became the Office of Management and Budget (OMB) in 1970, while the Civil Service Commission became the Office of Personnel Management (OPM) in 1979.

[8] The growth of the complex and intricate devices by which the U.S. government has tried to procure research and development as well as standard goods and services is traced in Clarence H. Danhof, *Government Contracting and Technological Change* (Washington, D.C.: The Brookings Institution, 1968) and Merton J. Peck and Frederick M. Scherer, *The Weapons Acquisition Process: An Economic Analysis* (Boston: Harvard University Press, 1962). For an informed, incisive, and humorous view of the outcome of federal advanced technical systems procurement practices, see Norman R. Augustine, *Augustine's Laws, And Major System Development Programs*, rev. (New York: American Institute of Aeronautics and Astronautics, 1983).

[9] Much of what we know in any systematic fashion about engineers (or scientists) comes from studies combining demographic analysis, oral histories, and social theory—studies such as Ann Roe's *The Making of a Scientist* (Greenwood Press, 1953), Robert Perucci's and Joel E. Gerstl's *Profession Without Community: Engineers in American Society* (Random House, 1969), and more recently, Robert Zussman's *Mechanics of the Middle Class: Work and Politics Among American Engineers* (University of California Press, 1985). In addition, see Robert Perucci and Joel E. Gerstl, eds. *The Engineers and the Social System* (John Wiley & Sons, Inc., 1969), a collection of essays exploring the occupational and work roles of engineering, recruitment, and socialization, and the social dimension of engineering careers. The value of insightful and informed readings of documentary sources is amply demonstrated by Edwin T. Layton, Jr., *The Revolt of the Engineers: Social Responsibility and the American Engineering Profession*, 2nd ed. (Baltimore: The Johns Hopkins University Press, 1986).

[10] Dr. Hans Mark, Deputy Administrator of NASA from 1981 through 1984. The agency's leadership was defined as current and past program administrators and center directors. See Appendix A.

[11] Given an average turnover rate of about 5 percent, the number of scientists and engineers who actually crossed NASA's threshold over the period was materially larger than 9875.

[12] Ames Research Center, Goddard Space Flight Center, Lyndon B. Johnson Space Center, John F. Kennedy Space Center, Langley Research Center, Lewis Research Center, and George C. Marshall Space Flight Center.

[13] Because of the small percentage of minorities and females among NASA's engineers (see Appendix B, table 7), a random sampling for the purpose of interviews would not, in all probability, have resulted in any interviews with non-white males. However, because the experiences of minorities who began to enter the agency in the 1960s could reflect the environment created by the majority in this (as in any other) organization, the "nominee" group includes a sampling of minorities and females supplied by NASA's Office of Equal Employment Opportunity.

Chapter 1
Beginnings: 1918–1932

Almost ten thousand engineers began their careers with NASA during the Apollo decade. Slightly over 60 percent were born before 1935. It was mostly these older engineers whom NASA's leadership, as late as 1984, considered to be the "most representative" of the agency's Apollo decade engineers.[1] These older men (and they were almost all men) were the ones to leave the most lasting imprint on the space agency's culture.

1918 — the year that Robert Strong was born — was the year the guns fell silent, bringing to an end four years of human carnage in the forests and river valleys, plains and hillsides of Europe — and bringing to an end the world that had created western civilization as it was then known. What was left of a generation once 10 million perished from disease or wounds, and 20 million more later succumbed to a world-wide influenza scourge, suffered yet another kind of death — the death of "the old lie," wrote Wilfred Owen: 'Dulce et decorum est pro patria mori.'"[2]

On the other side of the Atlantic, life had gone on much as before. An American president proposed his formula for perpetual peace, and the Red Sox won the World Series. Not far from a jubilant Boston, in North Andover, Mass., an old New England mill town, a boy began a life that would reach far beyond the American Woolen Company mill where his father was an overseer. Unknown to the boy, Gustav Holst had already put to music the vision that would carry Strong into the last frontier.[3] The boy from Massachusetts would be among those who would launch the first human into the final vastness of space.

Robert Strong's career really began when he was eleven, the year Charles Lindbergh flew alone across the Atlantic Ocean. That crossing "is still one of the greatest achievements of the century.... North Andover was a small town; it couldn't have been more than forty-five hundred people in that town at that time [with a] small high school [of] about three hundred and fifty students. My oldest brother was playing baseball that afternoon. [We] had a little, small, ball park, hardly anybody there; just a few of us. And the umpire stopped the game and announced… he was pleased to report that Captain Charles Lindbergh had landed in Le Bourget Air Field." After Lindbergh's flight "several of my friends and myself got interested in building model airplanes…. There was a flying field close by. We'd go up and do spare jobs with the … airplanes that would come in from time to time …. Of course, kids my age all wanted to be pilots. But then, as I grew older and got interested in more scientific subjects, I decided I'd be an aeronautical engineer."

In 1934 Strong entered the Massachusetts Institute of Technology, where he discovered the work of the National Advisory Committee for Aeronautics (NACA) "through those marvelous books they put out — the technical reports and technical notes and technical memorandum…. At MIT [the] NACA was a renowned place, even then." It was as a student at MIT that Strong discovered Jerome Hunsaker, the designer of the first aircraft to cross the Atlantic, who had introduced at MIT, in 1914, the first college course in aeronautical engineering.[4] And it was at MIT that the NACA discovered Robert Strong, recruiting him in 1938, at the end of his senior year. "The kind of people who were attracted there," to the NACA's parent aeronautical laboratory at Langley Field in Virginia, "came from all over the states. During the Depression it was probably the only place they could do that kind of work…. At that time Langley was very small, it must have been two hundred fifty, three hundred people there, at the most."

On a late spring day in 1938 Strong and two others "rode the train to Washington and transferred to a boat and got off at Old Point Comfort…. The train ride… was ten dollars. I had a big steamer trunk with all my possessions, and got it on the boat, and that boat used to land at Old Point Comfort about 5:30 in the morning. You'd have to get off and spend the first night — as many did — in the Langley Hotel…. Hampton was a one stop-light town, at the corner of King and Queen Street, and that was it in those days. Many of the people, local, viewed the [Langley] group with a jaundiced eye. [We were] free spirits in many respects." Hampton people called them, less elegantly, the "NACA nuts."

A thousand miles from North Andover, below the southernmost foothills of the Appalachians, where the Gulf, Mobile and Ohio Railroad once crossed the Cahaba River, survives the small town in which Dan O'Neill was born. Centreville, Ala. was "a little place" when he was born there in 1920, and by last count it was a little place still, a town of about 2500. "There wasn't really much in a small town. You just didn't know much about what was going on in the world." The changes that would affect O'Neill's life were stirring when he was born, although few inhabitants of Centreville had the luxury, in 1920, of concerning themselves with the creation of the National Socialist German Workers' (NAZI) Party, much less the publication of Sir Arthur S.

Eddington's *Space, Time and Gravitation* — one of the first English language expositions of the theory of relativity.

O'Neill was one of seven children who "grew up on a small farm, like everybody else was doing in those days." His father "was ... a two-mule farmer" as well as "the local blacksmith." O'Neill is a maker and a fixer, which he attributes to the days when he was "just a small boy working in [his father's] shop, helping. My dad sharpened the plows for the local farmers. He did welding, welded wagon tires.... He fixed wagons and shod the mules and all those things.... A lot of woodwork he did by hand, making wagon axles and spokes. He could completely rebuild a wagon." O'Neill worked in the shop "turning the forge ... to build the fire up, holding the material while [his] dad worked on it, beat on it." As he grew up, working with his father, he learned a lot of carpentry, which he does to this day.

"Back in those days, most of the books that we had to read were more like the westerns or Doc Savage. We used to subscribe to Doc Savage, and that had...some quite far out scientific things.... He was a super sleuth ... he had all kinds of scientific things that were way beyond — not like Buck Rogers.... He had chemists, engineers, and doctors, and they'd go out and solve all of these big problems."

O'Neill's mother "never finished college." She "taught school for a few years before she got married." She was "a good mother. She cooked and took care of the family. And she was, I guess, my inspiration ... she could help me with my school work until I got past what she knew, which I did, eventually.... My parents ... saw that we went to school. All seven of us graduated from college." When O'Neill finished high school, he "really had no desire to go to college. I don't know what I would have taken, had I gone. I got a job with the Alabama Power Company trimming trees." The pay "was seventy five dollars a month. I ... paid five dollars a week for room and board. I was making good money. But after working a few months with the power company, I observed that people who had been there twenty years were still climbing poles and stringing wire in the hot weather and the cold weather, and I decided there must be a better way to do things. So I saved a little money and I decided to go back to school."

O'Neill's oldest brother "took agricultural science [in college] and worked in that field for a year, but I'd had enough of farming.... And as I had the idea that I'd like to fly, I thought, well, aeronautical engineering is the thing to do. So that's why I started in aeronautical engineering.... I didn't know much about it until I actually started to school and began to learn some of these things." In 1939, when O'Neill started college at the University of Alabama, "we weren't really involved in the war yet. But listening to your professors talk about their experiences in aeronautics and what airplanes could do, and what they would do in the future ... I began to realize 'well, this aeronautical business is really a coming thing'.... I guess I've been a dreamer all of my life.

"I put myself through college. I borrowed ten dollars one time to start my second year of college. That was [for] a bicycle so I could deliver papers.... I lived in a fire station.... I worked in a shoe store. And I delivered papers." The college education in engineering that O'Neill could get at the University of Alabama in the early 1940s was "not broad by any means.... I never was as smart as some people. I had problems, especially with math.... I did pretty good until I got to calculus, but I had problems with calculus." O'Neill struggled on for four years, working part-time, studying part-time. He was also in the Reserve Officers' Training Corps. Then, in March 1943, when millions of young Americans saw conscription looming before them, O'Neill surrendered and entered the Army's Officer Candidate School (OCS). "I went through engineering OCS right after ROTC and then I decided, if I was ever going to learn how to fly, now was the time. So I put in for flight training and I went through flight training as a second lieutenant and got my wings.... The next two and a half years, I enjoyed flying, but I kind of lost my desire to become an aeronautical engineer for some reason. That's when I went back to school. I transferred to industrial engineering.... I really didn't understand then as much about...the different kinds of engineering.... But I considered industrial engineering to be more in the management of business, rather than in designing.... I remember one college professor, whose name was Johnson. And he was an industrial engineer."

O'Neill finally got his bachelor's degree in engineering in 1949. He stayed with the U.S. Air Force Reserve, eventually retiring as a Reserve Lt. Colonel. "After I got my degree ... I went to work for a pipeline company that built ... gas lines. They called us 'progress engineers'.... I worked in Tennessee and Texas.... I worked on the line, on the powder crew, for four months ... loading poles and fuses and caps and shooting dynamite ... but ... like the power company job climbing trees, it was a job, but not much future.... When my job played out there, I went back home."

O'Neill and his wife married in 1949. They lived "in a trailer on the pipeline. And in order to have something to do, I started teaching school at a Veterans' Continuation School.... Some of the third graders could barely read.... That exposure really got me interested in education.... There were so many people who were not educated.... I lived about twenty-five miles from the University [of Alabama].... So I went to school in the morning and I got a master's degree in school administration and majored in elemetary education.... Then I taught school for four years — math, science, physics. In 1957 I decided it was time for a change. I had an interview with ABMA [the Army Ballistic Missile Agency in Huntsville, Ala.] and I came to work at ABMA, here on the [Redstone] arsenal, on the first of July, 1957.

"On the first of July, 1960 ... exactly three years from the time I started ... some five thousand of us transferred to NASA." (Congress had just transferred the ABMA's space facilities and personnel to NASA's newly designated George C. Marshall Space Flight Center.) O'Neill went "to work on Wernher von Braun's staff in his Technical Program Coordination Office, which [oversaw the] budget, funding, programming, and scheduling — making charts for meetings and presentations" for the Jupiter missile program. O'Neill has been at Marshall "ever since."

Located on what was once a vast mudflat whose Y-shaped rivers reached almost from Lake Michigan to the drainage basin of the Mississippi River system, Chicago was destined by its location as the water, and later rail, gateway to the American west, to become a great city. With the completion of the Erie Canal in 1825 and the

Illinois and Michigan Canal in 1848, Chicago became one of the United States' great geographic catch basins, gathering in its depths the raw material not only of much of this country's nineteenth century economic growth, but also its distinctive literary and social movements. Much of that raw material came from the second great European hegira, which brought to this continent the Italians, Poles, Serbs, Croats, Bohemians, and countless Jews from southern and eastern Europe who would constitute three-quarters of Chicago's population by the turn of the century.

Here, in 1920, Ernest Cohen was born, offspring of two families of Eastern European rabbis. "On my mother's side ... they came from somewhere up on the Russian-Polish border.... My grandmother might have come from Lithuania.... My grandparents remember the Cossaks getting drunk on Saturday night and ... running through the village.... My grandfather ... was a peddler and he peddled in a Polish neighborhood ... because he did know the language. And they had large families." Both of his grandfathers "were rabbis. The one on my mother's side was a scholar.... On my father's side ... they came from Germany. There was a great deal of difference in the way they ... cooked and the way they lived. Great grandfather" on Cohen's father's side "was a rabbi ... he didn't really work, but he owned a bakery.... The girls used to run the bakery.... My grandmother on my father's side learned to read and write and to figure, because she was too small to do the heavy work.... [Great grandfather] taught all of his sons to read and to write and to figure, but none of the daughters except my grandmother, so she could take care of the books for the bakery.

"Mother ... was the oldest of thirteen children.... The way the family ran, the oldest child used to raise the younger ones, and my grandma raised the babies. So mother actually raised most of my aunts and uncles.... We first lived next door to my grandma. And it was always more exciting for me to be at my grandma's place.... Part of the family would be fighting, the other part would be singing and having a good time.... I suspect that my grandmother probably raised me more than my mother."

Cohen's father "did a lot of things.... When he was young he was part of a blackface act" in Chicago vaudeville.... "He liked that kind of stuff. But when he got married, my mother felt differently.... He got a job as a milkman and he also was ... interested in the mail order business ... he got a lot of mail and he did a lot of writing. He liked that." But having been "a singer and [done the] soft shoe, he always missed it." Many years later, when Cohen's parents moved "to Los Angeles, he actually bought a small bookshop right very close to the old Columbia studios, and ... he and my mother both used to get quite a thrill when all the old movie stars used to come in and chat with them.

"We lived in an apartment building most of the time.... When I was small, my dad bought a house. The Depression came in '29... land values evaporated, and the place became a slum.... It was ... right ... on the west side of Chicago. But before it became a slum, it had a very large ... Italian population.... [They were] very, very nice people, except they were bootleggers.... We did eventually move to the northwest.... I was the oldest grandchild. I had all these uncles and I used — when I was small — to see most of the hockey games in Chicago. I'd get [to] the ball games, the boxing matches, the wrestling matches.... I had an uncle who was, like, two years older than myself.... I guess the families were beginning to run together.... Friday night was Sabbath for us, so Friday was a big baking day for [grandmother]. She baked the cholla in loaves, great big pies and stuff. One thing she used to bake was apple strudle.... She had one of these great big, round tables [and] used to stretch this dough. And she used to chatter all the time to me.... My grandmother used to... dress my grandfather ... help him on with the coat and sweaters, used to have the whisk broom, clean him, pack the lunches.

"When I was very, very small one of my uncles bought himself an erector set.... When we'd go over to visit him, to keep me quiet, he let me use the erector set. But then, after a while, I kept losing the screws and he wouldn't give me the erector set any more. So my parents bought me an erector set, and I played with that damn thing for hours and days.... They always knew where I was ... I was building with this thing."

Cohen attended grade school and high school in Chicago, not deciding on engineering "until the ... last year of high school.... I got real interested in chemistry. And ... I felt that maybe I'd like to be a chemical engineer.... No one in our family ever was an engineer before. We didn't know much about that.... Engineering was the last thing they ever expected me to go into. They probably thought — a lawyer, or medicine, or something like that. Those were the two professions ... that everyone knew something about. Maybe accounting, or something like that, but engineering kind of floored them ... because of my total ignorance of what engineering was all about." As it turned out, Cohen "was lucky [in] that I really enjoyed it.... I really consider myself extremely lucky to have chosen something that I just plain liked.

"Going to college ... was a real thing for my parents.... I'm one of the few people in my family that ever really did go to college." After he graduated from high school in 1938, Cohen went to the Armour Institute of Technology, which later merged with the Lewis Institute of Technology to become the Illinois Institute of Technology. "Money was... pretty tight... in the Depression," and Cohen largely worked his way through school. "My folks sacrificed a great deal in order to get me through college. I went to a private engineering college because they figured that ... it would be cheaper to go to...college in Chicago than go down to the University of Illinois and be away from home.

"Most of my friends that went to college with me ... used to work, bring all the money home, and we'd get an allowance.... And even after I got a job, I was living at home. I still brought all my money home and got an allowance from my parents. They bought all my clothes and stuff.... The college ... was pretty close to about 60 percent Irish Catholic, and they had strong family ties that way too.... It was hard to get money ... but ... there was a lot of ways for us to have fun. Saturday nights mostly we used to get together and dance. Anybody whose parents owned a house in Chicago always had a basement. They used to paint the basement Chinese red and wax it. And there was usually a ping pong table down there, so there was always a chance to have a party. And in the winter time it was always things like ice skating, and summer time, [there were] places to have picnics and go to the beach.... We could have a good time on a very limited amount of money."

At the Armour Institute, "there were only five kinds of engineering when I was there. It was straight engineering ... electrical, chemical, mechanical, fire protection, and architectural. And that was it.... There was two years of English ... the English and math departments were the strongest departments in the school because everybody had to take English and math.... When I went in, as a [high school] senior, I got a book and the book gave the program, all four years. And you didn't get an elective until your fourth year. It was a choice between differential equations and thermodynamics."

When Cohen graduated from the Illinois Institute of Technology he "got a job as an engineer in a small company" called National Die Casting. "The employees ... were tool and die makers...their engineers were essentially draftsmen.... They were making at the time — the war had started — demand oxygen regulators, for pilots ... and other aircraft instruments, and I sort of got interested in fluid mechanics and that kind of design.... I worked for about two years designing aircraft instruments.... Before the war it used to make orange juice squeezers...they made a lot of money [on them]. They had a lot of interesting things that they tried that were kind of foolish," including a mechanical scalp massager advertised to reduce hair loss, which was based on the orange juice squeezer design, and a die-cast juke box that failed commercially for lack of audio resonance.

The U.S. Army infantry claimed Cohen in 1944. "I was transferred into the [U.S. Army Corps of] engineers, and sent to Los Alamos, New Mexico [where] I was assigned to the Manhattan Bomb project for roughly about two years." He was discharged from the Army in 1946, got married and returned to Los Alamos to work for a short time, and then went to Cornell University. With the help of two stipends and the GI bill, he earned a master's degree in physical chemistry from Cornell. "From there I went to the Bureau of Mines in [Bartlesville], Oklahoma.... I was very interested in thermodynamics at the time and did fundamental research in thermodynamics.... My main job there was ...doing some bomb killer imagery there ...we published some papers on that.... We used to do statistical thermal calculations.... I didn't do it all that much, but we had guys who used to do that eight hours a day, over and over and over again.... I liked the job a lot...it was ...real exacting work. [But] after a while you were just doing the same thing over and over and over again.... I just felt ... too confined."

Cohen moved on to the University of Wichita, where "they had a research and development outfit that was associated with the school and did research and development work for Coleman lanterns and Coleman furnaces [and] other small companies around there.... It was a small group of people, about eighteen or twenty engineers or chemists. We all got along very well." He had enjoyed teaching as a student assistant at Cornell, and he warmed to the collegial university setting with its lectures and concerts. However, by the time he and his wife had moved to Wichita, they had four children. "I wasn't making enough money ... so it was starve or move on." In 1952 Cohen took his family "to St. Louis and went to work for part of an architectural design outfit, Sverdrup and Parcel." When Cohen joined the firm, for which he would do fluid dynamics, their main business was building bridges, roads, hospitals, laboratories, and other large facilities. The firm had had no experience building aeronautical facilities. Nonetheless, thanks to the war-time contacts of its founders, it won a government contract to build the Arnold Engineering Development Center, for which it built the transonic, supersonic, and hypersonic wind tunnels. "They did real well, because they hired a lot of good people who really knew how to do this work.... They were very honest [and] a good company to work for.

"But then," he remembers, "I got caught up in the space age." When the AVCO Corporation (an aerospace research and development contracting firm) came to St. Louis to recruit, Cohen interviewed for a job. "And the way they explained it, they'd got a project.... What they really should have said is that they were proposing one." Cohen went to work for AVCO, but "about a year [later] I decided, 'well, they won't do it.' There was ... about eighteen or twenty of us who were doing nothing because there was nothing to do." As it turned out, the boss Cohen had had at Sverdrup and Parcel had moved on to NASA; he worked at the Goddard Space Flight Center outside Washington, D.C. in Greenbelt, Md. "He came to see me one time, and he said, 'Hey, you know, you ought to come and work for me again.'" So, in the fall of 1960, Cohen moved his family to Greenbelt. "I never really intended to stay this long, but I've been here ever since."

New York City has been another great American catch basin, port of entry to the Land of Promise throughout the nineteenth and well into the twentieth century. It was here that Isaac Petrovsky, with his father, a once prosperous Lithuanian merchant, and his mother, an opera singer, caught his first glimpse of America in 1930. It was not an auspicious year for an Eastern European immigrant family in search of material security, if not prosperity. New York City's Bank of the United States, with its sixty branches and half a million depositors, closed its doors along with more than 1300 banks across the United States. Meanwhile, President Herbert C. Hoover signed the Smoot-Hawley Tariff, thereby assuring a precipitous decline in international trade. It is unlikely that the ten-year-old boy who stood before the immigration clerk at Ellis Island — or even the father who brought him there — knew or cared much about tariffs and banks.

The boy and his father, who had sold everything the family owned, left Lithuania with only their baggage. "We went by train to Bremerhaven, but before that we were stopped before we crossed over the border, and ... they took us back. So my father had to bribe them to be able to get out. He left me in a restaurant by the train. I waited there for about three hours and didn't know what was happening. Then we finally got over [the border] and we stopped off in Germany for one night, and then we got to Bremerhaven. It was a five to six day trip. So that's the beginning of my life.

"We came in on the *Bremen*. I was sick for five days. I and my father" shared a cabin with "two Hungarians. One of them smoked a terrible cigar." When they arrived at Ellis Island on April Fool's Day, "there was a crowd of people being pushed around ... we came over before the [immigration clerk's] desk.... I wanted to be an American, right then and there, and I ... wanted an American name.... They told me to write down something. So I wrote down Ike — I didn't know how to spell it.... And the most amazing thing was, they gave me an orange! I knew what an orange was, because my Dad was wealthy enough to import citrus fruits from Israel — or Palestine, in those days.... He told me that one orange cost ... one Lithuanian dollar. But it had an exchange value of ten American cents."

When they came to the United States, Isaac Petrovsky and his father knew not one word of English. At home the family had spoken Yiddish mixed with German and smatterings of Polish and Lithuanian. Their first refuge was Middletown, N.Y., where some relatives of the mother had made a home for themselves. "Eventually we moved to Brooklyn. My father felt very secure in that enclave of that type of people."

This American journey had begun in Kaunas, the capital city of Lithuania, where Isaac, as a boy, had "lived... in a very big apartment.... We did not have electricity. Heating was done by fireplaces. The kitchen was tremendous.... The house was full of servants...this was what distinguished you from people who could not afford it ... the number of servants you had.... Water was brought in two pails on a yoke — one of the servants would go down to the river and ... bring it up and put it in a barrel. We never drank any of the water; we drank tea, which means the water was boiled. My father was a businessman, and he apparently was quite well-to-do, because I never lacked for anything.... He was a 'luftmensch,' [which means] 'free agent'.... He started out ... when he was a younger man, before he was married ... in some lumber business. He bought lumber for some German firms ... and he imported and exported ... some medicines or perfumes.... My mother was a mezzo-soprano.... She was a beautiful woman." Her own family had emigrated to the United States a few years earlier, having (once she and her husband resolved to emigrate) left as soon as she could get an artist's visa. She survived by working with a traveling vaudeville company that presented exerpts from operas in between the silent movies then shown in theaters. "She knew the Sam Goldwyn people, and Warner Brothers, because they were starting out in the movies...back in the 'twenties.'"

Her son Isaac, an only child, stayed behind to be "raised by nannies. When I was old enough, I went to the ... Hebrew gymnasium.... Everything was in Hebrew, everything they taught me.... They would also teach us something about the Bible.... During the day I would go to that school ... then I went home. [In] addition to that, I had teachers. I had piano teachers. I had teachers that taught me how to write and read German. They came to the house. I was an only child. I was one of those lonely little ones."

After the family emigrated and moved to Brooklyn, N.Y., Petrovsky's father "went into all kinds of business. He started out with a cousin of his, that he met, with the ladies' stocking business. And apparently the cousin took the money and disappeared. My father went into restaurants.... He did whatever he had to do. He was a peddler, if he had to do that. He became very successful.... When I was in junior high, we lived [in] — I would call it now, in retrospect, a ghetto. It was an area ten blocks by ten blocks that was a Jewish neighborhood and an Italian neighborhood.... We never really left that area." At long last the loneliness came to an end. "Friends ... were all around the neighborhood there. I played stick ball and baseball, [but] I discovered really that I didn't have the patience for all of these games. I read, I listened to records, and I played the piano. I stopped playing the piano, I think, when I was about fourteen. My mother decided to give me violin lessons. I got tired of holding the fiddle after a while.... I discovered — of course, I didn't understand it then — that I didn't have a left hand.

"I went to Hebrew School ... all the way through junior high. We had Hebrew lessons in the morning and then the regular curriculum, and then I went to New Utrecht High School to finish off. I was what you call a standard C student. There were certain things that I took to quicker than other things. Like geometry was something that I could relate to. Algebra I could too.... I loved English because I was crazy about Shakespeare ... to me that was the most beautiful language in the world. I also took four years of French, three years of Spanish. When I graduated, I worked for a year in the garment district in downtown New York and went to Brooklyn College at night.... I went to Brooklyn College because I didn't have any money to go to the university.... And I was studying ancient history and Spanish because I wanted to go into the State Department or the Foreign Service. But after that my father got enough money together and I went to New York University.... My father says to me, 'you know, Ike, go to college. I got the money. Go to college.' So I went to the nearest school that was a college. That was New York University.... And I said, 'what's the nearest thing to a trade?' And they said, 'engineering'.... I needed a trade. I needed to have something that I could earn a living with. That's the reason I became an engineer. That was it.... And I said, 'OK, I'll take that.' So I signed up for civil engineering. And I started taking the preparatory courses."

In 1941, after the United States was drawn into World War II, Isaac "took ROTC because they gave me a uniform. I didn't have too many suits of clothing.... They called us up and they said ... 'you have to sign up now, because otherwise you'll be drafted. This way you can become a second lieutenant.' So I signed up. They processed us ... and they sent us to Fort Belvoir, Virginia for ten weeks ... and I went through all that basic training.... I felt good. I mean, I had muscles I never heard of before. When I finished basic training, they said, 'now you go back to working on your studies and get your degree and when we have an opening for you, we'll send you back to Fort Belvoir for another ten weeks.' And I didn't want to have tear gas thrown at me and all that. Then they said that all students studying aeronautical engineering would be sent to Miami Beach, OCS. So I went over [to the registrar's office] at lunch time. The girl had gone out to lunch, so I said, 'I just want to change my courses right now.' The other girl said 'what do you want?' She pulled out my master file, crossed out civil engineering, and put in aeronautical engineering. She went out to lunch and I went down to Miami Beach. [Miami Beach] was fantastic.... It was the first time that I saw the beach sand and palm trees."

Not long after Petrovsky finished Officers' Candidate School he learned that he was due to be sent overseas. "I said, 'My God, you can get killed wherever they're going.... They sent me down to Miami to pick up a flight and I was flying — they still wouldn't tell us [where]. And I'm flying and flying and flying and I see the jungle underneath me, and I said, 'My God, we're already over the Japanese!'" As it turned out Petrovsky had been sent to British Guiana, where he served as an aircraft maintenance officer until the war ended. In 1945 he returned to New York University to finish the course work for his degree in engineering, which he received in 1946. During the next year Petrovsky worked with Boeing Aircraft in Seattle until he was laid off. The separation was mutual: "I didn't care for aeronautics." He and his new bride returned to Brooklyn, where he worked briefly for an engineering company. He was on the road again in 1948, headed toward Florida to be close to his retired parents. Once there, he found work in civil engineering. That lasted until his wife, who did not get along with Petrovsky's mother, contacted friends in Hollywood, Calif., and arranged another cross-country migration.

Petrovsky settled down in Hollywood until 1966, working for various civil engineering firms as a structural engineer. "I was working and I had good jobs and I was doing very well.... I was recognized in my field, because I was never out of work. When a project would end with one company, I would get a call from another." Then, he remembers one day "walking up the stairs...and I think about the third or fourth stair ... a voice said to me in my head, 'you're going to be hitting that step for the next thirty or forty years'.... I missed the family...we had the children... my mother and father, they lived in Florida.... So that's when I decided to go back to the East Coast."

Back to Florida he went. Bendix Corporation hired him as a structural engineer at Kennedy Space Center, but he soon found that his job "was a paper shuffling job.... It was the first time I was involved with the space program, and I was completely shattered, because everything was paper, paper. Everybody was going to meetings. They used their own buzz-words, and I didn't understand a word of it, because I know steel, concrete.... I realized ... 'hey, you're stuck. You can't go back to California. Your furniture is on the way, so you're stuck here. You better make the best of it. The thing I need, then, is a job I can depend on. So I have to go work for the government.'" In 1968 Petrovsky landed his government job — with NASA, working with the organization that oversees the contractors who maintain the launch pad facilities at Kennedy Space Center. "When I got the job, I didn't even ask what it was all about. All I wanted was to get into the system. Well, I got into the system.... There were about ten guys ... and we were all tracking the requirements documentation to support the testing for the Apollo program ... it was paper ... and I learned one thing: you got to keep your nose clean for three years, so you can become a career [employee]. I did that, and I moved a piece of the paper beautifully. I punched the holes. I knew how to change the pages. I hadn't the foggiest idea what the hell it all meant.... I kept my nose clean for three years."

Years later the branch chief who hired Petrovsky told him why he had chosen him for the job: "You could do just so much page changes [his boss told him], and you wait for other offices to respond. So we would have discussions. We'd have about 10 or 12 guys having discussions. Each one is different. Each one has his input. They wanted all kinds." They thought a Pole would add something to their discussions, but they didn't have a Pole. Since there did not seem to be all that much difference between a Lithuanian and a Pole, Petrovsky would do.

———————

Deep in south central Michigan, about halfway between Lake Erie and Lake Michigan, the New York Central Railroad's largest maintenance and operations center west of Buffalo lay spread out in the town of Jackson, Mich. American railroading was flush when Henry Strassen was born in Jackson in 1922; he was the son and grandson of railroad engineers, and Jackson's railyards must have been lavish with the screech and soot of locomotives. The net annual income of the nation's railroads had surpassed the three-quarter of a billion level in the 1920s, approaching the billion dollar mark in 1929, a sum equivalent to 31 percent of the federal government's budget for that year. However, by 1932, as the Great Depression began to take its toll, that figure plummeted to a net loss of slightly over $100 million, recovered to its Depression era high of $220 million in 1936, and did not return to its pre-Depression high until it was rescued by the war-time traffic of 1942.[5] The human cost was, as most human costs are, incalculable.

To the affected families in languishing railroad towns like Jackson, the human cost was the cost that mattered. As a boy in his early teens, Strassen was "deeply impressed" as Jackson "was pretty much destroyed" by the Depression, its population diminished from 75,000 to 45,000. By the early 1980s Jackson's townspeople numbered fewer than 40,000. Thus, as a teenager, Strassen knew "damn well" that he was not going to let his livelihood depend on "some outside group like Goodyear or General Motors." He would try to make a go of it on his own.

For Strassen, as for Robert Strong, "probably the most significant thing in my life was Lindbergh." Strassen had learned about Lindbergh's solitary crossing on the family's old radio, "one with three dials and a big antenna.... I was seven years old when he flew the Atlantic, and I was terribly impressed.... It's probably as vivid to me as the Apollo landing. I used to go out to the airport all summer long and spend time just sitting at the airport, and working. I'd earn 15 cents washing an airplane, or I'd work for an airplane owner for a week, or just riding around." While his friends "were all more interested in automobiles," Strassen built airplane models. When the chance eventually came to pursue a career involving airplanes, he would be ready. Strassen was the youngest of three siblings; it was his eldest sister's husband, a successful lawyer, who first interested him in college — initially law school. But Strassen was also interested in mechanical things. Believing that patent law would allow him to combine a secure profession (legal practice) with his first interest — machinery — he entered the University of Michigan in a combined law and engineering program. Then, for him, as for so many other young men, the ghost of war intervened. "I woke up one morning and I had a notice: 'Dear Mr. Strassen, you have a nice low draft number and you're about to be drafted. If you persist in going to law school, we will draft you immediately. But if you stay in engineering, we'll grant you a deferment until you graduate.' So that was when I decided to be an engineer." Strassen transferred to the engineering school and "almost bombed out about halfway through.... I got the bug to go into the Navy.... I went over to Grosse Ile, near Detroit, where the Navy has an air base, and volunteered to become a naval aviation cadet.

"In those days they took you out and flew you around in a Navy aircraft. In this particular case it was a Navy dive-bomber. We went through the whole series of aerobatic and simulator dives. I can't imagine going through that today!" Strassen survived, but before he could sign up, the Navy recruiting officer urged him to return to school and get his degree. "It was the best thing that ever happened. I would have probably been a lieutenant at Pearl Harbor, flying out over the Pacific, and that would have been the end of that." In the fall before his graduation from Michigan, Strassen was approached by the Navy again, this time with an offer to send him to graduate school in exchange for a commission as an ensign. He could go where he wanted. He flipped a coin over MIT or the California Institute of Technology, and it came up MIT, which he entered in 1940. Before he could complete his degree, however, the Japanese attacked Pearl Harbor. The Navy commissioned him and put him on active duty. He remained in the Navy until 1962, doing technical intelligence work and program management in areas from advanced fighter aircraft to guided missiles.

Strassen's work with the Navy gave him more than a career; it provided ever greater exposure to the possibilities of space travel, and it was while he served as the Navy's representative on a special NACA advisory committee that Strassen met Wernher von Braun. By the end of 1962 the prospect of a manned landing on the Moon and safe return "had gotten too compelling." He retired from the Navy and went to work for NASA, believing "there was just no doubt that there was the place to be." True space exploration, however, "didn't really sink in…until [Neil] Armstrong walked on the Moon…. It took a long, long time to accept that manned [space] flight was … real."

From A. W. von Hoffman to Rudolf Diesel, from Werner von Siemans and Gottlieb Daimler to Hermann Oberth and Wernher von Braun, German culture in the 1920s continued a venerable tradition of engineering research. While the American intelligentsia has often been suspicious of technological change, leaning instead toward a world of pastoral images and populist values, science and engineering in Germany have occupied a well-established domain as respectable careers for those of aristocratic as well as middle class origins. Faustian ambitions of spirit and personality, rather than the aspirations of rootless tinkerers, seem to have fueled the German dynamo.

Born in 1923 in the old Prussian capital of Berlin to the family of a nationally prominent German banker, Werner Posen "had always an inclination and a great attraction…to mathematics, physics, chemistry, to natural sciences." The elder Posen had regretted choosing a career in banking over architecture and, for that reason, may have encouraged his son's fascination with the workings of the physical world. The boy's parents bought him "the right kind of experimental sets and gifts," and especially "erector sets. [I] loved erector sets." Soon he was entering annual competititions for the best erector set designs. "I got one of those awards.... My parents were proud of that." His school friends "didn't know what they wanted to be," but he did: "I wanted to be a scientist, in particular, a physicist.

"I also read a lot of science fiction ... and that got me into some close relationship to the rocket ship development, even though it was, at that time — the 1930s — certainly not something that everyone was familiar with." He remembers "many [science fiction] books.... We had a famous science fiction writer in Germany — Hans Dominic. I started with one [of his books] and I had to read them all.... He was, I would say, a predominant influence on my life."

Notwithstanding Posen's scientific leanings, his father insisted on a traditional liberal schooling for his son and sent him to a gymnasium in Berlin, where he had to learn Greek and Latin. "I didn't like it at all ... they didn't emphasize math and they didn't emphasize physics and all those things that I felt stronger in. [But] we had working groups for students with common interests, and one was a working group for physics.... We did gyro experiments and so on. So, I got ... as a young boy, the science fiction side and then, as a high school student, I got into serious matter. At that time I started buying — and my father actually helped ... serious books about math that went beyond school. I wanted to learn more than was offered to me.

"And then ... came the war."

Posen was drafted into the Luftwaffe, assigned to a communications unit, and sent to the eastern front. Illness saved him from the worst horrors of the German invasion of Russia, and he was returned to Germany, where he recovered in time to be sent out again — this time, to the North. "I got assigned to a station on the Baltic Sea...close to Peenemuende, which was, unknown to me, the development center for the V-2 and V-1.... I really marvelled about that.... There were so many millions of soldiers. And I was just picked for that right thing for me." Posen spent two years, from 1943 to 1945, "as a soldier assigned to do tracking. We call it now radar tracking of missiles ... it was all very much clouded in secrecy. But I had good eyes and I knew my physics to the point that I knew exactly what they were doing two days after I arrived." Best of all, "I even met von Braun ... and I knew ... he was trying to... develop rockets that would eventually go into space. With my background in physics and my background in science fiction, that really made me determined at that time that I wanted to keep doing that."

When he returned to Berlin in 1945 Posen began a study program in experimental physics at Berlin's Technische Hochschule. Working in the field of secondary electron emission of semiconductors, he soon became immersed in "fundamental research" in electronics, completing work for his master's and doctoral degrees by 1952. In the meantime, Posen began working as "a physics editor for what you call in this country 'Chemical Abstracts'.... It was very good preparation for me because ... I had already set my eyes on going over to the United States, and my English was very good."

Posen had "set his eyes" on the United States for several reasons. "I was really unhappy about the political situation in Germany.... [There was the] devastation, and I wasn't really sure that the next generation of politicians in Germany would be all that much better.... At least equally strong, maybe even stronger, was the desire to participate in rocket development. I knew the next step was space, and I wanted to participate in that, and it was very clear that I couldn't, in Europe, for many, many years." Aware that von Braun had gone to the United States, he asked an American friend in Berlin to help him locate von Braun who, by that time, had become technical director for the U.S. Army's Ordnance Guided Missile Development Group at the Redstone Arsenal in Huntsville, Ala.

"I looked in all kinds of books and there was very little about Alabama, very little." Nonetheless, in 1955, at the age of 32, Posen left Germany with his wife and child, heading for Alabama. "When we finally got here, arriving in New York, they say [sic],

"'Where are you going?'

"Alabama.

"'Are you *sure?*'

"My big problem, when I came [to Huntsville], was to listen to the southern stuff ... and even know what they are saying and, then, in turn, talk so that they could understand me. That was quite a culture shock.... I wished I had done that ten years earlier; I would have lost my accent." Nonetheless, Posen, like dozens of other German scientists and engineers, learned how to make himself understood. He remained in Huntsville — first with the Redstone Arsenal and then with NASA's Marshall Space Flight Center — working with rockets (since given the more recondite name of launch vehicles) and their payloads for the rest of his career.

The city of Baltimore, largest city in the border state of Maryland, has been washed by every current to flow across the American landscape. Its history embraces the slave trade, industrialization, the growth of the railroads, the influx of successive waves of immigration, foreign shipping, urban growth and decay, and H. L. Mencken. Before the completion of the interstate highway system in the 1960s, millions of souls on the East Coast knew Baltimore mostly as the place through which one lurched northward, stop light by stop light, on blistering afternoons in July and August, to escape from the hot southern summer. As they went, they passed miles of brick row houses with prim, plain fronts and white door stoops. These marked the boundaries of the neighborhoods where working class people lived, people like the parents of Philip Siebold, who was born in Baltimore in 1926, the year Robert H. Goddard launched the world's first liquid-fueled rocket at Auburn, Mass.

"My dad was a blue collar worker.... I grew up in a typical lower middle class, if you can even call it middle class, [area] in Baltimore." Siebold attended various Catholic schools in Baltimore, his aspirations largely limited to vocational education, so he "could learn to be an office worker, a secretary, or a clerk, or something like that." But he was a good student, good enough so that "someone casually said to me ... 'Why don't you apply to Poly?'" Baltimore Polytechnic High School, "back in those days ... took students from any place in the city because they had special programs, one being a program called the advanced college preparatory course, which was very heavily college oriented." Siebold took up the suggestion without much purpose: "I accidentally walked in and did it ... by God's choice — I don't know."

Between his mother's and his father's family "of nine or ten [each], of all of us, there are only about three people who have gone through college, one being a Catholic priest.... I saw all these people suffering through the Depression and the poor guys working in the shops and coming home dirty and filthy and dead tired, and struggling, and I decided that I wanted a white collar job. And I was going to be an engineer.... Father and mother ... really didn't understand [his interest in engineering], but "they were willing for me to go to high school." So he went to Baltimore Polytechnic High School because "I knew I couldn't afford to go to college.... I went there knowing that a lot of the people that went there came out and got into engineering type jobs as draftsmen." With a strong technical curriculum that included calculus, engineering mechanics, and strength of materials, "we were admitted to most colleges in an advanced standing ... even in the Naval Academy, they accepted our students without entrance exams." But college was not for Siebold — at least, not then.

When he graduated in 1942 he found a job with the Martin Company, which "recognized the people coming out of this [Baltimore Polytechnic High School] program as being capable of going into their engineering department. Particularly in those days everybody started on the drawing board.... They even offered a course in their drawing system, their engineering system, to us in high school on Saturdays. So I went on Saturdays.... We even studied an airplane called the '167', which is a predecessor of one of the lightweight bombers that Britain and France bought and used in the Battle of Africa. With that background, I no sooner finished high school — as a matter of fact, I was still taking finals — when I went down and was hired as a junior draftsman."

Siebold worked for Martin for over twenty years, interrupted only by a stretch in the Army after he was drafted. He proudly remembers virtually every aircraft or missile program he worked on: the Dyna Soar, the Martin B-26, "a number of Navy airplanes, all of the seaplanes, the P5Ms ... the B-57." In the 1950s he began working on missile programs. "A lot of them were military and a lot of them were research vehicles that came and went." As interesting as the work was, he "recognized that I needed to go to college.... If you're in an engineering department with lots of engineers and you don't have a degree and they do, it doesn't take you long to recognize that if you're going to get any place other than the menial tasks, you better get that degree." He began night school at The Johns Hopkins University, one of the pioneering institutions in continuing adult education, and earned his degree in mechanical engineering in 1961, at the age of forty.

During the 1950s Siebold worked on various advanced space vehicle designs as part of Martin's effort to get into the space business. "It was the little group of ten or twelve in so-called advanced design that put the basic concepts together. When an RFP [request for proposals] came in, we would look at those requirements and make the first cut at what the vehicle should look like, and then get more refined data from people that then supported us." By the time Siebold finished his degree, he "had left the design world and was now working more on the management side and [on] things called configuration management, control and configuration.... When the Titan III program started, I went to Denver as engineering rep.... Baltimore was doing subcontract ... engineering work under Denver's direction for that program. I became the engineering liaison man stationed in the Denver division for...about three years." When it was time to return to Baltimore in 1964, Siebold suspected that Martin was "going downhill.... I saw the handwriting on the wall.... I purely looked at it and said, 'Who's got all the money? Where's the best future?'.... NASA was it. They were at the forefront." On his way back from Denver he stopped off at NASA's Johnson Space Center in Houston "to talk about a job." His background appealed to the center, and he was soon hired and detailed to NASA's launch operations center at Merritt Island, Fla. When NASA combined its growing launch complex there with the new Kennedy Space Center in 1965, Siebold opted to remain with the Johnson Space Center and move to Downey, Calif., where North American (later Rockwell Corporation) was building hardware for the Apollo program. There he worked as JSC's resident test director for the first Apollo unmanned vehicle. He would stay at Downey, as a NASA representative working in on-site quality control, for the next twenty years.

The immigrant neighborhoods of New York, the Bronx and Brooklyn, were home in the 1920s and 1930s to countless boys who would grow up to leave their mark on the postwar expansion of American science and engineering. Whether these boys' families instilled in them a love of learning inherited from their European or rabbinical origins, or whether those families were convinced that a cosmopolitan profession such as medicine or science was the best vehicle of ascent from uprooted or marginal places in the American scheme of things, the effect was the same: the Bronx High School of Science and the Brooklyn Technical High School nurtured a significant proportion of the talent and training that would find its way into the U.S. space program.

Take Michael Goldbloom, born in Brooklyn in 1926. What led him to become an engineer? "I guess it's my father that led me in that direction. My father had no formal education. But he was probably one of the best educated men I've ever met. He was a voracious reader. He was interested in science.... He used to take me to the planetarium and the museum of science and industry when I was just 6, 7, 8 years old. I became very much interested [in science] at that early age." Goldbloom went to the Bronx High School of Science. He enlisted in the Navy in 1944, before he reached his eighteenth birthday, and was sent to radar technician school. Twenty months later Goldbloom was discharged and returned to school. Using his GI Bill benefits, he was able to complete his work for a bachelor of science degree from the College of the City of New York. He still keeps in his desk "the first good slide rule" that he ever owned, bought with his GI Bill money.

After earning a masters degree from Brooklyn College, Goldbloom took his first job, with the Sperry Gyroscope Company in Nassau County, N.Y. His training in the Navy and in graduate school had been largely in the field of automatic controls. "The reason that Sperry wanted me was to work on automatic pilots." In 1954 Goldbloom left New York, "never to return," and moved to Los Angeles to work for the Lockheed Missile Systems division. He stayed in California throughout the 1960s, working for various aerospace companies. He was working for the Northrop Corporation's planetary program division when Northrop decided, for business reasons, "to get totally out of the NASA marketplace." Goldbloom decided in 1970 to transfer to NASA in Washington so he could continue working in the planetary exploration program. What brought him to NASA was "the intellectual excitement of the job." Goldbloom had been fascinated by the notion of exploring the planets since he was a boy, "listening to Buck Rogers on the radio when I was six or seven years old. And the very prospect that I could earn a living doing science on Jupiter and sending a spacecraft to Uranus or Neptune.... I couldn't resist it."

Born in 1928, Charles Stern spent the first ten years of his life in Willimantic, Conn. and then moved with his parents into a middle class Brooklyn neighborhood of semi-detached homes. His father had graduated from Tufts University with a degree in chemistry, but had opted to go into business, working first in the haberdashery trade in Connecticut and then moving into a wholesale glass business in New York. Neither his father nor his mother — who had thought he would make a great accountant — had given him any particular encouragement to go into engineering. He was "not mechanically inclined. I'm not one of these kids from the sticks who was in my fourth car by the time I was fifteen, either.... I hardly knew what a car was. We had one, but I rode in it and that was it.... I had no great yearning to become an engineer or a scientist.... But World War II was on, and I thought ... 'Gee, I don't want to end up in a trench or in a tank.'" Stern chose to become an engineer "one hundred percent because of the war. If I'm going to get shot at, I want to get shot at up [in the air], not down here. If I'm going to fight, I'd like to fight clean." So he decided "I probably ought to go to a high school from which I could come out with some kind of technical training...and get into the [U.S. Army] Air Corps."

Charles Stern is another NASA engineer who received his schooling at Brooklyn Technical High School. He remembers it as "probably the finest technical high school in the country.... There were better scientific schools, but not technical. I took the aeronautical engineering course, which was ... a pre-engineering course, voca-tional ... not particularly suited as a college prep course because it didn't offer some of the math and language required to get into a lot of the universities at that time." When he graduated in 1946, Stern "figured [that] coming out of high school, I wouldn't have a chance to fly. At least not as a pilot. That was officer or college stuff." He would do "anything I could do that would get me a head start...in the aeronautical business.... It was, again, the war motivation, not any great desire to be a part of the national aeronautical research establishment." He applied for admission to Brooklyn Polytechnic School "because it was one of the few schools that would accept high school graduates with the kind of semi-vocational training I had: no language [or] math.... I didn't get in because there was this massive influx of veterans coming home from each of the theaters [of World War II]. So the next step was to ... enlist" in the Army Air Corps. "And I went down and failed the physical." He entered the hospital for successful medical treatment and "I hadn't been home more than a few more days...when I got a call from Brooklyn Poly: 'We have a vacancy.'" So fate finally smiled on Charles Stern and he got to go to college after all. "I took aeronautical engineering because that was probably all I was suited for — and because it sounded interesting. As I went through college, of course, it became more and more interesting and I did fairly well."

Stern graduated in June 1950 and war broke out in Korea shortly thereafter. Although he had applied for jobs with various naval research organizations as well as the NACA, he had hoped he would be able to work at the NACA's Langley Aeronautical Laboratory. But then, "all of a sudden, there was my greeting.... In November of 1950 I went to Fort Devens, was processed into Fort Dix, was processed down to Fort Eustis, Virginia, and spent my two years of Army [duty] at Fort Eustis." Fortuitously, Fort Eustis was "just up the road from Langley, which was wonderful, because it got me a head start." While still in the care of the Army, Stern was able to begin graduate work in a joint Langley-University of Virginia program in aeronautical engineering at Hampton, Va. He was released from the Army in November 1952 and began working at Langley before the year was out, completing his masters degree in aeronautical engineering during the evenings.

Aeronautical engineering did not become just interesting for Stern, it became downright exciting: He happened to enter the Langley laboratory at one of the aeronautical field's most creative periods. "You remember, we had a missile crisis gradually growing. In the early '50s we were trying to figure out how in the world to make a ballistic missile go intercontinental ranges — 5000 miles or more — reenter the Earth's atmosphere at almost orbital speed ... and survive till it reaches either the ground or air burst level. One of the things one had to do was study the [air] flow at those speeds. Or, if you couldn't simulate the flow at those speeds, you simulate the flow at the same energy levels, and at least you get a partial simulation for the heat transfer issues, which are the issues that are critical."

At both the Langley Laboratory and the NACA's Ames Research Center, established in 1939 at Moffet Field, Calif., aerodynamicists were struggling with the problem of designing a missile nose cone that would not burn up in the heat of reentry into the atmosphere. One way of simulating the extraordinary heat energy levels that affect nose cones on reentry was with shock tubes. When Stern went to Langley, he worked with the "aerodynamics of shock tube flows, shock tube boundary layers, shock tube heat transfer, shock attenuation behavior." It was through their shock tube work that engineers at Ames and Langley discovered the "concept of blunt body flows, which dissipate the energy in drag, heating the friction layer of the shock layer rather than heating the body" of the missile's nose cone itself.

"And you do that with a blunt body, not a sharp body, where all the heat goes into the skin."[6]

Stern's career with NASA was interrupted briefly when, succumbing to the lure of better pay, he moved to Massachusetts to work with the AVCO Corporation on reentry heating for ballistic missile nosecones. A year later, missing "the freedom to work in engineering science and not [to] have to worry about building [a] device," he left Massachusetts and returned to Langley.

———————

Henry Beacham is a sociological rarity among the older engineers who became part of NASA during the Apollo years. Born in 1928, he was raised in an upper middle class neighborhood in northwest Washington, D.C., the son of well-educated parents. His mother was an editor for *Vogue* magazine and wrote for the Baltimore *Sun*. She had also done publicity work for the women's suffrage movement and worked for the National Council for the Prevention of War. In the 1920s she and Beacham's father, a veteran newspaper man, formed an editorial research business, for which she wrote using a masculine pseudonym: "It was in the days when you didn't use women's names in the newspaper business." The theory behind their business was that "an editor could find out what happened ten years ago in a book, and he could find out what happened two weeks ago by looking through the papers. But there was an enormous gap of recent history — the ten year to one year ago [period]. The trick of the game [was] to give a writer an assignment that would be completed in a month and put into the mail and have that be something that editors all around the country would be interested in. And it worked."

To any one of the country boys who made their way out of rural America in the decade between the wars, Washington was the city; but those with cosmopolitan upbringings would look back on Washington in the 1930s and 1940s as "a very small town." To be active in local politics, as Beacham's parents were, was to be active in national politics. The elder Beachams "were friends of Justice [Louis D.] Brandeis, people like that." Beacham was sent to an exclusive private boys' school in suburban Bethesda, Md., where he mixed with the sons of lawyers, doctors, high-level civil servants, and affluent Washington area businessmen. His principal boyhood enthusiasm was boats; he built his own kayak and rowboat, boated on the South River near Annapolis, Md., and resolved as a teenager to become a naval architect. A brief experience working for his father proved generally unsuccessful, from both his and his father's points of view, and by the time he was ready to think about college, he had decided to make a career of engineering. After graduating from preparatory school in 1944, Beacham entered Duke University. There he majored in engineering with a minor in naval science, as part of the Navy's ROTC program. "Whereas the Army had ninety day wonders, the Navy was still playing around with officers and gentlemen.... They felt their officers should be college educated ... so they were going to let us get our degrees before we were commissioned and sent to sea." When he graduated, the Navy had more officers than it needed, so he was commissioned as an Ensign in the Naval Reserve. Since he was not called to active duty, he went to work for Eastman Kodak in Rochester, N.Y. "In Rochester they had two different labs: one, the film making; and the other, the camera operation. I was with the camera group for about a year and a half." Then his urbane upbringing caught up with him as he discovered (he thought) that he had in fact been "poorly educated." He went back to school at the University of Rochester, planning to take a graduate degree in physics — but not before taking courses in economics and government. "My father and mother were both newspaper people, and I missed a sense of what was going on in the world."

From the University of Rochester, where he obtained a master of science degree in mechanical engineering, Henry Beacham moved on to Syracuse University to do some teaching. Then, on the eve of the Korean War, he moved to the Naval Ordnance Laboratory at White Oak, Md. While working for the Navy could not guarantee that he would not be called to active duty, it might have helped; Beacham was able to stay at the laboratory for nine years doing "environmental testing and ultimately what used to be called operations research ... weapons analysis." In 1959 he transferred to the Navy's Naval Research Laboratory (NRL) at Anacostia. A few months after the Project Vanguard team was transferred from the NRL to the newly formed NASA in 1959, Beacham responded to the summons of a former NRL colleague and transferred to NASA's new Goddard Space Flight Center. There he began his NASA career by doing environmental testing for unmanned satellites.

Beacham could, he recalls, have gone to NRL in the early days and joined the Vanguard program, but "it never intrigued me." At the same time, NASA looked attractive compared to a career at the Naval Ordnance Laboratory. "You get bothered, after a while, computing ... the optimum way to kill ... the maximum number of people. I don't think I was especially excited about the space program. [I was] excited about the *challenge*, the difficulty of it, but I was never personally interested in flying and — I had no sense of the potential of what you might learn, in physics particularly, until I had been around a while. That makes it exciting now. But at the time, it was mostly an engineering challenge."

Bob Jones was one of those "kids from the sticks" who had regularly dirtied his fingers with auto parts. Born in 1932 in the shadows of Pittsburgh's steel mills, Jones left the industrial city as a small boy after his father (an electrical engineer) died, leaving his mother to fend for herself and her small son and infant daughter. There was a good bit of moving around as his mother fended. "Mother moved in with relatives in various small mill towns around the area. [Then] an adventuresome aunt," his mother's sister, also a widow, "went to Florida ... and wrote back to my mother about how oranges grow on trees and you could pick them, and why didn't she come down there? And so mother just picked up the two kids and went. The two sisters rented a house" in St. Petersburg, where Jones grew up, save for a year in North Carolina, where he and his mother moved with his stepfather, who worked for the A & P.[7] "We came back to Florida," where his mother made ends meet as a registered nurse, and "remained there except for some visits up north. By then I was a southerner and I didn't really care for the north."

Many years later, as a grown man, Jones grew nostalgic at seeing an exhibit at the Library of Congress of a "number 4 1/2 model erector set ... identical" to the one he played with as a youngster. "That was the toy I would never forget. I could hook it up early in the morning.... I remember all of those little parts, bolts, and brackets." Then there were the chemistry sets: "We made gun powder ... you know, kids get into things. We, in high school, got into building cannons ... take a four inch pipe, thread it, and put a cap on it, drill a hole in the cap and pour about two inches of lead for a good solid base, and then mix up your gun powder, which is saltpeter, charcoal, and sulfur. Pour that in there and ram toilet paper down in it for wadding, and put a handfull of ball bearings in there.... St. Pete's, at that time ... was not as built up, and the high school was considered fairly out ... so there were undeveloped areas nearby and we would take one of those things and go out in the vacant lot and tie it down to a tree and we made fuses either out of regular fire crackers, or you would take [a] fuse and soak it in gun powder and then put it in the oven to dry." The ingredients for gun powder could be bought at the local drug store. "Saltpeter is an anti-aphrodisiac for animals, and we would say, 'my father has a horse, you know'... potassium nitrate and powdered sulfur is used for any number of things.... We put a ball bearing right through the grammar school cafeteria wall one time. It made a neat, one inch hole.... That was the big thing, then, besides tinkering with cars."

Before he got his first car, Jones bought himself a "Cushman motor scooter. One of my good friends and I built the first — we thought — bicycle with a telescopic or sprung front fork, rather than a rigid frame, so that the wheel would follow, like springs on a car." Then came the 1941 model Ford coupe. "The '40 Ford was the 'in' car in the '50s because it had a little better ride than the '41, [but] I could not find a '40 that I could afford. So that was my first car. It was black. [In high school] my friends and I and our crowd, we dated and socialized, but not so much as the 'in' group — the cheerleader, football team, football heroes and socialites.... My friend's house was directly across the street from the high school. It had a big two-car garage.... We would be over there working on [the] hot '41 Ford, and those guys — you could see them there going to the dance. They wouldn't be dancing with much delight, except it was an excuse to steal booze if you could get a hold of some.... We were always working on cars. Frequently there would be a dance across there and we could sense that we were one type as opposed to the partying crowd. Usually they had a lot more money, too, and I worked different jobs. I worked at the news company packaging magazines ... during high school. And mostly worked in gas stations, and then got a job in a wheel alignment shop and continued that."

Growing up, Jones was not sure what he wanted to be. "Mother ... just let me kind of find my way.... She insisted I get good grades, scolded me when I didn't.... I made honor society. But she didn't really tend to drive me toward any career.... I knew I didn't want to be any of the human skill-oriented people, because I didn't think I did well with interactions with other people, and I tended toward things rather than people.... Psychology classes [in college], where you had to sit and talk about yourself, drove me crazy; but a physics class, I loved."

After he graduated from high school in 1950, Jones went to St. Petersburg Junior College, which was "dirt cheap, like, practically free. We didn't have any money and [the University of Florida at] Gainesville was the big state school.... I didn't know how I was going to make it up there, and wasn't motivated. Besides, it didn't have any engineering at all. [It was] primarily a business and liberal arts school]. Then I got an F in calculus, and that sort of just turned me off. So I continued to live at home and work at the Arrow Wheel Alignment Shop. They sponsored a quarter-mile stock car race, which I suppose was one of the reasons I went, because on Friday nights you could get the pit crew to a playing field ... in Tampa, and help ... mechanical things and contained energy.... That was heavy stuff!"

"All of my friends — the three guys that I ran with — one of them had dropped out in his freshman year and joined the Navy. My other good friend dropped out the semester before me, and let himself get drafted. And the third hung in there, but it was sort of like the neighborhood was coming apart. I didn't know where I was going, and I didn't know what I wanted to do, and everybody was going into the service, so I dropped out and went to work at the wheel alignment shop, knowing full well what would happen.... It took them about six weeks and they sent me my greeting. So I ended up in the Army, and I guess, subconsciously, I planned that, because I knew all about the GI Bill."

The U.S. Army sent Jones to Alaska, where he was stationed with a small company that ran a logistics depot. There he learned how to be a supply sergeant. Best of all, he could oversee the "weaponry, unit armor — which meant I got to maintain machine guns." While he hated the Alaskan winter, he loved its summer, and found a friend who introduced him to the natural wonders of the remote wilderness. "He was a registered big game guide, and I saw a lot of Alaska and had access to his car.... We went to Ghost Town, to the Kennecott copper mines. We went down to Chitina, salmon fished, and we hunted grizzly and shot caribou." Jones and his friend "hunted" with the camera too, often turning the lens on their buddies. But Jones was at heart a private person, and he still remembers the refuge he made for himself in the company supply room. "I even lived there for a while. I just put my cot in the back to get out of that mass — no privacy — type living, and an old cat came around and I befriended her. And so I had a companion. But they did move me out of there because of the fire hazard.... Those huts were so dry. At 30 below there is no moisture in the air."

While Jones was in the Army he realized that he knew what he wanted to do after all. "My interest had always been in the relationship between physical objects, and especially motion and linkages and those kinds of things." He would be an engineer. Two years later Jones returned to Florida; he managed, with the help of the GI Bill, to graduate from the University of Florida in 1958 with a degree in engineering. He realized that he had a personal need for "security," and as a result he "wanted to stay around Florida." Helped by good grades, he interviewed successfully with various engineering companies. "Ford came and wanted to make a regional service manager out of me. I knew enough about regional service managers to know that that was complaints, and that was really working with the public, and I didn't want to do that. Bendix did one of those 'fly me' [offers] up to Fort Wayne.... It was about ten feet of snow on the ground and they do the typical recruiting trip. You had lunch and they met you at the hotel and took you around. And I remember this — what they call bullpen.... They all had white shirts, and they all had ties on, and one guy was working on, like, a little bracket. And I thought about that, and the cold, the snow in my feet." Jones also got an offer from Florida Power. But "that's making steam, making electricity. Man, you make electricity day and night, day and night.... I had liked my power plant courses, [but] that's all you do."

His true career would begin with the Army; he was due to be interviewed by the U.S. Army ordnance department from Aberdeen Proving Ground. "It was automotive and mechanical and things that go 'clank'.... I thought, that was the place for me." But an Army officer he was to meet with "didn't show, and here I was in my new Sears, Roebuck suit, and I wandered down the hall and there was this outfit called the Army Ballistic Missile Agency. It was interviewing for engineers to work at Cape Canaveral.... They painted a pretty rosy picture ... interviewing specifically for an engineer to work in the weight and balance section of the booster and nose cones down there — in the assembly test section they called it — to determine the center of gravity and the weight of the warheads and the thrust units for the Redstone and Jupiter missiles.... There were some photographs of this thing that looked like an oil rig, and the guys up there were in leather jackets and they had boots on, and a tie. The idea of working outdoors with the hardware, hands-on — [and] I could be close to Mom and Gerry [his sister, a "starving artist"], and it's warm." Most of all, Jones would be close to the sheer mechanical power that had always excited him:

"I got [to Cape Canaveral] just as they were finishing up the Redstone program.... I was there for the first lunar probe, and ... there was a Juno that went up and turned ninety degrees. It was sitting there, and it came back on the pad and a shock wave came up the flame trench and blew the covers off, and a cigarette machine outside was pierced and the candy bars and cigarettes went everywhere and big chunks of concrete — I thought, 'this is sporty business! This beats the hell out of drawing brackets!' There's something about working on the rockets that's different than working on the space station, space craft, or facilities.... I suppose it's contained energy. I remember working on the Saturn I and IB. You remained on the pad while the LOX [liquid oxygen] prechilled, with xenon lights, and the wind blowing, and as those pipes chill, they scream. The vents are blowing and you are clear and the techs are buttoning it up. You're in a headset ... and this thing is groaning and moaning and the hydraulic pumps are coming on.... The real highs were either in the blockhouse, as a nice GS-5, GS-7 weight engineer, at the moment of ignition, hearing that sharp crack, or, if my alternate was in there, being at the road block, which was a quarter of a mile away ... sitting in the pick-up truck. We would watch that thing ignite a beautiful, absolute, thunderous roar, zillions of horsepower, and you visualize them valves workin' and them turbo pumps goin' ch-ch-ch-ch-ch-ch —." Or when the rocket was just "clearing the pad, just before the structure went back, during final closeout. The liquid oxygen on board. The thing is smokin' and ventin' and shakin' and screamin'.

"That's watching the hardware."

————————

Robert Strong, Dan O'Neill, Isaac Kuritzky, Ernest Cohen, Isaac Petrovsky, Henry Strassen, Werner Posen, Philip Siebold, Michael Goldbloom, Charles Stern, Henry Beacham, and Bob Jones: born between World War I and the eve of the Great Depression, they were the progeny of an America that would be barely recognizable to the younger men and women who would be working with them at NASA at the height of the Apollo era. They were the sons of an older industrial America, predominantly from the upper Midwest and the Northeast. Only one came from the impoverished countryside of the deep South, and none came from west of the Mississippi. Three came from the Eastern European immigration that populated this country's older urban centers and trades. Only three were sons of engineers. And only two, by any stretch of the imagination, could be considered offspring of an intelligentsia which, in this country as much as in Europe, dwelt principally in capital cities. With these two exceptions, theirs was the class that experienced the pain of the Great Depression more than any other, with its longing for a more secure place in the world, for salaried middle class stability. What they sought could be found most directly through the profession of engineering, unencumbered — partly because of its novelty — by the social barriers entrenched in some of the older professions, such as law and medicine.

With the exception of the three who attended Duke University and MIT, all attended public institutions and supported themselves partially or wholly while going through school. They were in the first cohort of young Americans to benefit from a nearly fourfold increase in the number who were able to go to college (from 8 percent in 1920 to 30 percent in 1959). They included the six from "blue collar" backgrounds who would be among the first in their families to go to college, as well as those who were of age to begin college when World War II broke out. In career aspirations as well as education they were not, as a group, particularly drawn toward airplanes and spacecraft. Two, it is true, had been inspired by Charles A. Lindbergh's 1927 solo flight from New York to Paris; these two, thus inspired, were among the first university-trained aeronautical engineers; both studied at MIT. (These two, one of whom also attended the University of Michigan, and the graduate of New York University, were among the earliest beneficiaries of the Guggenheim Foundation's effort to promote aeronautical engineering.)[8] For the rest, however, what propelled them forward was something more basic. Engineering provided not only relatively ready access to a salaried profession; it also provided an acceptable alternative to active military service, for engineers were eligible for draft deferments. The military's ROTC programs held out comparable inducements. One astutely noticed that aeronautics was "the coming thing," while two others recall having read science fiction as children. Only two confessed outright to having had an intellectual interest in science or engineering, although a few indicated as much when they remarked simply that they "liked" engineering or machinery.

All except the oldest, who was already at work at the NACA's Langley Aeronautical Laboratory when World War II broke out in 1939, joined the military as enlistees or draftees during World War II — one of them on the German side. Most of the eleven began their careers in the 1940s working for engineering firms; only one ventured to make a career with the military. Seven of these eleven engineers had no less than nine, and in two cases had had as much as twenty-one, years' experience working in private industry before they went to work for NASA. This group included two of the six who had been working with NASA's predecessor organizations — the NACA, ABMA, and NOL — when NASA was formed in 1958 and were thus among the new agency's initial engineering corps. Five joined the agency between 1958 and 1970.

Sharing, with few exceptions, generally similar social origins and career aspirations, these eleven men were bound together by the fact that the route toward the fulfillment of their aspirations was eased by the nation's need to mobilize not only military troops, but military technology, in the service of war. All were initially employed by either federal engineering agencies or private firms stimulated by wartime demands. That they were equipped for the jobs they found, or for which they were in some instances recruited, was attributable to the fact that the federal government, directly or indirectly, encouraged them to pursue engineering careers. Private aspirations converged with national need as World War II (like so many previous wars) became an engine of social change.

---

[1] See Appendix C, table 4.

[2] "It is sweet and fitting to die for one's country" (Horace), quoted in "1914," by Wilfred Owen (1893-1918).

[3] Holst, an English composer, completed his orchestral suite "The Planets" in 1918.

[4] Jerome Clarke Hunsaker served as chairman of the NACA from 1941 to 1956.

[5] *The Statistical History of the United States from Colonial Times to the Present*.(Stamford, Conn.: Fairfield Publishers, 1965), Series Q 106-116, Y 357-367.

[6] The discovery of the blunt-body theory was made in 1952 by Harvey Allen at Ames Research Center. See Elizabeth A. Muenger, *Searching the Horizon: A History of Ames Research Center, 1940-1976*, NASA SP-4304 (Washington, D.C.: U.S. Government Printing Office, 1985), pp. 66-68.

[7] Atlantic and Pacific Tea Company, a supermarket chain.

[8] The Daniel Guggenheim Fund for the Promotion of Aeronautics was established in 1926. Guggenheim grants went to eight major universities: California Institute of Technology, Massachusetts Institute of Technology, New York University, the University of Michigan, the University of Washington, Stanford University, Georgia Institute of Technology, and the University of Akron. See Richard P. Hallion, *Legacy of Flight: The Guggenheim Contribution to American Aviation* (Seattle: University of Washington Press, 1977).

The draft is the largest educational institution in the world.

Robert S. McNamara
Secretary of Defense (1961–1968)
Remark to Reporters, 1966

Chapter 2
Beginnings: 1932–1948

The last time Hank Smith — now a facilities design engineer at Kennedy Space Center — piloted an airplane was in 1959. He was a senior at the University of Florida, but by then he had already put in a successful stint training as a Navy fighter pilot. A Korean War veteran finishing college on the GI Bill, he was in an all-veteran fraternity, and "there was this guy ... he was probably 22 or 23, who had a little airplane." Smith's fraternity buddies, no doubt impressed by heart-stopping tales of combat flying, pestered him to fly the fellow's airplane. "I never flew a really light airplane — they call them puddle jumpers — like little Piper Cubs. This was a little high-wing tail-dragger. I said, 'I don't know how to fly your airplane.'" The owner of the tail-dragger was insistent; "he said, 'aw, come on.' Well, the fraternity guys kept bugging me, 'come on Smith, you're a big hot shot Navy pilot! You go fly his airplane.'"

So "one day in the spring, I said, 'OK, well, tomorrow morning we'll go fly, if it's nice.'" It was nice, and the two men took off in the little plane. "I sat beside him. He took it up to a couple of thousand [feet]. He said, 'OK, do you want to fly it?' I said, 'OK. Now, I'm going to tell you something that we learned in the Navy. When I say, 'I've got it,' I've got it. I'm in charge. Get your hands off. Put 'em over your head. I don't care what you do.' Then I said, 'when I say, you've got it, *you've got it*. We've got to do that, because I don't know your plane.' So he says, 'OK, that's a deal. If we have trouble, *you've got it*.' I say, 'OK, I've got it.' So I took this thing through some 15 angle bank turns — you know, you had to use rudder pedals to coordinate the whole flight. Then I say, 'OK, you've got it.' He says, 'come on, fly it!' I say, 'OK, I've got it again.... Will this thing do 30 degree angle bank turns?' He said 'yes.' I say, 'will it do 45 degree angle bank turns?' He said, 'yes.' I say, 'will it do 60 degree angle bank turns?'

"He says, 'I don't think so! I don't think I've ever done over 45 degree angle bank turns!'

"I said, 'look back that way,' because I knew where we were going. By the time he stuck his head back there I cranked that thing up, put on every bit of power I had, and did a 60 degree angle bank turn, rolled it back, did another one, rolled again, did another.... I didn't know if I could do it, but I had just enough power to hang in there.

"Then I said, 'you've got it!'

"This kid's eyes were huge! Big!"

That a fraternity brother might own his own airplane was almost unthinkable in 1934 when Smith was born in Oneonta, then a small city of 12,000 in upstate New York. "We lived out in the country ... a mile outside of town ... that's all dairy country." Smith and the other youngsters worked on the farms, putting hay up in barns and hauling and spreading manure. "We went through all that. Then, in the fall, the next big thing was to put corn in the silos.... We'd work from 8 or 9 o'clock until dark.

"We did ... a lot of odd jobs. I worked in the filling stations. One time a boy and I—for several years we took about a half an acre and grew vegetables, and sold them over in the city. We always had a garden. My mother canned and froze and did everything like that.... We grew carnations.... Easter Sunday morning there'd be four or five people making corsages.... We'd be up all night and I'd start delivering about 4 or 5 o'clock in the morning to the Catholics.... I'd deliver until noon-time. I never made it to church on many occasions. In the afternoon, it was plants, lily plants. I had to get all those delivered."

Oneonta was a railroad town, one of those places through which the Delaware and Hudson passed on its way from Pennsylvania through New York State to Canada, mostly carrying coal to Montreal. Smith's father, like "just about everybody's father, worked on the railroad. He worked in the shops area. They did a lot of fabricating of box cars, repaired cars. They had built passenger cars in the old days. There was a big roundhouse there where they fixed locomotives.... We used to go down and play on the trains ... in the empty box cars. Dad used to take us every once in a while down to the big old roundhouse where they repaired things, and if they wanted to move it around, we'd get on and watch it go around." Smith was impressed by the locomotives, "those big powerful things. I always can remember the filthiness of them, how dirty everything was.

"At one time [Smith's father] worked with his hands. Then ... in later years, he ran the storeroom, handling parts and materials. He ran it, kept it stocked, and serviced it." While his mother was mostly a homemaker, she had gone "to a little business school" and worked occasionally as "a legal secretary for the various attorneys around my home town ... back then, to make ends meet."

Going to college had become, by the time Smith was growing up, the normal expectation of Oneonta's "solid" families. "We'd all go to college; we'd all graduate.... If you were a good student, you went on to college." The expectation of a college education had already begun to work its divisions on the town's high school students. "There were three curriculums: there were the guys who were jocks—did the PE [physical education] stuff, and shop. They also had business courses." And then, "for the good students," there was the precollege curriculum, in which students took mathematics, biology, chemistry, and physics. Smith was a good student, and he "loved math." His father and mother "were eager for me to go to RPI [Rensselaer Polytechnic Institute]," and Smith, too, "always wanted to go to RPI, [to] get an engineering degree there."

But he never made it to RPI. Instead, he went to one of New York State's two-year technical institutes, where he began a course in electrical technology. Before he could finish, he "got inspired to go into the U.S. Navy." Naval recruiters came to the campus "and started recruiting…. The uniforms were really sharp — the blues, the golds, the white hats — really sharp! Big time stuff! … They told everybody back then that you were the top 10 percent of American youth. You know, like the 'Marines need a few good men.' And … the guys that were accepted into that program were good…. When I started in all the testing … there were, like, 38 guys from all over that were getting physicals, testing, both mental and physical. Out of that group … seven of us made it…. The rest either couldn't pass the mental test, which I thought was easy," or the physical. And thanks to "all that good farm work, [Smith] was in good physical shape."

He was accepted into the Naval Aviation Cadet program when he was twenty years old. He stayed with the Navy for four years, undergoing rigorous flight training and officer's ground school at Pensacola, Fla. and the Naval Air Station at Cecil Field, near Jacksonville. By then he had become a Florida resident, which meant that he would have had to pay out-of-state tuition had he wanted to go to RPI. Because he had gone into the Navy during the Korean War (although he was never sent to Korea), he was eligible for GI Bill benefits. He enrolled at Jacksonville University — "a small private institution" — where his new wife had a teaching position. "I went two years there…. I took all this pre-engineering stuff, the chemistry and all … to get all this stuff out of the way."

Two later he transferred to the University of Florida, where he earned a degree in civil engineering in 1962. He and his wife had "bought a little home," and when it came time to look for a job he applied to the U.S. Army Corps of Engineers in Jacksonville. The Corps "had started all the design for NASA for the Kennedy Space Center…. In the process, they decided — since it was getting so big — that they needed a Canaveral District office…. So they formed that spring the Canaveral District office, and in July of '63, two or three hundred of us came down here." Smith worked with the Corps for about a year, until March 1964, when he went to work for NASA as a facilities design engineer. "This whole place … on this side of the river,[1] I've seen come out of the ground…. We buried jeeps in the mud — had sand in the hair and face." He never left.

Paul Dussault was always something of a misfit, someone who "oscillated around" a lot when he was young, before he decided what to do with his life. His life began on the south side of Chicago, now in the inner city; he lived in a flat with his mother after his father left home when Dussault was too small to remember. Born in 1932, he led an adventuresome boyhood, watched over by a parent who was both tolerant and "hard-driving." His mother had been an Army nurse during World

War II, which meant that he also lived, off and on, with his grandmother. "When I was in elementary school, I was at the top of my class. I got good grades.... We went out and did lots of things when I was a kid. We'd go over the whole city exploring. I think every weekend there were a bunch of us who would always go downtown to the museums and things like this, and ride on the streetcars all over the place. It was cheap transportation. Our parents let us go around ... when I was about eleven years old, twelve years old, I was riding all over the subways. Then something happened when I got to high school. There was some misfortune there in the print shop class ... there were a lot of other things that go on with people of that age. And so I thought to myself, 'Well, I'm just going to get by from here on out.' So that's what I did.

"I got red Fs all through high school.... I would go about four days every week. I knew if I was absent more than that, you automatically flunk. But ... I always had it calculated right down to the last day. So you could miss 20 percent of the time and still pass.... I would take off every Friday. [Mother] knew I was messing around and she knew I was a lot smarter than that. I don't think she was too worried. She figured I'd straighten out. I was ... interested in something different than everybody else.... I've always been interested in airplanes ... I used to work on model airplanes. And when I got to high school ... I got interested in World War I airplanes." So on the days when he skipped school, Dussault scoured old magazine stores for flying magazines from the 1930s and built airplanes. Everybody else was "interested in World War II airplanes ... but I wanted to go back further, because this was something that wasn't so well known.... I used to — rather than work with kits and stuff like that — I'd rather make my own drawings and work from there and build them up.... I would work with the whole structure of the airplane.... They didn't fly very well.... They were too heavy; I built them strong.... But I had a lot of fun building them."

Dussault did his calculations right and managed to graduate from high school and enter a "junior college anybody could get in in those days. I was there for a couple of weeks and decided I didn't want to do that either.... I was playing on a basketball team, and ... I was also working in this hospital [as an orderly] where my mother was the head nurse.... I just went there because there were a lot of student nurses there.... So I quit the school, I played basketball eight hours a day at the Y." And when "basketball season was over, I joined the Army." By then the United States was at war in North Korea, and Dussault hankered after the excitement of combat: "I kept volunteering to get there.... I always liked the military.... I was trying to make myself look older during World War II, so I could join up." His luck held, and he managed to join "a special regimental combat team where General William Westmoreland was the commanding officer.... I enjoyed the whole thing, because seeing places like Tokyo and stuff like that in Asia was good experience.... I was in the paratroopers, which was kind of fun.... I liked airplanes."

When the Korean War was over Dussault knew for certain only one thing: he did not want to stay in the Army. He tried junior college for a few months, taking liberal arts courses, working "a little harder this time, and [I] got pretty good grades." But he still had no idea what he wanted to do with himself, and he needed money, so he went to work for a meatpacking company in the Chicago stockyards. A brief inspiration to become a pilot for the U.S. Air Force came to nothing, and he supposed that he could stay close to airplanes by becoming an aeronautical engineer. Since the University of Illinois "would, then, admit anyone regardless of grades," he went there and after two years majored in aeronautical engineering.

At the University of Illinois one of his professors introduced him to orbit theory, which he was studying when the Soviet Union launched Sputnik I in 1957. "The people at the University of Illinois did some crude tracking of the spacecraft to pin down its orbit. And we were making some calculations on it ... it was kind of exciting." Then he began taking courses in rocketry and design, and decided that astronautics might be even more exciting than airplanes. Two years into the "space age" he realized that he would have to go to the University of California in Los Angeles (UCLA) to find the "courses in orbit design and ... planning missions, space missions in the future" that he wanted. He got a summer job with the Rand Corporation, which was hiring graduate students. "They were doing all kinds of exciting things there.... I worked on some interplanetary orbits." He had gone to UCLA principally to study with "this guy ... who was from the old school that had thought up some nice, elegant ways to calculate all of these orbits by hand. But when the computers came along, it kind of put him out of business."

In the summer of 1960, half-way into a master's degree program, Dussault ran out of money and began looking for a job. He found one at NASA's Marshall Space Flight Center. Dussault's career at Marshall was brief. "I hadn't finished my master's" thesis and "people were a little irritated with me at Marshall, because I was working on my thesis while I was there.... I did mainly my stuff, which was on libration point satellites." A libration point, he explains, is "an equilibrium point in an isolated, two-body gravitational system, such as the Earth and the Moon, [which] are somewhat isolated in the solar system. Or it could be the Sun and the Earth, or the Sun and Jupiter. It would not be the Sun and the Moon, for instance, because the Moon is really going around the Earth.... There are five equilibrium points in this two-body system. This is a general sort of thing that holds throughout the universe.... Now, if you place a spacecraft at one of these points, with just the right velocity, then it will stay in the same configuration relative to the other two bodies. So it's kind of in equilibrium with them." The notion of a gravitational equilibrium between the Earth and the Moon has been an inspiration for space colony enthusiasts, who have proposed locating colonies at libration points.[2]

Dussault mailed his thesis to UCLA and then decided to become a mathematician. He returned to the University of Illinois and "did almost all the course work for a degree in mathematics, but I didn't like the pure mathematics courses. I despised them.... And I didn't take linear algebra and real variables. Those awful things. I couldn't take that stuff at all." Again he ran out of money. He found work for a summer at the U.S. Naval Ordnance Laboratory. "And you know, you get out there in the real world and things are kind of dull and kind of drab.... I wanted to go back to school again."

During his last year at the University of Illinois, Dussault had become "obsessed with one subject — general relativity theory and cosmology. I really got into the thing, and all of the mathematics that they had in it. I took courses in tensor calculus … it had so many physical applications, I really liked it. So I thought 'I'll try to get into mathematics up at Berkeley.'" On his way back to California he made a detour through Queen Elizabeth College at the University of London, England, where he planned to work with a physicist who shared his enthusiasms — and, he confesses, enjoy the company of the college's many comely young women. "I was over there all of three days after going over there on the Queen Mary. It was a nice trip. But … I decided, 'Gee, I don't like the way students live over here.' It was pretty bad. You live in hovels. I thought, 'I'm not used to this anymore; I don't think I can take this.' So I took an airplane home.

"I had no job, no money, nothing. And I said, 'Gee, I'd better go back out to California and see if I can get a job.' So I just drove my car out to California, and started looking for a job…. It turned out, I got there at just the right time." He found a job at Lockheed Missiles and Spacecraft's research laboratory at Palo Alto, where he worked with John Breakwell and Stanley Ross, specialists in orbit theory. "Ross, at that time, was working on a contract for Marshall Space Flight Center to do the interplanetary flight handbook for NASA. And people still refer to this thing…. So I helped him draw up all the plots … he gave me a lot of crummy work to do and I seemed to do it with relish, so … he liked to have me around."

John Breakwell, meanwhile, had become "a professor at Stanford University…. We were within a stone's throw of the university…. Breakwell, being over there … encouraged me to come back…. I got into the school all right, because my grades were good…. In the meantime, I got married … my wife had lots of money and all I had was lots of debts." His mother had remarried and built up a profitable nursing home business. Between the two women, there was enough money to put him through school.

He completed all of his course work at Stanford but "kept putting off the oral examinations." Money began to run out; he was being paid "a paltry sum," and it was time to look for a job again. This time he found one with a space mission planning group for NASA's Electronic Research Center, located in Boston. "I'd have to go back and forth to ERC all the time. And I had a terrible fear of flying, but I overcame it…. I used to jump out of planes." But as a passenger, "I didn't have any control over the situation. That's what I don't like." He worked for the Electronic Research Center for three years; most of the time he was actually located at NASA's Ames Research Center. Meanwhile, with the help of Stanley Ross, he was able to get a NASA fellowship at Stanford University to complete his doctorate "working day and night, weekends, everything — well, I was really interested in what I was doing, too.

"I had a lot of ideas I had developed in my thesis. One of the main ones that had some applications as far as NASA was concerned was a data-relay satellite for communications off the far side of the Moon. And it involves being in a libration point orbit … and controlling this spacecraft, because the libration point orbits are not stable…. So I did all of the first work on this stuff. And then I thought, 'I'm going to see some of this stuff used, because I'm not interested in just writing papers'…. I tried to get this started when I was at Ames … but people just kind of laughed. And there were scientific applications also, putting a spacecraft in a halo orbit about the

Sun and the Earth where it could monitor the solar wind as it came in towards the Earth.... I took that [idea] to some of the space science guys at Ames ... and they said, 'Nah, we're not interested in that'.... I said, 'Hey, you can put it in the tail of the Earth and just leave it there all the time.' 'Nah, we aren't interested in that.' Most of the people that you find working at NASA are specialists in one thing. And they don't seem to want to know what anybody else is doing.The one thing I did get with my jumping around in different areas is, I have a pretty good background in physics and space science and mathematics and engineering. So [it was the] perfect thing for a systems engineer coming into NASA, and then all my model airplane work early on, when I get into the spacecraft systems, it's the same type of thing."

Once at the Electronic Research Center, Dussault discovered that "they weren't interested in space science, but they were interested in the communications on the far side of the moon. And the lunar landings were taking place around that time [and] the orbiting of the Moon. And it became pretty obvious that they were having problems communicating with these guys on the far side. So I thought, 'Gee, I'm in NASA now, I'm going to start writing letters.' So I wrote a letter to George Low, saying, 'Hey, you ought to worry about the safety problem here, you know'.... He wasn't too happy getting it. 'Who is this upstart telling me I should do something different?'" Dussault got "a very short reply, just 'Thanks for your information; we'll file it somewhere.' The people at the Electronic Research Center (ERC) were pretty interested in this.... But nobody took ERC very seriously; that place was the outer edges of the NASA system."

NASA's Electronic Research Center was closed down in 1969, and its facilities transferred to the Department of Transportation. Dussault, who (along with his wife) had not liked living in Boston anyway, had to look elsewhere for work. Finally he found a place for himself at Goddard Space Flight Center, where there was some interest in a lunar communications satellite. That interest was short lived, but Dussault stayed on at Goddard, continuing to work out his ideas in the development of trajectories for unmanned satellites.

George Sieger, like Paul Dussault, was left fatherless as a small boy and also marvels over the freedom for adventure that meant when he was growing up. World War II not only provided his mother an occupation and an income (as it had Dussault's mother), but exposed him to an early and lasting enthusiasm: airplanes. Sieger was born in Toledo, Ohio, where his mother operated a boarding house to support herself, George, and his two sisters. There she sheltered enlisted men (and, after the war, veterans) as they passed through town. There were "steam-fitters who worked at the local refineries. We had a semi-pro basketball team in there. We had country 'n western singers.... They'd go through and stay anywhere from a couple of days to weeks at a time," remembers Sieger. "After they would leave, they would send various packages, mementos, stuff that they had gotten overseas.... So I had a continuous source of everything from war relics to tons of balsa wood — literally huge boxes of balsa wood.... A couple of the people that we had got me interested in modeling various airplanes.... They'd send me aircraft recognition manuals, and I became very interested in the military services, and in particular, flying."

The self-confidence he would later need hovering over the controls at mission operations at Johnson Space Center during an Apollo mission came to him as a boy. "It came from the fact that to a great extent I was on my own to pick and choose and make my decisions from a very early age. I used to drive my mother nuts. One day, I'd be there coming home from high school." Then "I'd have a couple of days off from work, and I'd hitch-hike to see the air races — say, 'Hi, Mom, I'm going!' Christ, if my kids did that to me today, I'd have cardiac arrest!"

When Sieger "was in late grade school and early high school, I was ... building my own airplanes. Originally, I started off from kits, and found out that the kits left a lot to be desired. I had [acquired] a hard and practicable knowledge of aerodynamics, just in the process of building various airplanes. And I finally came to the point where I started designing my own airplanes." His first flight happened when he was a teenager; a brother-in-law took him to Franklin Field, where he had the first of many flights in "an old Piper J-2 Cub." Sieger's interest in airplanes and flying readily transferred itself to spaceflight, as he began to devour, in the 1940s, articles by "the Wernher von Brauns and the Willy Leys who [had] written in several of — I guess, at that time, what was considered pulp magazines ... those were the only magazines that would publish some of their far-out thoughts."

By his senior year in high school at Toledo Central Catholic, Sieger was ready for an imaginary venture into space, writing for his first term paper "a thesis ... on going to the Moon, where I had taken some of the more advanced thinking of the von Brauns and the Willy Leys and, to a great extent, sketched out the basic type machine that would go to the Moon. I was naive enough to believe it could be as simple as a three-stage rocket.[3] I designed all of the interior portions of the rocket.... The unfortunate thing is, I never thought how to get back.... And when I was in the Air Force over in Formosa, in October of '57, I also had the opportunity to see the impact of Sputnik I on people in the Far East. There was no doubt in my mind that I wanted to be associated with space at the earliest opportunity I could. But at the same time, I was also interested in aircraft flying."

High school had been especially important to Sieger. "They had an extremely good engineering school associated with [it] ... a coop program, where, as you finished your second year of drafting, you then picked a direction, whether you would go into the mechanical side ... the surveying side ... the electrical side. They had several good instructors, who turned me on to ... looking forward to going to college. I also had some fine chemistry and physics teachers." He would not be the first, nor would he be the last, youngster to be taken under the wing of a dedicated and enterprising teacher determined to live and act the pieties of a democratic American education.

Things were tight in the Sieger household as George, his mother, and two sisters all worked to make ends meet and have enough left over for the sisters to attend nursing school. For Sieger, the fruits of hard work turned into a mixed blessing. On one hand, he earned two scholarships — one to the U.S. Naval Academy, and the other to a Naval ROTC program at Notre Dame. But "I had been carrying several jobs throughout" high school, including a job "at the A & P warehouses, and the standard fare down there was … a quart of chocolate milk and some brownies for supper every night when you got home from school; I had been doing that for a couple of years in a row." The result was diet-induced diabetic symptoms, and he "flunked both of [the] physicals" required by the Navy.

Undaunted by this reverse in the fortunes of one of her charges, Sieger's history teacher at Central Catholic, "Sister Mary Mark … gave me the encouragement to go off and believe that I could get through college on my own. She … kept me going on…. My father was a World War I veteran, and she had done enough research to find out that … the State of Ohio Elks Association provided funding for schooling for [children of] deceased veterans of World War I." Sieger won a modest scholarship from the Elks — "it was five hundred dollars a year; in the early '50s, that was a hell of a lot of money" — which he took to begin work on a B.S. degree program at Parks College in East St. Louis, Ill. Parks was one of the few aviation schools in the country that offered a B.S. degree, and Sieger was keen to get into a U.S. Air Force aviation training program, which required one year of college. His sisters would work successfully with him to repair his diet, so he could pass his physical. But there was more to Parks College than convenience. "I liked their basic philosophy — that in order to graduate from school you had to be able to design an airplane, build an airplane, and fly an airplane…. As you were approaching the end of your curriculum, you would get into a two-year design project where you would actually take and build that … airplane at Parks College."

He finished work for his B.S. degree in three years and in 1954 applied for and received his appointment for Air Force flight training. During the nine-month hiatus between graduation and his reporting date, he worked for McDonnell-Douglas Aircraft at Lambert Field in St. Louis. There he learned "an awful lot about aircraft flight test data reduction [working on] one of the first of the true supersonic airplanes, the F-101A, [and] the XV-1 Convertaplane, which was a pulsejet-driven helicopter." In the spring of 1955 he finally began his flight training for the U.S. Air Force, graduating from basic to propellor and then jet-driven aircraft before being assigned to a fighter squadron. It was during that training period that he met another person who would make a large difference in his life: Morris Coleman. "He was a barnstormer, crop duster, and flight instructor. He taught you an awful lot, not only about flying, but about people. And I think he was very instrumental in developing a large amount of my attitudes [about] working with people…. His philosophy in dealing with your crew chief was one of the most instrumental … because the crew chief's the guy who is ultimately responsible for you, your ass, and your airplane. You take good care of him and he'll take good care of you…. You've got to earn respect, so right off the bat, you proceed to earn it. He also taught me to fly."

Sieger was attached to the 13th Air Force and sent to Korea to fly F-86s. "We got an opportunity to fly all over the Far East…. We ranged down into Okinawa, Formosa; we got down into the Philippines…. We were all over in Thailand, and we got an opportunity to see the Far East…. It was the best flying in the world." Flying tankers (what the Air Force evidently had in mind for him next) would have been too much of a let-down; Sieger left active duty and returned to McDonnell-Douglas in St. Louis. He had hoped to get a slot as a test pilot, but "at that time they were knee deep in pilot slots, so I picked up a flight test engineering slot." He began work for McDonnell, about 1958, at Holloman Air Force Base working on F-101B and F-102B aircraft and on McDonnell's new missile program. For two years he worked for McDonnell, learning what he could from the experience of "hands-on operational engineering."

By 1960 NASA's Space Task Group, newly formed at Langley Research Center to orchestrate the Mercury — the first American 'man in space' — program, was advertising in *Aviation Week* for capable young men with operational engineering experience. Sieger applied and was accepted. He soon found himself working in the control center at Cape Canaveral during the Mercury launches. In time, millions around the world would see the back of his head as he peered at display screens or bent over controls at NASA's mission control in Houston; few were aware of the cool-headed temperament needed to talk men — however much of the "right stuff" they might have — through the perils of the remote and unforgiving sea of space.

The Southern Railway passes along the eastern slopes of Virginia's Blue Ridge mountains and crosses the James River at Lynchburg, the city where Ed Beckwith was born in the worst year of the Depression. Surrounded by the rolling hills of some of the loveliest country in the East, home of Virginia's fabled gentry, Lynchburg has struggled off and on to sustain its mixed community of small factories, merchants, bankers, rail entrepot, and local and neighboring colleges. The city itself ushers the southward bound toward the Piedmont's small manufacturing region that spreads loosely from Danville down through North Carolina, a result of the water power that flows east from the mountains. "My birthday," says Beckwith, still sensitive to the deprivations of poverty, "is 1933, which indicates probably a small family. I was the only child. Of the people I knew, almost all were either single, or only had one sibling.... We became close to one another ... through the family." The two principal industries in Lynchburg at that time employed Beckwith's parents. "Father was with a railroad express company ... he was always called 'the extra board,' which meant that he did a job each week or so, looking at the board to see which jobs were available according to seniority. Sometimes he rode the mail car or freight car to various cities from Lynchburg. Sometimes he just handled freight." Beckwith's mother worked in the Craddock Terry shoe factory.

"I wanted to be a pilot.... Across the street from me lived Woody Edmondson, who was the national aerobatics champion for several years during the war.... I was just a little kid. I knew him — not well.... I could see him drive in and drive out." And so Beckwith became enamored of airplanes. "I was the first kid on the block to build stick models and that kind of thing.... Back in those days, you were fortunate to find a balsa wood kit. They were pine, because balsa was being used by the military in World War II.... I was in sixth grade in school; I remember carrying my first model to the auction and auctioning it off. It was very popular, and it went very quickly.... I was excited."

Beckwith had finished high school and begun college at Lynchburg College when disaster struck his family. "My parents both were in an automobile accident and neither worked for a while. I stopped school and went to work at Craddock Terry…. I nailed on shoe heels." However, a friend of the family who knew of Beckwith's enthusiasm for airplane model building suggested the NACA's apprenticeship program at Langley Research Center near Hampton, across the James River from Newport News. Beckwith applied, and after hardly a month of nailing heels into shoes at Craddock Terry, Beckwith began work at Langley in June 1953. "Immediately I wanted to get into the model shop…. Of course it was filled up. I went into the sheet metal shop."

The NACA also helped Beckwith finish college. Under its cooperative education program, he returned to school at the Norfolk Division of William and Mary, and at Virginia Polytechnic Institute, while he was working at Langley and accumulating credit toward an advance in grade and salary. His college studies under the coop program were a "straightforward [curriculum] in aeronautical engineering…. The only thing that the coops did not have to do … during those days, was — for one English course we were allowed to substitute reports that we had to write back at NACA…. We didn't get any credit for it; we just didn't have to take it.

"During the coop plan, each time you came back to work after spending a quarter at school, you went to a different organization…. During those early days, coops were cheap labor, so we spent a time in the sheet metal shop…. I had already spent a year there, [and] in the machine shop, the wood shop — which is the model maintenance shop; in the instrument research division, in which we used to calibrate instruments … and then, after those had been covered, you went into some research organization — hypersonics, subsonics, whatever."

Finally, in 1958, Beckwith earned a bachelor's degree in aeronautical engineering. "In my travels around [Langley] field … working at various places, I learned to know people…. I was fortunate enough to be able to get to enough places in engineering — besides research scientist — to know where I wanted to go, and they were willing to have me back, so I went to what was called the free-flight tunnel … flew models in a wind-tunnel." It had been a long way there, but he made it.

———

One of the few black men to reach the upper tiers of NASA's management hierarchy,[4] William McIver was another child of Brooklyn, where he was born in 1936. He was one of five children; his mother was a homemaker, and his father was a freight inspector for the Lehigh Valley Railroad. He remembers his boyhood as having been "fairly sheltered. I was largely interested in athletics and science ever since I was a kid. I used to listen to these radio programs like Captain Midnight and … the Green Hornet. I … always remember sending in for secret decoder rings and … got interested in all that sort of stuff. And particularly during the Second World War, there were all these things about secret weapons and NAZI agents … hiding out in Patagonia developing a secret weapon and so forth. So I got interested … in science and engineering from a sort of adventure standpoint."

While he does not say so, his parents must have urged schooling on their children, for of their four offspring who survived childhood, one became an electrical engineer, one a political scientist, one went into business administration, and one, William, obtained a doctorate in aerospace science. The strongest influence on his career was one of his father's godsons, a chemical engineer who gave William a summer job working in his company. "I used to work part time [for him]. He'd let me do drafting.... In hindsight, now, I can see that it was really just busywork, but at the time it was great.... He had a small company, a precision machine shop, so I got a chance to actually get my hands on a lathe and a drill press."

McIver went to Brooklyn Technical High School, "one of the three competitive [science and technical] high schools in New York City. There's Bronx High School of Science. There's Peter Stuyvesant and there's Brooklyn Tech. Those are the science and engineering high schools. Then there's the school of needle trades, the school of fashion and design, the school of music and art.... I went to the engineering school largely because it was in Brooklyn, and because of the athletic teams.... There was also some snob value in going to a competitive high school like Brooklyn Tech. And then, probably the key thing was that CCNY [the City College of New York] in those days was absolutely tuition free.... If you had something like an A average in high school ... you could go to CCNY tuition free, which is, thank heaven, what I was able to do. And that was very lucky, because then I really didn't have to work full time or anything like that when I was in college. I could study.... I was very fortunate."

McIver now chuckles over his great expectations when he graduated from CCNY in 1957 with a mechanical engineering degree: "I — as [were] many City College guys — was fairly self-confident. I decided I wanted to come to Lewis [Research Center] and I had heard about people like Si Ostrach, Frank Moore, and Harold Mirels.[5]... I wanted to join their research group — with my bachelor's degree!" When he was interviewed for his first job at Lewis, McIver was politely told that he might not be quite ready to work with the likes of Ostrach, Moore, and Mirel, but that he could get his feet wet in some research at Lewis, and, after he had some experience, he might move into "analytical research." He was hired by George M. Low,[6] then chief of the special project branch of the supersonic propulsion division at Lewis. Low encouraged him to do graduate work at Case Western Reserve with NASA support "as long as I made up the time on Saturdays or Sundays." This McIver did, earning his master's (1959) and doctoral (1964) degrees while working at Lewis.

McIver finally got to work with Simon Ostrach who, in addition to being his branch chief at Lewis, was his professor at Case Western Reserve. "Those were the glory days ... of aerodynamics and high-speed research." Like so many aerodynamicists in the 1950s, McIver was drawn to the problem of protecting the nose cones of intercontinental ballistic missiles from burning up on reentry. Where his own work converged with the problem was in the possibilities of sheathing the blunt-shaped nose with an ablative material that would burn away as the missile reentered the Earth's atmosphere. McIver stayed at Lewis until 1969, when he was lured by NASA's "career development" programs to Washington, where he began a second career on the executive staff in the administrator's office and a program office at NASA Headquarters.

———————

Among the characteristics that distinguish NASA's Apollo era engineers, none is so striking as the fact that virtually all of them are white males. Only among the youngest — those who arrived at NASA in the late 1960s — did the percentage of blacks creep to 3 percent, or the percentage of women to 4 percent. Compared to black and women scientists and engineers employed nationally in 1970 (1 percent and 5 percent, respectively), a black engineer had a better chance of employment with NASA, while a woman engineer fared slightly worse.[7] By 1984, 13.1 percent of NASA's scientists and engineers were women, while 8.7 percent were black. (Nationally, in 1984 about 12 percent of all employed scientists and engineers were women, while 2 percent were black.[8]) Blacks continued to find NASA, a government agency, a relatively more ready employer than did women. Richard Ashton and Marylyn Goode were two other NASA Apollo era engineers — one a black man, the other a black woman — who managed to thread their way through the eye of the needle. Both were from the South and were beneficiaries of that region's network of black educational institutions and communities with strong religious foundations that had emerged from the hopefulness of Reconstruction. Both gravitated toward Langley Research Center.

Ashton's father was a farmer from Westmoreland County in northern Virginia. The land was everything, the southern black family's succor and hedge against the future. The Ashton farm had been in the family since Richard's great, great grandfather cultivated it. "When he passed away my great grandfather left the provision in [his] will that any Ashton that wanted to could take up homestead there. I've got a number of relatives living up there on the farm right now." Stability and continuity also marked Ashton's mother's family. His grandmother had lived "around the corner" from his great grandmother in Norfolk until she died at the age of ninety-five. Ashton, his mother, and grandmother all grew up in the same house. Each parent's family was large, with eight or more children, while his parents themselves produced a large family — Ashton was one of eight siblings. Ashton himself has four children. "It makes a very warm, close relationship, having a very large family." What is more, he observes, "out of that group you've got to have a couple of good ones. And later on the older kids, they always tend to serve as role models for the younger ones." Ashton is also the son and grandson of men who fought in segregated armies. His father managed to enter Hampton Institute in 1942 on a baseball scholarship only to be drafted and sent to fight in Europe and the Pacific. Then there's "great, great uncle Joe that fought in the Spanish American War, and my grandfather [who] fought in World War I."

In his own way Ashton knows that a national need for technical skills has promoted social and economic mobility, as he remarks that he and his brothers and sisters "came through when they had the Sputnik era in space and everyone was hired on, going and working for NASA and so forth.... Most of us went into the technical fields, with the exception of one brother who went into business administration and one sister that went into elementary education." Indeed, it would seem as if the "space age" was as liberating for Ashton's generation as the Union armies had been for his great, great grandfather's. Four of his five sisters have been employed in some facet of engineering — one as a mechanical engineer for the Navy, another as a nuclear technician (also for the Navy), another as an electronics technician, and the fourth as an electrical engineer for the Northrop Corporation. One brother, an Army officer, like Ashton has a degree in physics.

"Resourceful" best describes the kind of childhood Ashton and his brothers and sisters had, one in which they learned mathematics not only because their father insisted on it, but because the boys all "worked" a paper route. "From when I was eleven to eighteen, I had a paper route for ten miles…. Counting became a part of me and the rest of my brothers, and we just passed it on down. Even my sisters, from time to time, worked that route. My older sisters, they used to work in stores. They had to do a lot of counting." It was their resourcefulness, too, which enabled them to learn basic fluid dynamics when they first became interested in moving things. Living in Norfolk, "on the water," Ashton amused himself by making boats, and then airplanes.

"All the materials I needed to make airplanes or submarines were right back there [on the water front] … reeds, and crates…. The most I would have [to] buy would be rubber bands." He learned how to put "together an airplane so that it would glide and fly pretty well, how to balance it, [the correct] wing spread…. I wasn't reading books,… I was just trying the various designs, [doing] a lot of experimentation…. I was just crazy about airplanes. I had an encyclopedia of all sorts of airplanes from World War I and II…. My brothers … we all used to make planes, submarines. We used to make submarines that would go under the water and come back up [with] rubber bands [to move] a propeller…. Submarines have diving planks and you turn them down and the power from the propellor pushing them forward causes the submarine to dive down just as an airplane will go up. As long as the submarine was being powered, it would stay down…. I used to carve [the propellors] out of [tree] limbs, old clothes pins." One day in 1957, when Ashton was thirteen years old, he made his "first metallic rocket. It was too heavy to fly. But I was in a metalwork class and I made a rocket. I didn't have anything that I could use for a propulsion system, because I wasn't that knowledgeable about chemistry and making explosives. Then, if I *had* put an explosive in the rocket I probably wouldn't be here today." Two years later, when Ashton was in high school, the Soviet Union launched the first man-made satellite, and after that he "had dreams of joining NASA."

Richard Ashton's father feared that his son would be crushed if he did not abandon those dreams. In the ninth grade Ashton had to choose between his high school's "general" or "college preparatory" curriculum, in which he would "get a lot of analytical courses, the mathematics, the sciences." Ashton's father wanted him to take the more vocationally oriented general curriculum. After all, he insisted, the purpose of schooling is to get a job. Ashton's guidance counselor urged the college preparatory course. He took the college preparatory curriculum and "although we didn't have calculus, we had algebra, trigonometry, solid geometry, a little bit of analytical geometry, physics, chemistry…. The school was … fundamentally good in the sciences."

Norfolk State (the Norfolk Division of the Virginia State College) was one of the many state-supported community colleges available to youngsters like Ashton who would have been unable to attend college otherwise. Ashton, like his brothers and sisters, entered Norfolk State after high school. "Being there, [it] gave us an opportunity to work in the summer to get enough money to go to college during the other part of the year. The tuition was low, and you could walk to school." Once in college Ashton began studying for a concentration in mathematics or electrical engineering. "But my father showed me this [news]paper back in 1962 and said, 'look at all of these electrical engineers looking for work in California. You don't want to be an electrical engineer.' He told me, '[become] a physical education teacher. You can always get a job because they will always need teachers.' My father … didn't want to take any chances. Then again, at that time there weren't that many black engineers and scientists and he probably thought, if I'd gone into that area I'd have come out and wouldn't have had a job. So he thought [being a] teacher would have been a safe thing for me to do — or go into the post office." Not only did Ashton decline a career in physical education or the post office, he changed his college major from mathematics to physics. "I enjoyed working the problems [and] decided I'd switch over to physics and stay with physics…. I liked the applications."

"I enjoyed math, I enjoyed science," and when Ashton's college physics teacher suggested in 1964 that he participate in Langley Research Center's cooperative training program, he was thrilled. "I came here [to NASA at Langley] to be a scientist. I had an idea of winning whatever prize there is to [be] found — a Nobel or Pulitzer Prize in science and engineering…. That was my goal, [and] also to get a Ph.D. in physics." But he was soon disappointed, although not in the way his father had feared. His first coop assignment at Langley was in the standards section of the instrument research division, which calibrated instruments. "The civil servants really didn't do much there. [The work] was mostly done on contract … other people monitored contracts, [did] paper pushing — nothing, really, in terms of 'hands on.' The coops do all the sorts of things that the engineers don't want to do … xeroxing, running errands, walking through purchase requests, picking up travel, doing a few mathematical computations, but not much…. I'd always had jobs, working hard, during the summer shoveling rocks [and] doing hard, difficult, tedious labor type jobs in which people stand over you all day long. And if you had half an hour for lunch they made sure you didn't take one second beyond the half an hour…. And every minute you had to be busy, working very, very hard. So I came to NASA, and … it was my first encounter with people coming in and drinking coffee, reading the paper…. The people around me weren't all that productive. And I said to myself 'Gee Whiz, now I know why the Russians are beating us in space.'"

Ashton toughed it out. He "got through it" with the help of "a very good mentor and good person to talk to." Next to disenchantment, what he had to "get through" was being one of a handful of black engineers at Langley Research Center. "I had never been in a different environment like that. When I grew up I went to [an] all-black elementary school [and] high school. Norfolk State was a black college. When I came here ... I had to learn to adjust to ... a different culture. It took me a long time.... My adjustment wasn't as difficult as some other people. I think I had it pretty easy. There were some people that got here before me, [black] engineers and scientists ... they had a terrible time." After three months Ashton was able to get reassigned to one of Langley's research divisions, where he could work on things he "really enjoyed — optics, spectra of meteorites entering the atmosphere, cameras, determining things about the energy, the density [of the atmosphere].... I just loved that. It was scientific, and I thought I was making a contribution.... Usually black engineer scientists didn't work in research areas at Langley Research Center.... They worked in more operational support [areas], calibration labs, the computer facility running computers ... operational sorts of things."

About a year after he had been working at Langley in earnest, Ashton was able to go to the University of Virginia graduate school, where he earned a master's degree in engineering physics — a program for which NASA paid his "full salary, tuition, everything." But when he returned to Langley, Ashton was repeatedly assigned to jobs in various support or operational activities. What he wanted to do was research, and a true research assignment always seemed to elude him. He had turned down offers from Westinghouse and IBM, at 50 percent increases in salary, in the hopes of moving into one of Langley's research areas. At long last he was able to get reassigned to the same research division he had worked in earlier. "I was working on optical properties of various satellites, materials, and their surfaces ... and also studies of the atmosphere, [the] determination of atmospheric ozone.... Then I went on to actually working with the experiments that were designed to actively measure the constituents of the upper atmosphere, [or] aeronomy." He also worked on "lifetime" studies of satellites, or studies to predict the effects on a satellite's life of its movement through the Earth's atmosphere and the interplanetary medium. Although Richard Ashton would never get his Nobel, or Pulitzer, or Ph.D., he was finally doing research.

NASA offers its mid-level professional employees a "career development" program to give them an opportunity for the varied experiences they might need to advance. In the late 1970s Ashton went to NASA Headquarters for a year of "career development." But his career failed to develop; by 1981 he had been sidelined to an administrative staff position, where he has remained, one of the 30 percent minority of NASA scientists and engineers who, after more than fifteen years service, had not achieved a grade higher than a GS-12.

———————

Like Richard Ashton, Marylyn Goode comes from a large southern black family. And like Ashton, she volunteers the information that her parents were able to send all of their children to college, and that all five children were able to become professionals. Goode herself is an engineer. One brother is a dentist and a minister, another is a doctor, and her two sisters are both teachers. Richard Ashton's father had urged him to become a teacher because there would always be a need for teachers, and it appears that many young black people had followed that advice; both of Goode's parents were trained as teachers at a Presbyterian college in Knoxville, Tenn. (Goode's mother stayed in elementary school teaching, but her father abandoned it in favor of the insurance business.)

Born in 1942 in Asheville, N.C., Goode attended church-affiliated schools in her hometown. It was as a schoolgirl that she discovered her love for mathematics and science. Although advanced course offerings were negligible, an appreciative teacher encouraged her, and she began "thinking about medicine." But when it came time for Goode to go to Hampton Institute, she "majored in teacher education because my father — realizing when I went to school in 1958 [that] there were not very many jobs open for blacks [and] teaching was a field that black women could get into — insisted ... that I get a degree in teacher education. I did not want to teach." Nevertheless, she yielded to her father's wishes and pursued her high school's "teacher education" curriculum rather than its "general studies" program, which would have enabled her to major in mathematics and science. Still, she clung to the hope of a career in some area of science. "My solution to that was ... I took everything ... required for teacher education, but I [also] took the higher-level math courses as electives."

Her father had been right. Goode supported herself for two years after graduating from Hampton Institute by teaching. But as she taught, she took graduate courses at Virginia State College in Petersburg. One of her physics professors must have admired her determination and ability, for he offered her a teaching assistantship in aerosol physics, which enabled her to stop teaching and work for her master's degree in physics. Meanwhile, she had married and started a family. In 1967 she earned her degree and took a job at Langley Research Center because her husband had found a teaching job nearby. She began her work at Langley "as a data analyst.... At that time they were hiring most of the women as what they called 'computers' and they were putting them in an office together" where they worked on Friden calculators. Although Goode had already had experience with FORTRAN and programming IBM computers, she, too, was put in the "computer pool."

Langley had only just disbanded its racially segregated all-female computer pools, and Goode spent most of her time with the survivors of the black female computer group once located at the edge of the center. Goode found the computer pool deadly. "Men coming here with math degrees were never put into a computing pool; they were just put out in the sections with the engineers. And they were usually converted to engineers within a very short time. So I asked the division chief about that, and he says, 'Well, nobody's ever complained ... the women seem to be happy doing that, and so that's what they do.' And that was it." Goode never rested, and after five years of tedium she was able to get an assignment to an engineering section. At the same time (1973), her two children were now old enough to tend themselves, and she began a protracted and ultimately successful struggle to earn a doctoral degree in physics.

The hurdles she has overcome have been considerable, but she readily acknowledges the support of individuals who sympathized with her and supported her. She recalls one supervisor in particular, who told her that when he thought of " 'a woman working, it was someone who you always had to make excuses for because she didn't do her work right' or something to that effect. He really thought that a woman should be at home, and when she was out here working she was just sort of a bumbling something. And *I* said, 'Well, gee thanks. I'm sitting here, a woman.' He said, 'Well, I don't think of you as a woman.'" Her efforts to complete her work for a doctoral degree were handicapped by supervisors who evidently "didn't think it was worth their while ... to educate the women out here, because they thought the women would quit."

Persevering in her determined way to master a field of advanced aircraft design, "sonic boom propagation," she found herself in "left field" when public funding for a supersonic transport all but vanished. If and when commercial supersonic transport revives on a large scale, Goode suspects she will be "one of the few around who's working it because those who *were* very into it in the late '60s, and there were a lot of them who did a lot of work in it, they are retiring.... You know, things you try that don't work are not always written up. So they might have to redo a lot of [that early work].... We write up the successes, but you don't always write up something that you've tried and that didn't work."

Matthew O'Day, like George Sieger, came from a Catholic family in Toledo, Ohio. O'Day's father, unlike Sieger's, survived World War I, but his initial enthusiasm for engineering did not. The elder O'Day had been one of the fortunate few to enter college — where he began an engineering program — in the first decade of the twentieth century. When he returned, he chose to make dentistry his life's work. (O'Day's mother had gone into nursing, one of the few professions then open to women.) Nonetheless, O'Day's father retained his interest in mechanical things and shared that interest with his growing son, who "spent a lot of ... time just watching what he was doing" while his father repaired the family automobile and did "do-it-yourself types of things" around the house.

O'Day remembers that "most boys" were interested, as he was, "in airplanes and building model airplanes.... I was doing things like that along with the people that I grew up with." At the same time, he was doing well in school in "subjects like physics, chemistry — things like that.... The teachers that I remember the most are the ones that were involved in the technical subjects, like algebra or chemistry.... They gave you aptitude tests" in school, and "in areas like engineering ... there was an indication that I would do well."

The assumption in the O'Day household was that the children would go to college. "I wanted to go to a Catholic university, [and] some place that offered aeronautical engineering." So after graduating from high school in 1954, O'Day went to the University of Detroit, which was located sixty miles from Toledo and offered the special attraction of a cooperative work-study program with the NACA. "I certainly remember when the Russians launched Sputnik.... I was in college.... I was more interested in the aeronautical part [of engineering], and still am, than I was in the space part of it, because that's all there was when I was growing up. There was a little bit of publicity about [what] Robert Goddard had done [and], in the Second World War, what the Germans were doing with their rockets. But that was an aspect of things that I didn't particularly care for because they were weapons of death rather than things that would really benefit mankind." Later in his life O'Day would reject working on military or classified projects, having resolved to apply his talents to "peaceful" uses.

At the University of Detroit O'Day concentrated on aeronautical engineering, ultimately specializing in structures and strength of materials. Both at Detroit and the California Institute of Technology (Cal Tech), where he would later do graduate work, he was exposed to nontechnical subjects and later came to appreciate the relative breadth of his education. "In engineering [at Detroit] I had courses in accounting and economics [which were] required. Being a Catholic university, you had to take philosophy courses or you studied logic and ethics and things like this. But with your engineering courses, you didn't have the time ... to take courses that I think I would have liked to have taken. That's one thing that impressed me about Cal Tech, because there was a requirement for a humanities course in the master's program.... I took a course in ... American and English history.... I did well in it ... enjoyed the humanities courses." After two years at the University of Detroit, O'Day entered the coop program, which "provides you with the wherewithall to complete your education. That was not a major consideration for me." However, the coop program did introduce O'Day to Lewis Research Center, where he began working during alternate quarters in bearings and icing research. After he got his bachelor's degree in aeronautical engineering in 1959, O'Day went to Cal Tech — again with NASA help — for a master's degree. Since the NASA graduate study program was "relatively generous, I saved enough money to go another year of graduate school ... and got what's called an engineer's degree in 1961." Cal Tech "provided you with the kind of background that you would need if you wanted to go into a research type of engineering career as opposed to the manufacturing or something like that. So it all pretty well fit in with what I planned to do when I finished graduate school, which was to return to Lewis."

A certain idealism, possibly shaped by the relatively broad curriculum he had had at the University of Detroit and Cal Tech, led to an important detour in O'Day's early career. While he had been at Cal Tech, "John Kennedy had been elected president. He pushed forward the Peace Corps program, and I found that to be an interesting concept. So I applied ... and in August, '61" — only a few months after returning to Lewis from California — "I was selected for a program that was to go to West Pakistan.... The Peace Corps tour of duty was two years.... What I did essentially was teach engineering subjects. One of them was strength of materials, in a government polytechnic institute.... I also taught a course in hydraulics. I never had a course in hydraulics myself; it took a little fast footwork to keep ahead of the students!"

A measure of O'Day's dedication was that he had to resign his job with NASA in order to join the Peace Corps. Virtue had more than its own reward, however; before he completed his two-year tour in 1963, Congress passed legislation reinstating government employees in their old positions, so O'Day "had a job waiting for me back here at Lewis." He began working with materials and structures for advanced propulsion systems, and remained with NASA, at Lewis, for the next two decades.

———————

"The thing was — if I go back through my life," reflects Ed Collins, "I'm a Christian, and I believe in God, and that He had his hand on my life." Perhaps it was a divine hand that guided Collins from Charlotte, N.C., where he was born in 1940, to Langley Research Center toward the end of the Apollo decade. His father had owned a contracting business and operated a do-it-yourself franchise store, and Collins' growing up resembled the fabled "all American" boyhood of the 1950s. "I raised chickens and sold eggs. I sold Christmas cards … door to door…. I was in the Boy Scouts. I was an eagle scout. I liked sports. I ran cross-country [and] track all through high school [and] college."

Perhaps his faith that God has guided his life is due to the vacillations of his own purpose — as distinct from a desire simply to "do well" — as a boy. Unlike some of the older Apollo era engineers, Collins did not play with airplane models or erector sets. He might have gone into business. When he was about sixteen, his father found operating both a contracting business and a franchise too burdensome, and turned the store over to his son "to just kind of run it for him. I really enjoyed doing that…. I liked to put up displays, figure out the advertising, and things like that. My goal at that time — I would have stayed in that store, had it made it. I probably wouldn't have gone to college."

But "the store didn't make it…. That was my senior year in high school, and all of a sudden I had to decide what I wanted to do…. I had decided at that time, even though I liked business and all, there was more future in engineering." Collins had been a good student: "I did pretty well in everything…. I graduated … in the top 5 percent in the state [in] math, verbal, everything…. Nuclear engineering looked very attractive to me at that time; it was exciting, and a new field." Besides, North Carolina State University, where most of Collins's family had gone to college and he was destined to go, "did not have business administration. They were not a liberal arts school…. It was either go there in some technical field or go somewhere else." It also happened that North Carolina State was one of the few institutions that had a nuclear reactor, so he figured, "this might be a really good jumping off place."

Collins entered North Carolina State in Raleigh in 1958, planning to major in nuclear engineering. "I made average grades my first two years. I played around a lot because … my mother [had] held pretty close strings on me. I hadn't really sowed any oats…. When I went to college I joined the fraternity and I became an officer in the band," for which he played the trombone. "I was running track and cross-country, indoor and outdoor…. In my senior year I was a senior senator for the student government, and I liked to get into activities like that. I was in the YMCA on the campus and played volleyball for them." He also joined "Mu Beta Psi, which is a music fraternity." Once he settled down into his major program he "made all As and Bs, because I really got interested…. We had a lot of one-on-one and you could go and talk to your professor if you were having a problem…. In the nuclear engineering classes we sort of became a team, because they would give us problems to work and we would do them together."

Once he graduated, in 1962, he was in danger of losing his draft deferment, and, not wanting to go into the military, he turned down a lucrative but probably short-lived position with a national heating and air conditioning firm to take a job with the U.S. Navy. For a few months he worked with a unit that went down into the bowels of ships to design changes in piping, "where the pipes would go, determine what the weight changes would be to the center of gravity of the ship, and determine the parts that were needed, and an estimated cost, estimated time…. But I didn't want to do that the rest of my life." He contacted a friend who worked for NASA at Langley Research Center, and before the year was out he was able to arrange a transfer. "They still had a lot of slots at that time. This was still in '62 and the space agency was hiring and it [was] the big heyday. Everything was flowing pretty freely…. I was brought in to do research on semi-conductor devices … mainly with radiation damage effects." NASA also arranged for him to return to school, to the College of William and Mary, where he earned a master's degree in integrated optics in 1965.

After working at Langley for a number of years, he was faced with another career decision and would awaken to the fortuitous nature of the divine guidance he believed he was receiving. He had been offered an opportunity to return to North Carolina State and study for a doctorate in acoustical engineering. He and his wife had already started their family: "We decided we wanted three children, and I said, 'we are going to have to have our third one now, before all this is done.' So we did. During that time is when I became a Christian, and I began to see God's hand in my life and began to pray and ask for guidance. I felt He wanted me in some type of project work, and I developed a real desire to work on a project. I began thinking about the team efforts that I had been involved in … all the way back to college … and how enjoyable they were…. I put everything together. I decided I didn't want to go back to school…. A Ph.D. would look nice on my record, but it wouldn't really get me another promotion, and it would really take time away from equivalency. I believe after a certain number of years of research, a man is equivalent to a Ph.D. whether he has a title or not. So I decided that was what I was supposed to do, after much prayer, and thinking, and talking."

In the end, project work would not provide the avenue of advancement that Collins had expected, and he tried repeatedly, and unsuccessfully, to shift into management to earn the promotions he thought God intended him to have. Instead, Collins would spend his NASA career working on several innovative engineering research projects, most of which were abandoned as the agency scaled down after the heyday of Apollo. Meanwhile, he would continue attempting to broaden the circle of Christian fellowship among his friends and co-workers.

———

A few of the NASA engineers who first sent men into orbit in tiny capsules were already well into their careers with the NACA when Hank Martin was born in 1943 — the year word of German experiments with long-range rockets began to slip into the British war ministry. The son of a research chemist for a multinational oil firm, Martin was raised in Woodbury, N.J., across the Delaware River from Philadelphia. Woodbury was "a typical small town,... an interesting mix ... of blue collar and white collar." His mother was a homemaker, and the family socialized mostly with the families of his father's colleagues.

Martin came to engineering quite purposefully. "I was always into how things worked.... I wanted to take things from ... basic concepts and make ... spectacular things to happen." He had a chemistry set, "of course. I did all kinds of strange things, and that led to my interest in rockets and explosives.... I used to like to play with fireworks, and then make my own." He used to shoot them off "across the school ground.... They didn't have any kind of organized model rockets or commercial versions.... If you wanted a rocket that really flew, you made it yourself. You got the match heads and the gun powder and you built the thing." He was also intrigued by electronics. "I was fascinated about how you could split water into hydrogen and oxygen ... and so I used to try to accumulate vast quantities of hydrogen and oxygen and make them react with each other, make water.... I was usually building a burglar alarm or a crystal set, or something like that."

After going to Catholic grammar and preparatory schools in New Jersey, in 1962 Martin entered Catholic University in Washington, D.C. While there was no doubt he would go into science or engineering, he is not bashful about admitting that he chose engineering over science to avoid foreign language proficiency requirements. "I knew I wanted something that involved labs and science.... But I had a terrible time with languages, and I knew that if you wanted to get into pure science, you had to have French, German ... and I really didn't want to deal with that stuff." Besides, "by that time I was into my car phase.... I could see engineering ... associated with cars. And I always thought that was really neat. So ... I started out in chemical engineering, and then switched over to mechanical engineering."

Catholic University proved difficult for Martin, or rather its mathematics courses did. "I never really had that much of an aptitude for pure mathematics ... but I did take a shine to computers." Equally important, Catholic University introduced him to philosophy and conceptual approaches to problems. "The school is geared towards you probably going on and doing some graduate work as opposed to the type of engineering school where you might come out and know how to do something.... I came out with a general approach to problem solving ... a way to think about things ... a way to break big problems down to small problems and then build up the answers until you had something that worked."

By then he had also acquired a taste for philosophy, just as he had acquired an abstract interest in space exploration. He remembers seeing the 1950 film *Destination Moon*, based on Robert A. Heinlein's 1947 juvenile novel, *Rocket Ship Galileo*, and *2001: A Space Odyssey*, released in 1968. When he saw *Destination Moon*, "that was back in the days when you could sit through and see it a second time ... and I did. I was hooked from that point." As for Stanley Kubrik's *2001*, "I liked the philosophy in the picture better than I liked the picture as a science fiction picture." He became an avid science fiction reader—necessary, he thought, to understanding much of what went on in a film like Kubrik's. As with science fiction, so with philosophy: "I think it gave me a much broader view of what was going on…. Philosophy … had a profound effect on the way I think about things…. You just don't … take everything as truth…. And I'm always looking for alternative explanations, alternative ways of doing things."

Perhaps, but when he graduated from Catholic University there was only one alternative: NASA. "There was status, working for NASA…. You were somebody on the block if you worked for NASA." He began working at Goddard Space Flight Center in heat transfer, conducting thermal analysis and design for satellites, or ensuring that satellites in orbit operate at the right temperature to protect their delicate instruments. "I could not have walked out of school — any school — at the time, and sat down … and done a thermal design on a satellite. No one was teaching you how to do thermal design … they were doing it all with electrical analogy at the time. And digital computers were starting to be of significant value…. It was a brand new field, and that's probably one of the things I liked about it." Although the organization Martin entered in 1966 "changed names, changed leaders, came under different divisions," the fundamental problems it was trying to solve remained the same, and Martin continued working with it for the next two decades.

Like Hank Martin, Richard Lockwood is the son of an engineer, but an aeronautical engineer who spent most of his career working with the NACA at Langley Aeronautical Laboratory. His father "was pretty well immersed in his work. His work was kind of his life." The new middle class[9] and the era of postwar affluence into which Robert was born in 1944 offered the increasing possibility that preference — rather than necessity — might decide the outlines of one's work life. Robert's mother wanted him to "look around" when it came to deciding on a career; his father, he insists, "didn't push" him into aeronautical engineering. But then, his father did not have to. Robert had "always had a natural inclination towards mathematics and science — always enjoyed them." He built model airplanes and worked on his own car. He followed his father's work and "occasionally watched wind tunnel tests at Langley."

After attending schools in Hampton and Newport News, Va., Lockwood went to Virginia Polytechnic Institute (VPI). There he took part in a cooperative work-study program with the U.S. Army's Redstone Arsenal in Huntsville, Ala. He worked at Redstone for alternate quarters during the last three years of his five-year degree program in aeronautical engineering, doing "trajectory analysis on computers, both analog and digital," as well as computerized "structural analysis." When he graduated from VPI in 1964, he transferred to NASA's Langley Research Center and began working "in the twenty-two inch helium tunnel — it was a hypersonic tunnel — doing experimental research. My own research was mostly in … studying the effect of mach number on boundary layer transition."

He was again able to take advantage of a work-study program, as NASA bore the costs of graduate courses at the University of Virginia while he worked at Langley. During the process, he discovered a fundamental difference between doing analytical and experimental work. "The work is different. And it takes a special kind of a person to be a good experimentalist. You really have to be a nit-picker on detail. And I've always hated minutiae." Thus he decided to do further graduate work, so he could earn a doctorate and continue working in the realm of analysis. Lockwood also realized that he preferred physics to mathematics: "I've always enjoyed the connection between reality and theory. You learn something about certain equations ... and then, by George, you go out in nature and you see it happen.... It gives you confidence that what you're doing is real. I couldn't be an abstract mathematician ... who plays abstract games that, in their lifetime, they [sic] may never see a concrete example [of]. It's just a bunch of equations on a piece of paper." He may have disapproved of mathematicians' preoccupations with equations on paper, and he may have disliked minutiae, but Lockwood was increasingly drawn into computerized analysis. "I don't know why I work with computers, because they're almost one hundred percent minutiae." Computers are also full of numbers and equations; but they are, he says, merely tools, tools that encourage one to "start thinking a lot more about form.... And it tends to have you make things more orderly. And I think that it's useful to try to reduce that chaos."

With NASA's help, Lockwood managed to earn a master's degree from Harvard and, after transferring to NASA's Ames Research Center in California, a doctorate in aeronautics from Stanford University in 1969. He denies that his pursuit of successive degrees in a field that did not normally require the doctorate represented any special career ambition; rather, it enabled him to do what he wanted to do, which was to develop computer programs to simulate air flows and turbulence around aircraft — or computational fluid dynamics. He really did not care about "moving ahead, [and] and I never have moved ahead." He's "very comfortable" making "more money through investments than" he does from his salary at Ames.

Although deeply immersed in the computerized mysteries of modern aircraft design, Lockwood is a space program enthusiast, but for pragmatic reasons that echo some of the controversies of his own generation: "We need to find outlets. It's healthy to have outlets for creativity and work and everything other than war.... In the past, the primary mover of technology has been war. It's kind of nice to have something peaceful that pushes technology." He cares that NASA is a civilian, not a military, agency. "I don't think I could work to build better hydrogen bombs.... I'm not anti-nuclear.... Human nature being what it is, we can't trust the other side."

Fred Hauser claims no special aptitude or enthusiasm for engineering, having become an engineer mostly because his father was one. Born in 1946, he grew up in the Philadelphia and southern New Jersey area, where his father was a mechanical engineer for the Radio Corporation of America (RCA). "He tried to be objective and not force me into something that I wouldn't want myself [but] had he not been an engineer, I probably would not be. I don't know what I would be, but I probably would not be an engineer." Hauser's mother, a trained nurse, "worked some, part time, and the rest of her time was devoted to housework.... She did not sew or do decoupage or thinks like that, like some women do." She also died "relatively young, when she was fifty two." If his mother appears to have worked constantly, his father found time to garden, which he preferred to working on cars. Nor has the younger Hauser worked on cars or been a "fix-it" person. "I'm just not that way."

The family took its Catholicism seriously. Hauser's father had gone to Villanova University, and Hauser resolved that he, too, wanted to go to a Catholic college. He also knew that he wanted to leave home and live at school. He admits to not having agonized much about where he should go to school, nor had there been much debate in the family whether he would go to college to at all. Notre Dame just seemed the place, and he started there in 1964, beginning a program in mechanical engineering "probably because my dad was a mechanical engineer." After the first year he decided to switch to aerospace engineering. When "I entered college … NASA was going strong, and I think I was very heavily influenced by that." As it turned out, "aerospace was just a fancy name, and they just added a course or two to the curriculum that related to space flight. My undergraduate education, if you had a specialty … would have been in the area of flight dynamics" — a field in which he has done little work since leaving college.

There was another disillusionment as well. College "was tough. It was difficult, truly…. The difficulty I had with engineering is just simply due to intellectual abilities…. I probably just don't have the raw intellectual talent…. I worked very hard, and I think I probably did almost as good as I could have. I was in the bottom half of my class". Although he read a lot — novels, not science fiction — he learned "early, in fact, I probably learned by the time I was a sophomore in college, that I don't really like sitting down and working detailed engineering problems. And I'm just not very good at it."

Hauser stayed at Notre Dame in a graduate degree program. It was 1968, and the number of American troops in Viet Nam was growing from 385,300 in 1966 to 536,100 by the end of the year. Casualties were growing too; over 10,000 American families had lost their sons or daughters to combat in Viet Nam since 1965. The Tet Offensive of January had intensified the polarization over the war among policy makers and public alike, and by the end of the year more stringent draft exemptions provoked further student unrest on campuses across the country. Hauser found himself in danger of losing his student draft deferment and quickly decided it was time to go to work as an engineer for the government. He called Marshall Space Flight Center, where he had located an opening, and soon found himself in Huntsville, Ala.

Once on the NASA rolls, Hauser began the work that would take him into the next decade: the preliminary design, planning, and "costing" of future programs. Apollo 11 would land its crew on the Moon's surface the next summer, and NASA engineers were busily defining the possible missions to carry them over into the next decade. He continued working, for the remainder of his career, on "phased program planning," the last planning phase for a space project before metal is bent. Having limited confidence in his intellectual and engineering abilities, he found that planning and organizing were things he could do and liked to do. "I think I do have management talent. I do have abilities to plan and organize and coordinate. If I was seventeen, I wouldn't go into engineering."

By the winter of 1949 World War II was becoming a thing of bittersweet memories and the lineaments of the postwar era had been drawn. As the U.S. Senate ratified the agreement creating the North Atlantic Treaty Organization and the creation of two separate German states assured the continued dominance of the Soviet Union over much of Eastern Europe, the Communist Chinese drove the Nationalists off of the mainland, whence they retreated to the island of Formosa. In the United States, New York audiences thronged to see Richard Rodgers' and Oscar Hammersteins' "South Pacific," while in France, Simone de Beauvoir ignited one of the war-fueled revolutions of modern times with her feminist treatise, *The Second Sex*. More subtle harbingers of things to come occurred that year when Northrop Aircraft, Inc. took delivery of the BINAC, a guidance computer for its new missile projects for the Navy,[10] and domestic economic and federal procurement policy became intertwined as the Truman administration initiated the practice of awarding military contracts to "distressed areas."[11]

Ronald Siemans, born in 1949 in Oil City, Pa., would still be a schoolboy when John F. Kennedy issued his challenge to the nation's space agency in 1961 to send a man to the Moon and bring him back. He would be one of the last new engineers to join NASA before the end of the Apollo decade, first going to work at Johnson Space Center in 1967 as part of a cooperative work-study program at Finn Engineering (later Cleveland State University) in Cleveland, Ohio. The son of a mail carrier, Siemans grew up in a household little involved in the new age of science or technology — indeed, his parents, neither of whom had attended college, "didn't know too much about" education at all. Nonetheless, they managed to start their first child, Siemans's older brother, in college. Lawrence had shown some inclination toward science or engineering in high school, but was discouraged from pursuing a scientific career by guidance counselors who warned of humanities requirements for most undergraduate science curricula. "I wasn't too interested in getting into literature.... I didn't want to get off into a lot of the humanities type education requirements that were required for the pure science background ... so I picked engineering.... You had to take your science courses; it's just that you're not required to take the heavy amounts of history and English and literature and all that sort of stuff, which was not one of my stronger suits."

Another thing Siemans worried about was money: how would he pay for college? Finn Engineering offered financial aid in the form of a cooperative work-study program with NASA, so he chose Finn and began his studies in chemical engineering. His first coop assignment was at the Johnson Space Center, where he worked during alternate quarters after his freshman year. There he began "working with what engineers do, plotting, just [being a] technical aide. It was right after the Apollo fire.[12]... A lot of people were involved in trying to figure out how to make the fixes and changes required to get the Apollo [program] back on schedule. But there were still teams looking at Moon bases and Mars missions and space station." Siemans was assigned to a group that was doing "trade studies" for a possible manned orbiting space station. Trade studies examine the trade-offs to be made between cost, weight, fuels, environmental systems, and other design features in which an improvement in one may result in disadvantages elsewhere in the design. "I did a lot of schematics ... just to look at which was the most optimum way to go as far as the type of chemical systems that were used in the environmental control system of the station. The area I went into was the crew systems division, which is responsible for the environmental control systems, EVA [extravehicular activity] systems, and thermal systems".

Siemans had entered the coop program not only because it would help to pay his expenses, but in the widely shared expectation that he would have a job waiting for him at Johnson Space Center when he graduated. In this expectation he was sorely disappointed. "If you don't get it in writing, you'd better not believe the government, because they really put it to us." NASA's budget sank to its lowest ebb in fiscal year 1974; the decline had begun with the fiscal year 1969 budget.[13] 1971 "was the year the RIFs [reductions in force] were occurring, and the promise of a guaranteed job didn't hold up that year."

He managed to wait out the ebb tide by entering a master's degree program in chemical engineering at Rice University, in nearby Houston, Tex. "Rice was a far superior school ... and the depth of the education and expectations for each course was higher.... But I can't say, honestly, that I've used much of that extra education ... well, yes, I have." When Siemans was able to return to a real position at Johnson Space Center in 1972, he used his Rice training in catalysis to promote an air communication device to improve the environmental system on the then-new space shuttle orbiter. From that point on he would spend his career with NASA working on environmental systems for advanced manned spacecraft designs.

The transformation of American society that had begun during the early lives of the NASA Apollo era engineers who were born between 1918 and 1932 was virtually complete by the time the guns had been silenced at the end of World War II. The twelve younger men and one woman who talk of themselves in this chapter share some characteristics with the earlier group. Most still came from the old Northwest and Northeast; a few more came from the South; none came from west of the Mississippi. Of the younger group, more grew up in urban than in rural areas, but about the same proportion (or more) were the sons of manual or service workers in the older group; three of the younger engineers' fathers had been employed by the railroads. Four of the five whose fathers had been salaried professionals were sons of engineers; the fifth, the single woman in the group, was the daughter of school teachers. More so than in the older group, attendance at college — and thus the promise of middle class employment — had become the normal expectation.

While virtually all had shown special abilities in science and mathematics, they gravitated not toward academic careers, but toward engineering or engineering research. Relatively more of the younger group were attracted not only to engineering, but to the kind of engineering that would bring them ultimately to NASA; NASA's cooperative work-study programs enabled more than a few to fulfill their ambition. More than half had been fascinated by airplanes; a few had flown them. Several were fascinated by rockets as well.

Their educational experiences were similar to those of the older group. Few, as before, attended the elite or prestigous engineering schools or universities; when they did, it was to complete graduate programs, and their advanced work was subsidized by NASA. The availability of publicly funded higher education was significant for virtually all of them, especially the three blacks in the group, which included one woman. The three out of four who did not do most of their undergraduate work in publicly supported state colleges attended Catholic colleges or universities.

The federal government was the employer of first resort for virtually the entire group. A few took temporary odd jobs — in a classroom, a factory, a metal shop — as a means of surviving before settling into their careers. But even those who did not begin working with NASA shortly after graduating from college worked in government jobs; one was a volunteer engineering instructor with the Peace Corps. And only one — George Sieger — spent any significant amount of time working in private industry, for a large government aerospace contractor. Half the group began working for NASA within a year of graduating from college. And with the exception of one who went to work for the NACA's Langley Laboratory in 1953, and another who began his first job at the NACA's Lewis Research Laboratory in 1957, all began their NASA careers in the 1960s.

The wars that marked their generation were the Korean War and the Vietnam War, but those wars left little mark on this group; only three enlisted during the Korean War, and only two of them experienced combat duty. The two youngest, who might have served in Vietnam, escaped by obtaining draft deferments as civilian engineers working for the government (the Navy and NASA). One must assume that the majority, who did not enlist, were eligible for deferments by attending engineering schools. Their mobilization was of another kind.

No engine designed or built to launch men to the Moon was as powerful as the engine of the U.S. government itself. Modern technology is the product, first and foremost, of vast organizations; it was the federal government which above all else ensured that NASA, the defense establishment, and the aerospace industry would have the armies of trained engineers needed to design, develop, and build the machines that would fly — long before anyone decided just what those machines should be, or where they should go. The GI Bill, the military services' reserve officers' training programs, cooperative work-education programs, the draft — with its exemptions and deferments for those in engineering school or working for the government in engineering fields — all generated in this country one of the great social and occupational changes of the twentieth century.

With one eye cocked on the growing joblessness and labor unrest that followed demobilization in 1919-1920 (the miseries of which were exacerbated by an inflation in the cost of living of over 100 percent between 1913 and 1920), and the other on the languishing supply of scientists, technicians, and medical personnel as young men marched off to war or into the factories that would supply the front, the federal government went into action itself. During World War I students in scientific, technical, and military fields began to receive deferments from the draft, instituted in May 1917. The Student Army Training Corps, administered through over 525 institutions, paid for the support and education of no less than 140,000 students who enlisted, prepared to go into active duty when called. Uncle Sam continued the policy with the National Defense Act of 1920, creating the Army and Navy Reserve Officers Training Corps at American colleges and universities. The fortuitously compatible motives of containing unemployment and building a technical workforce continued in the creation of the National Youth Administration, which educated 620,000 young people between 1935 and 1943. The next year Congress passed the Servicemen's Readjustment Act (better known as the GI Bill), which, along with its Korean War counterpart, kept millions of veterans out of the job market and sent them to school instead.

The federal government thus became not only an agent of occupational change, but of social and economic change. Where once higher education had been the preserve of a genteel minority with a virtual monopoly on "higher learning," by the dawn of the post-World War II era, attending college — any one of the 900 institutions added to the 951 in existence in 1910 — became possible for the offspring of parents who had never dreamed of admission to the realm of the salaried professional. The social and economic aspirations (and accompanying insecurities) thus released have yet to be measured, but they are etched in the middle class experience common to most of us.[14] This is the phenomenon that largely unites NASA's Apollo era engineers, for all their individual diversity, and that brought them to the threshold of the space age.

---

[1] The Banana River separates John F. Kennedy Space Center from the Cape Canaveral Air Force Station, site of NASA's launch pads.

[2] See, for example, Gerard K. O'Neill, *The High Frontier* (New York: William Morrow, 1977).

[3] The mammoth Nova booster, envisioned by NASA engineers in 1960 as necessary for a direct ascent to the Moon, incorporated four stages; the Saturn V (AS-506), used for the lunar orbit and rendevous manned Apollo Moon landings, consisted of three stages (S-IC, S-II, and S-IVB). See Roger E. Bilstein, *Stages to Saturn: A Technological History of the Apollo/Saturn Launch Vehicles*, NASA SP-4206 (Washington, D.C.: U.S. Government Printing Office, 1980).

[4] The arcanum of NASA's management hierarchy can have more nominal than substantive significance. From the top down, it goes something like this: Administrator, Deputy Administrator, Associate Deputy Administrator, Associate Administrator for line or staff functions, General Counsel, Inspector General, Assistant Administrator, Assistant Associate Administrator, Deputy Associate or Assistant Administrator, Division Director, Branch Chief, and Section Head. Division directors and above are normally members of the government's senior executive service.

[5] The building of a flight propulsion laboratory for the NACA was authorized by Congress in 1940. Located adjacent to the Cleveland, Ohio municipal airport, the laboratory began operations in 1942 and in 1948 was named the Lewis Flight Propulsion Laboratory in honor of Dr. George W. Lewis, the NACA's Director of Aeronautical Research from 1919 to 1947. In 1958, the laboratory became a part of NASA and was renamed Lewis Research Center. Simon Ostrach, Franklin K. Moore, and Harold Mirels were members of a small group of "resident geniuses" at Lewis who were allowed virtually complete freedom to pursue basic research in aerodynamics, especially problems of heat transfer. All three have been inducted into the National Academy of Engineering. See Virginia P. Dawson, *Engines and Innovation: A History of Lewis Research Center*, NASA SP-4306 (Washington, D.C.: U.S. Government Printing Office, 1991).

[6] An Austrian by birth, Low was detailed from Lewis to NASA Headquarters in 1958 to serve as chief of Manned Space Flight (programs). He moved to NASA's new Manned Spacecraft Center in Clear Lake, Tex. for the Mercury program and held various high-level line positions in NASA's manned spaceflight programs until returning to Headquarters in 1969 to serve as Deputy Administrator (1969 to 1976).

[7] See Appendix C, table 7 and National Science Foundation, "Characteristics of the National Sample of Scientists and Engineers, 1974," Part 2: Employment, NSF 76-323 (Washington, D.C.: National Science Foundation, 1976).

[8] NASA Personnel Analysis and Evaluation Office, "The Civil Service Work Force as of September 30, 1984" (Washington, D.C.: National Aeronautics and Space Administration, 1985) and National Science Foundation, "Women and Minorities in Science and Engineering" (Washington, D.C.: National Science Foundation, January 1986).

[9] The "new middle class," as described in C. Wright Mills' classic *White Collar: The American Middle Classes* (1951), is a twentieth century class consisting of salaried workers — primarily managers, salaried professionals, salespeople, and office workers. It is a class which has largely replaced the "old middle class" of the nineteenth century, which was composed of well-to-do farmers, entrepreneurs, and independent professionals.

[10] Developed by J. Presper Eckert, Jr., and John W. Mauchly, the BINAC was the first airborne computer. A much simpler machine than the ENIAC, which used a decimal system, the BINAC operated with a two-digit binary code and was actually two

computers which constantly checked one another. Harry Wulforst, *Breakthrough to the Computer Age* (New York: Charles Scribner's Sons, 1982).

[11] Official Washington had been persuaded by wartime prosperity that full employment was the key to a healthy economy. This conviction resulted in the Employment Act of 1946, a measure which signaled the federal government's acceptance of a responsibility to "promote maximum employment, production, and purchasing power." The economic downturn of 1948-1949, which prompted the administration's decision to use military contracts to reduce unemployment, was followed by a revival, which intensified with the onset of the Korean War.

[12] Apollo astronauts Virgil I. Grissom, Edward H. White II, and Roger B. Chaffee perished in a fire on January 27, 1967 in the Apollo command module during a simulated countdown for mission AS-204.

[13] NASA's total budget authority declined from a pre-1980 high of $5.25 billion in 1965 to slightly over $3 billion in 1974.

[14] See Frederick Rudolph, *The American College and University: A History* (New York: Knopf, 1962), John S. Brubacher and Willis Rudy, *Higher Education in Transition: A History of American Colleges and Universities, 1636-1976* (New York, 1976), *The Statistical History of the United States from Colonial Times to the Present* (Stamford, Conn.: Fairfield Publishers, 1965), and Ross M. Robertson, *History of the American Economy*, 2nd ed. (New York: Harcourt, Brace & World, Inc., 1964).

Chapter 3
What Goes Up ...

The careers of the many men and a handful of women who worked as engineers with NASA during the Apollo decade combine to tell a story — as do most careers — of personal triumphs and disappointments, of growing confidence and creeping self-doubt, of discovery and intellectual frustration. Their careers are also about making one's way through the complexities of organizational life, marked out — like the flags on a strategist's map — by organizational units named and renamed, elevated and diminished, and by innumerable accommodations to personalities and forces beyond anyone's apparent control. In keeping with most engineering careers, many moved farther and farther away from the "hands on," "heads under the hood" experience that attracted them to engineering in the first place. To move up in the NASA organization was, and still is, to move into management.

For those engineers who had worked for the NACA, the shift in career pattern came about as the NACA, an organization charged principally with aeronautical research, was transformed into NASA, designed to be a research *and development* organization. Then again, an increasing disassociation from engineering practice experienced by upward-moving NASA engineers was compounded by a policy throughout the federal establishment of relying on private-sector firms for engineering research and development, as well as production and routine services. What the lure of management and the increasing shift of NASA's actual engineering work to the private sector has meant for these careers is explored in chapter 6. Also explored in a separate chapter (chapter 5) is a problem of professional identity somewhat special to the Apollo generation: the popular press typically described the successful Apollo venture as the triumph of the nation's *scientists*. However, those close to the professions of science and engineering certainly were aware that a scientist was not an engineer. How they differed, if in truth or only in perception, has also helped to shape the careers and outlook of these men and women.

———————

Abraham Bauer came within a hair's breadth of being sent off to war in 1942, after finishing college at the University of Missouri, but was able to get a deferment to work for the Tennessee Valley Authority (TVA) as a chemical engineer. The effort to produce strong but lightweight materials for aircraft and military hardware was under way there, as elsewhere. The project at TVA that "made the most impression" on Bauer involved "a big electric furnace … about ten feet in diameter" that "used a carbon electrode sixteen inches in diameter." When "lowered down into the center" of the furnace, "an enormous power source was turned on, with materials in there that were to be processed at high temperatures, and an arc was struck which produced a tremendous amount of heat." Bauer "designed some auxiliary equipment to work on that furnace." He found the project "exciting" and has kept the drawings he made. A related project was an attempt to extract aluminum from "low-grade ores" embedded in clay. "Aluminum was very important during the war to make airplanes, and the Germans were sinking the ships bringing aluminum ore up from South America." The project succeeded, and within two years Bauer was ready to move on.

Bauer had "heard that there was something going on at Oak Ridge, Tennessee … only a few hundred miles away." With little idea of what they were headed for, Bauer and a friend took jobs with the Eastman Kodak Company, or Tennessee Eastman, a major contractor for the Oak Ridge National Laboratory. Tennessee Eastman had been contracted to operate a uranium isotope separation plant "using extremely large-scale mass spectrometers. What you do with a mass spectrometer," explains Bauer, "is … inject a beam of ions — ions being molecules that have been stripped of one or more electrons — and shoot them into a magnetic field at high speed. And they… travel a curved path in a magnetic field…. The heavier particles swing to the outside, as you might expect; the lighter ones curve more sharply. So you can separate things out according to … their particle mass. And that was the technique that was used to separate the uranium 235 from uranium 238…. These devices … had tracks … consisting of ninety-six of these mass spectrometer units, each of which was about twelve feet high. And each one of them was operated by a girl who was a technically untrained person. They had people who were called technical supervisors, who wandered around to see if everything was going well, and if they had problems, they helped them to solve them." And Bauer "became that person."

After a while, "these units would fail. They would run for some number of hours and then they would … break down in one way or another…. They would get pulled out of the big vacuum chamber and pulled into the service area. We were asked … to inspect them and see what had gone wrong. And we did. And then we made a record of the collected data on why they were failing and then we made inputs back into the management structure, saying, 'you really ought to change this a little bit, and if you do this, it wouldn't fail there.' So we were trying to get them to run longer before breaking down. And that was important in a production sense because they were very slow producers.... Running all that equipment, you would only get a few grams per week. And so it took a long time to build up a quantity of uranium 235 that they needed in order to make a bomb."

"We gradually became aware of what we were doing. There was tremendous security associated with the place — but right up to the time of dropping the bombs on Hiroshima, the general population in that plant didn't know what was happening.... In fact, there was some concern that there might be a major postwar scandal because ... [it] was regarded as a possible boondoggle. Eighty thousand people down there working — and nothing is coming out. There were some fairly famous physicists who were floating around there. The whole basic design of that plant was based on work at the University of California at Berkeley, and in particular, E. O. Lawrence. So I saw E. O. Lawrence walking around the plant there on one or two occasions, and J. Robert Oppenheimer.... I remember him as being a very nervous individual ... slender ... he looked almost like a hunted animal — he was darting around all the time."

When the war ended in 1945 the Oak Ridge plant was closed down, and Bauer went to the University of Tennessee to teach physics. "Soldiers were coming back by the thousands" and virtually anyone who knew anything about physics — which, by then, included Bauer — was sought out to teach. He was only twenty-six, and many of his students were older than him. When his parents and his sister moved to the West Coast, he tried to join them by getting a position as an instructor in physics at Stanford University or the University of California at Berkeley, but those West Coast institutions proved more picky than the University of Tennessee. Bauer was casting about for other possibilities when he encountered a recruiter from the NACA, and by the summer of 1948, he was on his way to the NACA's Ames Research Center.

Spread out alongside the U.S. Navy's Moffett Airfield, Ames Research Center lies in a rich, aquafer-fed basin that opens at the southern end of San Francisco Bay. Luxurious foliage combines large evergreens with tropical plants that bloom in Chagall colors through much of the year. To the west are the gentle green slopes of the San Mateo mountains, while the eastern horizon is curtained with the rose and ocre undulations of the Santa Clara range, outlined in sunlit yellows and shadows of deep purple and brown.

In this opulent natural setting aeronautical engineers imported from the Langley laboratory were already at work in 1940 when Abraham Bauer arrived, probing one of the fundamental technological barriers that would have to be surmounted not only to refine the technology of intercontinental ballistic missiles, but to enable a guided missile to deliver a human being into Earth orbit and return him unharmed: how to prevent the incineration of the missile and its occupant as it reentered Earth's atmosphere? The initial approach to the problem had come from high-speed, high-altitude flight studies, especially the search for the best design for hypersonic[1] aircraft to be used largely by the military: assuming an engine powerful enough to

61

propel an aircraft of a given weight and the right shape and construction five times faster than the speed of sound, what ought to be the aircraft's "right" shape, its "right" construction? Before engineers could decide those questions, they had to replicate with models the phenomena of flying objects bursting through the sky at almost unimaginable speeds. This NACA and NASA engineers tried to do at Ames and Langley Research Laboratories throughout the 1950s and early 1960s, designing and building various devices, such as hypersonic wind tunnels and shock tubes.

Bauer was hired by H. Julian (Harvey) Allen, who had recently been brought to Ames to head the laboratory's theoretical aerodynamics section and was, by the time Bauer arrived, in charge of the high-speed research division and Ames's supersonic wind tunnels, where aircraft models were subjected to the aerodynamic flows and pressures of supersonic flight. However, "in the early years of NACA," Bauer recalls, "the great thrust was always to go to higher speeds." That meant hypersonic flight, the understanding of which would become as important for space flight as for high-performance aircraft. Extreme heat and pressures result from the kinetic energy of hypersonic flight, and before engineers could design a vehicle capable of withstanding such extraordinary temperatures, they would have to be able to simulate hypersonic flight. Conventional wind tunnels could not be used because "the gas in the [wind tunnel's] test section was extremely cold and would drop down to the liquifaction temperature of air. If you tried to push it any faster, you'd be getting some liquid air droplets, and, at those low stream temperatures, when the gas recompressed on the face of the model, it still just came back ... to room temperature. One of the features of hypersonic flow that was important to simulate is the hot temperatures ... that are developed in the flow, because the high temperatures affect the flow.... They are responsible for the hypersonic heating that was a primary concern. So the heating problems couldn't really be adequately simulated in ordinary wind tunnels." Bauer remembers that "there were shock tube advocates ... people who worked in shock tubes simulated the thermal part of the flow, but not the aerodynamic part. The people who worked in the wind tunnels simulated the aerodynamic part, but not the thermal."

"Harvey had had an idea to go beyond what wind tunnels ... were ... capable of doing.... He wanted to get up to extremely high hypersonic speeds by using gun-launched models. You put a model of something that you're interested in a gun, and then you put a charge of gunpowder in there and ... shoot it out, and it comes out at several thousand feet per second. That idea was not novel.... The novel idea was to combine that with the conventional ... supersonic wind tunnel, which was built here at Ames and came to be called the Supersonic Free Flying Wind Tunnel.... The gun would be fired, and the model would go shooting upstream through this supersonic air stream and it would result in a very high test velocity."

"There were a number of design engineers who were working to put the thing together, and I was asked to figure out what to do with it when it got put together.... It proved to be an enormously valuable device," simulating both the thermal and the aerodynamic aspects of hypersonic flight, the effects of which were recorded with Schlieren or shadowgraph photography. "For a period of ... about 1950 to 1968, it was one of the most productive means available of developing an understanding of hypersonic flows.... We did pioneering research in hypersonic aerodynamics, and we were able to do things with this facility that couldn't be approached in any other way."

To simulate the thermal and aerodynamic aspects of hypersonic flight was not, however, to know how to design the nose of a ballistic missile — or manned spacecraft — so that it would not burn up on reentry. Aerodynamicists had known that friction exists at the interface between a solid surface and a fluid, and they called the friction "drag."[2] Reducing drag was an important part of making an aircraft aerodynamically "clean," and the shape of the aircraft was what normally determined its drag. Immediately next to the surface of an object moving through air or water lies a thin boundary layer, and the characteristics of the flow of air through this layer — whether it is steady, or "laminar," or whether it is turbulent — determines the extent of friction to which the object's surface is subjected (or its drag) as it moves through the air.[3]

As aerodynamicists turned to the problem of bodies reentering the atmosphere from hypersonic and high-altitude or upper-atmospheric flight, one of the largest problems that faced them was the reduction of drag, and hence friction and heat, at the aircraft's laminar boundary layer. Conventional wisdom, based on atmospheric flight experience, was that drag would be minimized in slender, streamlined designs. (If more heat-resistant alloys could be found, they, too, would help to overcome the thermal barrier.) That was the approach taken with the experimental rocket-powered X-15 aircraft, begun in 1954 as a joint NACA, Air Force, and Navy project. However, as Harvey Allen puzzled out the problem, he came to the unorthodox conclusion that a reentry body should have a high, not low, drag shape. The streamlined shape of conventional wisdom would absorb half of the heat generated by friction at reentry, but the kinetic energy of a vehicle returning to the heavier lower atmosphere could be absorbed by the "shock layer" of air between the shock wave and the body of the nose, instead of the nose itself, if the nose was bluntly shaped.

So far, so good; still, there were many possible variations on the "blunt" body shape. Bauer and his co-workers in Allen's group began to experiment with various high-drag shapes. "Now the carryover from subsonic aerodynamics had been that bodies should have a favorable pressure gradient — like a sphere — something where the pressure is continually falling from the nose as you go around the sides, that this would help to maintain the boundary layer laminar." Bauer and his fellow research engineers persisted. "We tried a variety of things. We tried bodies that were pointed. We tried pure cones. We tried cones that retained the pointed tip but introduced curvature along the sides so as to keep a favorable pressure gradient. Nothing worked."

Then "one day a blunt piece of plastic accidentally flew down the channel and one of my colleagues, a good friend of mine ... saw the shadowgraph pictures from that shot and he looked at it, and he said, 'Hey, look! This is laminar!'" The piece of plastic had a "flat" shape (actually, it was slightly curved), "and we started making up models that were flat." By the time the NACA was absorbed into NASA in 1958 and the new agency's focus shifted to Project Mercury to launch a man into Earth orbit,[4] the blunt-body concept had been refined to the Mercury capsule's nearly flattened bottom end. "We solved problems of the early generation of ballistic missiles," Bauer proudly asserts; "we did tests which led to the selection of shape for the manned space vehicles — Mercury, Gemini, and Apollo."[5]

During the 1950s at the NACA's Langley and Ames Research Laboratories, engineers in supersonic aerodynamics and reentry physics worked head to head to increase their understanding, with its urgent practical implications, of supersonic, hypersonic, and transatmospheric flight. They, too, struggled to find the best shape for the first generation of manned space vehicles. Bill Cassirer was drawn to Langley in 1949, after finishing a master of aeronautical engineering program at Cornell University, by the sheer excitement of it all. He was followed there three years later by Charles Stern. Cassirer "had thirteen job offers, which was a lot for those days.... NACA was the lowest in salary." But the NACA had managed to obtain Italy's leading aerodynamicist, Antonio Ferri, through the efforts of the Army's Office of Strategic Services, which brought Ferri to the United States in 1944. Ferri knew a great deal about the progress the Germans as well as the Italians had made in replicating transonic flight in wind tunnels, and the prospect of working with him was more than ample compensation for Cassirer. "It was my plan that I would come down here," to Langley, "if I could work with Tony ... for about a year or so, and then leave.... Ferri left" (in 1950, to teach at Brooklyn Polytechnic Institute), and Cassirer stayed on. "The reason I stayed was — until I had been here a lot of years — nobody ever told me what I had to do."[6]

Cassirer concentrated on supersonic aerodynamics research until 1960, when he shifted to reentry physics. Both he and Stern, for whom he was something of a mentor, were working in the early 1950s on the "aerodynamics of shock tube flows." The shock tube was a laboratory device researchers used to generate shock waves by breaking a fragile diaphram between the low-pressure and high-pressure sections of a tube. Both researchers, recalls Stern, and others working with them, were interested in "shock tube boundary layers, shock tube heat transfer, interaction with the main flow of shock, and shock attenuation behavior." Phenomena such as these interested them because they held the keys to understanding "the unsteady flows in experimental ramjets." Cassirer "had been working on unsteady flows in inlets — not necessarily ramjets — but inlets in general. One characteristic of unsteady flow was called 'buzz'.... You get an instability in the flow and a shock wave bounces in and out.... What it is, is an oscillating flow which could easily be termed 'buzz.' The question was, 'what causes those instabilities?' One of the ways to learn about the shocks and shock boundary layer interactions was through the instantaneous unsteady flows associated with shock tubes. So we were using the shock tube as a diagnostic tool to try and learn more about ... 'buzz.'"

Cassirer and Stern worked together on shock tube research to gain a better understanding of supersonic engine inlet performance and "buzz" for four years, until 1956. As the 1950s and ballistic missile research progressed, Stern remembers, "there began to be interest in the use of the shock tube for simulation of the high energy flows associated with reentry. Two things were taking place simultaneously. Out at Lewis Research Laboratory, a couple of guys were working on similar things to what we were doing — shock tube flows as a means of simulating unsteady flow characteristics and shock boundary layer interactions.... We went into some interesting discussions, and arguments, and fights, and competing reports." Meanwhile, "with the interest in the ballistic missile program came the question, how does one simulate the extremely high energy flow field associated with the reentering missile? Some people up at AVCO [Corporation in Massachusetts] were coming to use the shock tube in a different way entirely, simulating very strong shocks flowing down the shock tube which set up behind them the high energy flow that was characteristic in many respects of ... reentry."

Stern had been at Langley for four years when, in late 1956, he said to himself "'I'm now ready to go out and brave the commercial world and make a lot of money.'" The NACA "was a great place to get one's basic training in research.... It well fitted individuals to go out and go into applied research or ... to where one could just, hell, rise a lot faster.... And there was the ballistic missile crisis — they were hiring like mad, and I did get a pretty good offer from AVCO. So I went. At that time [AVCO was] the prime contractor for the Titan ballistic missile nose cone. Martin Marietta was the missile contractor. The big competition was General Electric, for the nose cone of the Atlas, and AVCO, for the nose cone of the Titan. And both were going the direction of ... blunt bodies. And I ... worked about a year in various pieces of what I'll call applied research for AVCO, and got myself involved in this same reentry problem: The matter of how one understands the flow around blunt bodies reentering the atmosphere at extremely high speeds and predicts what's going to happen to them so that one can design survivable nose cones."

Stern remained at AVCO for only a year. "At Langley we were ... trying to fully understand flow.... I was interested in shock tubes for their use in simulating unsteady flows that would be experienced in engine inlets — I wasn't interested in this engine or that engine.... When I went to AVCO, we were still doing research, but we were now trying to apply it to a specific use.... We were now in the business of trying to build a nose cone that would survive reentry after having been launched on the back of this big Titan missile. I decided that ... I really liked it better at Langley.... I liked the freedom to work in engineering science and not to have to worry about building the device.... So I ... came back to Langley and worked almost exclusively on the aerodynamics and thermodynamics of reentry. We continued some more shock tube work, but it was now finishing up." Because shock waves occur in atmospheric gases, and their first effect is on the physical density and (through altered temperatures) on the molecular composition of the gases themselves, "we were getting into aerodynamics mixed with physical chemistry, where the aerodynamics of extremely high speed flows gets into chemistry and physics."

When Stern returned to Langley in 1958, Cassirer and other Langley researchers had already begun to move into space-related problems of hypervelocity flight and reentry. Throughout the Apollo decade, from 1960 to 1970, Cassirer remained in reentry physics. "We were working on reentry — predicting reentry heating for Apollo…. What our job was, was to predict what heating the…body would experience — both convective … and friction…. When the second Apollo landed," in November 1969,[7] "we were working on making predictions for a manned Mars landing, not the Viking, but the manned Mars landing…. You just keep asking, what's next, what's next. At that time, space looked like it had a limitless future." Perhaps it did, but Cassirer had a hunch that there were still important breakthroughs to be made. In 1969 "people started saying, 'what's new?' I told my guys, 'look, we're going … out of reentry and back into high-speed flight — hypersonics.'" Recurrent interest during the 1970s and 1980s in hypersonic aircraft and transatmospheric "vehicles" would prove him right.

———

Other research avenues converged on the problem that faced NACA engineers at Ames and Langley Research Laboratories in the late 1940s and early 1950s. H. Julian Allen's "blunt body" concept promised to reduce the surface heating to which vehicles reentering Earth's atmosphere would be subjected — but not enough to fully protect the interior. Certain materials — like the nickel-chrome alloy Inconel-X proposed for the body of the X-15 — could endure rapid heating to temperatures above 1000° F without significant losses in strength. There were two possible solutions to the problem: cover the nose cone with a heat sink, or cover the nose cone with an ablative material. The heat sink, which had been used successfully before 1958 on early intercontinental ballistic missile (ICBM) nose cones, was a highly conductive metal that absorbed reentry heat into a mass sufficient to prevent melting. The principle of the ablative surface — which was less well understood in 1958 — was the dissipation of heat through the burning or vaporization of the material covering the nose cone. An ablative nose cone had been tested successfully on the Army's Jupiter-C ICBM in 1957. Ablative or heat sink: the question would have to be solved before NASA could send the first American into space.[8]

William McIver began working on the reentry heating problem shortly after his arrival at the NACA's Lewis Research Center in 1957. While at Lewis he also worked toward his doctorate in aerospace science at neighboring Case Western Reserve University (which awarded him a Ph.D. in 1964); his thesis was a study of Australiasian tektites, small pieces of glass of uncertain origin first found in Australia and Indonesia. "Tektites are little pieces of glass … on the order of a centimeter or so … found all around the world." They "have very little oxygen … very little water in them. It's presumed that they could not have come from some kind of terrestrial origin because — let's say … there is a meteor impact on the Earth … sand is melted and stuff goes up in orbit and then the wind carries it all around the world." But if textites were of terrestrial origin, as they "melted in the atmosphere … they would contain a lot of moisture and oxygen. Well, these things contain very little moisture and very little oxygen. So the theory was that they were actually, as a result of a meteor impact on the Moon ... splashed from the surface of the Moon, up into cislunar orbit, and then gradually, by the Earth's gravitational field, sucked into the Earth. When these spheres from space enter the Earth's atmosphere, they come down and they melt.... On one side, they show signs of melting on the front ... on the back, they're perfectly spherical."

That was the theory. McIver wanted to test it. "I built a vertical wind tunnel" to simulate the opposing forces acting on an object entering the atmosphere, "the wind blowing up and the gravitational force pulling down ... that's why you get these ring waves developing" around the object, "because you have the balance of these opposing forces.... I proved that's how it *could* have happened."

NASA engineers would debate and test, test and debate, the relative merits of the beryllium heat sink and ablative heat shield right to the threshold of the first manned space launch. "Big Joe," which combined the U.S. Air Force's mighty Atlas ICBM as booster and a full-scale Mercury capsule with an ablative heatshield, was tested successfully in September 1959. It was this combination that sent John H. Glenn, Jr. into orbit on a winter day in 1962.

When David Strickland left the Georgia Institute of Technology in 1944 after receiving a degree in aeronautical engineering (with the help of the U.S. Navy, in which he had served as a missile guidance officer), he went to work in the aircraft industry. "I got involved in the airplane business, since there wasn't any space business at all.... Until the Saturn" launch vehicle, the multistage launch vehicle with clustered engines developed for the Apollo program, "everything that was done in space was done with a ... derivative of the ballistic missile. And that was sort of ... coincidental.... It could have gone to the automobile industry or anyplace else, but the aeronautical industry was the place that it went, because ... everything in space had to go through the atmosphere.... The industry was in place, and it had the kind of technical disciplines, the structures, and the electronics and the communications." A transition from aeronautics to space engineering was a part of Strickland's career, as it was a part of many other aeronautical engineers' careers. After another year in the Navy and a master's degree program at the University of Michigan, Strickland went to work in 1952 at Consolidated Vultee Aircraft Corporation (Convair) in San Diego, Calif. He stayed at Convair until 1958, working as an aerodynamicist on aircraft.

When Strickland went to San Diego, Convair was working on a new fighter-interceptor plane for the U.S. Air Force, the F-102. With its bullet-shaped fuselage, sharp-edged delta wings, and powerful Pratt and Whitney J-57 engine, the aircraft was intended to fly at transonic speeds. However, tests in the NACA's Langley Research Center's wind tunnels showed that it could not pass through mach 1. For the next two years Convair worked on a redesigned prototype that applied the "area rule" discovered by Langley aerodynamicist Richard T. Whitcomb.

For years aerodynamicists had assumed that streamlining the fuselage of an aircraft was the best way to diminish drag. Puzzling in 1951 over the way shock waves pass over airplanes at transonic speeds, Whitcomb imagined that the total cross-sectional area of a plane's fuselage, and not simply its diameter, was what determined the extent of drag. With Whitcomb's "area rule," the wasp-waist or "coke bottle" came into being as the design solution to the problem of drag at transonic speeds. Convair redesigned its prototype, following the area rule, and, during tests in December 1954, the F-102A proved Whitcomb's discovery. Built for the U.S. Air Force, the F-102 and its more advanced successors became a critical part of the U.S. continental air defense for the next three decades.[9] Convair engineers — including Strickland — spent a lot of time at Langley Research Center in the early 1950s.

In 1958 Strickland left Convair to return to Ann Arbor, Mich., where he worked for the Bendix Corporation and hoped to earn a doctorate in engineering from the University of Michigan. But he had married and started a family. "I found after a while that I just wasn't going to do it, so I went back to Convair.... Rather than the airplane division, I went to the astronautics division, whose responsibilities were the Atlas and the Centaur."[10] From 1962 to 1965 Strickland worked on advanced projects and the Atlas space launch vehicle for General Dynamics (parent company of Convair). "We carried responsibilities for very major aspects of the Mercury program ... on our relatively inexperienced shoulders, and it didn't faze us.... Atlases blew up, and the next day we went to work and we sat down and tried again. And nobody ... expected perfection then." In 1965, by now well schooled in the intricacies of sophisticated hardware development, Strickland left industry and went to work for NASA in the first of a series of project and program management positions he held for the remainder of his NASA career.

———

To make the transition from atmospheric to transonic and space flight, engineers had to try novel vehicle designs and structural materials. Even that need was predicated on their ability to design the "power plants," or engines capable of propelling aircraft or launch vehicles at the speeds necessary to travel faster than the speed of sound, or the thrust ("specific impulse") necessary to burst through the heavy barrier of Earth's atmosphere and gravity. It was, for example, the development of the jet engine in the late 1940s that intensified the search for new aircraft designs and construction materials to minimize air drag and heating during high-speed flight.[11]

Space travel, especially for long-duration missions to other planets, compounded the technological challenge by demanding highly efficient, minimal-weight integral power and propulsion systems for spacecraft. Common to all high-performance power systems — whether for aircraft, rockets, or spacecraft — was the problem of developing designs and materials that could withstand the unprecedented temperature extremes and pressures to which such systems would be subjected. Thus much of the critical engineering work done by NASA during the 1960s would be in materials, structures, and heat transfer.

———————

Matthew O'Day's first introduction to Lewis Research Center occurred during his junior year in college, in 1956, when he began working at Lewis as part of NASA's cooperative work-study program. In his coop work at Lewis, O'Day "had worked in a number of areas.... I started out in bearings research, and I worked in icing research." Five years later, with a master's degree from the California Institute of Technology in hand, he returned to Lewis. His last coop work experience at Lewis had been in orbital mechanics; "there's lots of mathematics, physics involved," but it was "an area that I really had no interest in." Instead, he was interested in structures, and found work in Lewis's materials and structures division. "Lewis is NASA's propulsion center, so all of the structures work here was to advance" work in propulsion systems such as "jet engine structures or propellant tanks for rockets."

Achieving the specific impulse necessary for rockets to lift heavy loads into space depends, among other things, on reducing the molecular weight (the sum of the atomic weights of all the atoms in a molecule) of the gases which, when combined with an oxidizer, produce the combustion that pushes the rocket forward. The lower the molecular weight, the more dramatic the increase in the specific impulse of the rocket or launch vehicle. The lowest molecular weights are found in light gases such as hydrogen — and, of course, the oxygen necessary to produce combustion. However, the volume of gas required to fuel any large rocket would be so enormous that efficient gaseous fuels had to be condensed into their liquid states. That required extreme cooling and pressurized plumbing and also produced the same structural stresses of contained liquids in motion, or "sloshing," that forced the makers of ocean-going tankers to build baffles into their holds. Thus structural engineering continued to pair with thermodynamics or heat physics — since rocket combustion itself created astronomical temperatures — as critial areas of aerospace engineering.

Learning how to handle cryogenic fuels — gases cooled to temperatures below 240° F— was critical to post-World War II work in the United States on intercontinental ballistic missiles and launch vehicles for space missions. American engineers at first relied heavily on German cryogenic technology for V-2 rockets, but by the early 1950s cryogenics had became an established engineering discipline in U.S. industrial and government research centers. Shortly after his return to Lewis, O'Day "got involved with one particular program to test titanium pressure vessels. I had the opportunity to pretty much plan the program.... When you're working with liquid hydrogen, it is kind of a hazardous situation ... so safety issues were a pretty sensitive area. It was relatively basic research ... not only testing pressure vessels, but also testing materials' reactions to cryogenic temperatures." He also worked at "developing instrumentation ... because this was fracture mechanics," and among the things one examines is "the growth of cracks."

O'Day spent about thirteen years working in Lewis's materials and structures division. "Roughly the first half of that was devoted to the fracture mechanics ... of structures.... We were doing this work" on "cryogenic pressure vessels, working with titanium and aluminum." And then there was " ... writing reports. We'd finish a chunk of research and, back in those days, that was the only way you'd get a chance to travel — if you put together a paper and presented it at some kind of conference." Modestly, O'Day insists "much of my early work ... was really of a short-term benefit, with a relatively small incremental increase in knowledge of no particular interest to anybody."

Around 1969 O'Day's division "decided to get into another up-and-coming area ... the area of advanced composite materials ... like graphite epoxy, boron epoxy, boron aluminum, and more recently, kevlar epoxy composites." In the process, O'Day turned from "cryogenic testing to ambient temperature testing, and an entirely different category of materials, composites. But again, it was the same type of work: trying to characterize these composites. And one important way of characterizing composite materials" is by "subjecting them to biaxial loading ... as well as putting shear on the structure itself."

By 1978 O'Day was at work on the Centaur liquid hydrogen fueled upper stage. Work on the Centaur had begun in 1956 for the Department of Defense's Advanced Research Projects Agency; combined with the Atlas lower stage, the payload and communications carrying Centaur became a workhorse in the NASA stable of launch vehicles for heavy communications satellites and space probes. "The Centaur ... used welded stainless steel tanks.... We tested steel, using different welding techniques. We made spiral welding tanks and tested those. We were involved not only in fracture mechanics but in stress analysis, so we could have done stress analysis work on model Centaur tanks.... It makes so much sense to me now," reflects O'Day. "Why weren't we doing research to support the Centaur? Why were we testing titanium? Why were we testing aluminum?" Had they written "something that was a definitive stress analysis of a Centaur tank, it would have been used up until today," and "answered a lot of questions that still aren't answered." But around 1977 "Lewis was going through reductions in force and reorganizations and the whole character of the work was changing. My initial desire was to be involved with research. But it seemed like that portion of the work here was being deemphasized, was shrinking, and the area involved with projects was growing."[12]

John Songyin began his engineering career at the National Bureau of Standards, where he went in 1950 after graduating with a degree in mechanical engineering from the City College of New York. For the next three years he worked on "developing strain gauges to get better sensitivity to measure stress and strain." Naval vessels, not aircraft, were the immediate cause of the work. "One of the big problems that we were looking at was the oil tankers during World War II that sailed in the North Atlantic. Due to the cold, a lot of the bulkheads were fracturing.... People were looking at the designs where the bulkheads met, and the kind of cutouts to allow oil to flow from one hole to the other," to get a better grasp of the "stress concentrations" in tanker construction. "Most of my work was looking into better ways to increase the sensitivity of strain gauges."

The strain gauge then most commonly used consisted of "fine wires that were attached to structures so that when the structure would strain, this would be picked up by these thin wires" as changes in resistance. "We were looking into other means" as well, "like applying paints of metallic solutions, and looking at the change in strain — how that would affect the change in resistance of this painted-on solution. It was something like that, that eventually developed into printed circuitry. In testing for these strain gauges, we would just take a flat bar stock and paint these things on with the proper kinds of substrates, and then put them into a tensile machine" with a "very optically correct apparatus that gave us the reference points, and then see what the upward change in resistance" was and "how that could be related to the reference change in strain. The strain gauge ... is very much a basic part of mechanical engineering.... A lot of work was done by mechanical calculators ... that put up such a clatter. Put in something," divide one number by another, "and this thing would churn away and clatter away and then read out these numbers. It was very, very cumbersome. It was only a little better than a slide rule."

Songyin left the National Bureau of Standards in 1953 for New York, where he worked briefly, and unhappily, for an engineering consulting firm "that contracted out to architects and engineers for buildings and institutions." He managed to find another job with General Electric in Evandale, Ohio, "where we worked on jet aircraft and rockets. And that's where I started specializing in ... heat transfer. We were working on military jet engines, [as well as] the nuclear jet engine program too.... But those were essentially paper studies and nothing [to do] with any hardware.... I remember using a lot of the NACA engine data." Then things "started to phase down at GE," while "things were really booming in Cleveland." Songyin served his two years in the Army and moved to Cleveland in 1961 to work at Lewis Research Center, beginning his NASA engineering career doing stress analysis for a new breed of "power plants for space. That was the SNAP program — Systems for Nuclear Auxiliary Power.[13] At that time Lewis was devoted to developing technologies with no specific application" but that "we expected would find an application in the near future. One of the things that we foresaw as a mission was interplanetary travel to Mars.... We were concentrating on converting the heat power of a nuclear source to electrical energy."

Songyin's "whole division was working ... on this SNAP project." Some branches studied "the rotating machinery"; others looked at different components, such as condensers and boilers. Still others probed how various aspects of the system should be tested. But growing public concern over fallout from nuclear accidents in space prompted a search for alternate power systems for long-duration space flight. So "we went from the SNAP system into the Brayton system ... around 1967."

The Brayton system operated on the principle of a "thermodynamic cycle that, instead of using a working fuel that undergoes a phase change from liquid to gas or vapor and then is condensed back into a liquid, just uses a single phase — a gas in this case — which gets heated ... powers a turbine, and then is cooled down in the heat exchanger. There's no condensation; therefore, no change in flow is involved." In this instance, "the heat of the Sun" provided the energy for the heat cycle. "We used a large mirror which focuses into a cavity, through which the tubes carry the gas, pick up the heat, and deliver the energy to a turbine which turns an electrical generator. The working fluid — the gas — then gets cooled down and gets pumped around and recirculated.

"I concentrated mostly on the heat receiver that gets the reflection from the mirror into this component," shaped like "the frustrum of a cone, which absorbed the heat from the Sun and transferred it to the gas.... The tricky part" was to design the system for "low Earth orbit — like two hundred and fifty miles altitude." The system would be "exposed to the Sun for sixty minutes" and then would be in the shade "for about thirty-six minutes." It would "have to absorb enough energy from the Sun to tide it over during the shade part of the orbit.... The way we did that ... was to use these salts that would melt in the Sun and then give up" their heat as they solidified in the shade.

"A lot of [Songyin's] heat transfer background came into" that work. "Lithium chloride undergoes quite a volume change — something like thirty percent ... as it solidifies and shrinks.... You have to be aware of the pattern of solidification," which produces "voids all over the place. That means when you come back into the Sun, the Sun — with high-intensity solar flux — could be focusing on an area in which there's a void where the salt has shrunk away from the surface, and therefore" there is "nothing to take away the heat of the Sun. Therefore there's a danger of overheating the container and burning a hole in it.... A lot of our attention was" on trying "to control where the shrinkage takes place to insure that there wouldn't be these evacuated areas." Songyin's group tested the design "under 1-g" conditions, "and we figured that if we could control" the shrinkage "under 1 gravity," the system "certainly would work under zero gravity." But the big long-duration mission "never came off. So all of that technology was shelved.... Now [1986] they're talking about" possibly using a Brayton cycle power plant for the Space Station. Some of the Brayton hardware "has been taken off the shelves, out of the mothballs.... I think there are two or three units that were built." After twenty years NASA's "picking up exactly where we left off."

Songyin worked on the solar power system for about five years, into the early 1970s. "At that time we were" also "looking at the Mercury Rankine System," for use in long-duration space missions, "the Rankine being similar to a steam power plant, but instead of water you're using mercury as the working fluid. It goes through the same cycle of boiling and condensing and activating a turbine which generates electricity.... The whole cycle would be closed," and "the same mercury would be circulated." Songyin's own work was devoted to mastering the heat transfer aspects of the Rankine system.

"We were looking into the problem of mercury condensation; we were worried about the effect of zero gravity on ... the condensation of the mercury. My responsibility was to ... come up with experiments that would simulate zero gravity, to give us an idea of whether there really was a problem with zero gravity. This involved experimentation in the lab, here, and also installing a condensation rig in the bottom bay of an AJ-2 bomber,[14] which went through a zero-G maneuver, and, in those ten to fifteen seconds of zero gravity, to get high-speed photographs and to analyze the droplets to see if we could get better insight into the phenomena of mercury condensation and see if there would be a problem in long-term zero gravity … conditions.

"We were doing the basic spadework for a mission we thought would be coming…. Our aim there was not tied to any particular schedule leading to launch and takeoff." Songyin's group was attempting to answer the technological questions so that when the mission was identified, and schedules made, the technological answers would be there for the system people to put it all together.

Sandra Jansen has been working at Lewis Research Center longer than most. After earning a teaching degree with a major in math in 1947 from Ohio State University, she worked for a year at various odd jobs. In 1948 she started working at Lewis, where she joined the dozens of women who worked as NASA's human computers, reducing data from hours and hours of tests run in the center's engine research facilities and wind tunnels.

Sandra Jansen's career parallels the rapid evolution of computers from the noisy mechanical desk machines of the 1940s to the high-speed electronic mainframes and microcomputers of the 1980s; she has worked "entirely with computers" throughout her career. "I had grown up with them … worked … in machine language, in assembly language, in interpretive languages [like BASIC], and then in FORTRAN." In the early 1950s, "the first things that we had were … punch card computers." Most of the data they worked with came from tests of pressures inside and on the surfaces of engines.

"We had … manometer boards [and] … people that sat and through magnifying glasses … read the level of mercury in those manometer columns." In time, film was developed "that could be taken automatically and kept on a continuous roll, so that you could get a shot here, and then a shot here, and a shot here…. You would sit there, and there was a cross hair that you'd move by hand-maneuverable wheels…. You would cross those hairs at the top of a particular manometer tube, press a button, and that would punch into a card. Then you'd move to the next manometer tube with your cross hairs, punch the button with your foot…. The way in which the data was reduced was all manual, by hand. We had four different … sections of girls…. Computing at that time consisted of row after row of women … who sat and did line after line of calculations on desk-top calculators." The women, few of whom had college degrees, "had forms set up for them with instructions as to what to do.

"We had big books of exponential functions and logarithmic functions and of the various trig functions you needed to do your job — the things that you, today, can push one key on a pocket calculator and get." Jansen's job was to "set up those sheets that [the women] used to do their calculations. I was a math major, so I could take the equations and translate them into the various sheets they needed to do their job. They didn't have to do the math; all they had to do was follow the instructions.

I prepared the instructions ... and the girls who worked there were called computers." Within a few years Jansen was promoted to a job as supervisor "of an office of about twenty people." She was still "setting up the sheets and handing out... assignments ... and tracking to make sure they got done on time." By the mid-1950s the new computer age took root at Lewis, and Jansen began developing programs for electronic computers as part of various research projects, "doing," she remembers, "the same work as the engineers. The first ... that we had were [IBM] 604s, which were punch card coded.... You put your instructions as well as your data in through punch cards. This eliminated the need for people sitting at desk calculators. We learned how to code these equations into these punch card computers."

Meanwhile, the need to obtain increasingly subtle and accurate measurements for more sophisticated test engines stimulated the invention or development of new automated pressure-measuring devices. One device consisted of "hundreds of pressure capsules, little thin membranes ... mounted on the outside of a pressure tank. The tank was maybe two or three feet tall. And coming to the outside ... of these membranes were plugs ... that were actually sensing pressure inside the experiment cavity.... They evacuated the chamber down to a very low pressure and then gradually allowed that pressure to rise. And as the pressure on the external side of this capsule and the pressure in the tank became equal, there would be a snapping of the membrane.... Now what they were really sensing was ... the time from the beginning of this change in pressure inside to the end of the change in pressure inside. And they calibrated the time *with* the pressure." Using a conversion formula, "you could take the time and, with a small equation, come up with what was the pressure."

By the mid-1950s Lewis engineers also developed a central computerized automatic digital data encoder, or CADDE, "the purpose of which was not to sense data, but to record data in an automated manner via land lines from the facilities, without anybody having to write anything down." The CADDE was "not a general-purpose computer"; it was developed specifically for Lewis to service several test facilities, including the 10 foot by 10 foot tunnel.

After the first UNIVAC computer (the 1103)[15] arrived at Lewis in 1953, "there was a whole gradual development of continually automating both the acquisition of the data — so that you didn't have to have people writing anything down in the test cells or taking pictures of manometer boards — and the processing of the data by having the more powerful computers ... to do what you needed to do. The new machine did those calculations for the tunnel ... that were being done by the girls with those desk-top calculators" in a moment, instead of in "an hour's or day's or week's ... turn around." The UNIVAC's "primary goal in life was to support [Lewis's] 10 foot by 10 foot wind tunnel ... but you didn't need all of that computer power just to support the tunnel. So extra time was used to do other types of research."

Greater computing power, along with more advanced automated measuring devices, enabled Lewis to centralize test data collection and processing. Data from wind tunnels, and both large and small engine research facilities, could be recorded and "fed by line ... through a central data collector ... put on tape, archived, and made available directly into the large computers for processing." The growth of electronic, high-speed computation as a new technological discipline was reflected in a change in the organizational location of what would not be much longer, "the girls." When Jansen first went to work at Lewis, she and the other computing women worked in "sections that sat within the R & D divisions. And then ... sometime in the '50s, there was a conglomeration of all the people into a computer services concept, a division that did nothing but this work."

Remington Rand's UNIVAC (which Jansen says "never became a really popular computer at Lewis") soon gave way to machines produced and marketed by IBM, which moved quickly into commercial computers, sold primarily to the government and defense contractors, after Remington Rand's initial success with the UNIVAC. "About 1956 we got some IBM 650s which were truly open shop type machines.... An engineer who could read and learn how to write a program could sign up for an hour's worth of time on this machine, key punch his stuff up on decks of cards, and run it through, and do the calculations.... We had three of those at our peak ... located in the 8 foot by 6 foot [wind tunnel]. They were so heavily used that ... if you were really doing some heavy computing ... you would run at night, you would run on holidays, you would do whatever you needed to get your computer time.... They became very popular, so the IBM world sort of infiltrated here.... Then, when we went for our first major large computer that was going to be truly scientific, and open to the users to write programs in FORTRAN, it was an IBM 704."[16] However, before the 704 was delivered, Jansen left Lewis to have her first child.

"When I left I was working in ... engineering ... developing programs on the computers, and writing reports in basically ... internal engine research. I was actually doing research. I had been given a project, and I was developing the equations and the programs and doing the actual work on the computer.... The last report I wrote was on boundary layer interactions." Both Lewis and Langley Research Centers were working on boundary layers. In Jansen's case, she was investigating the "boundary layer external to ... the blade rows of the compressor" within an aircraft engine, "as opposed to the boundary layer of the airfoil. The theory is the thing — the fact that you're working with cascades of blades and rotating machinery makes the process much more complex."

Jansen was away from her work for over three years, during which time she was miserable, watching from the outside while "the space program was coming to the forefront in everyone's imagination, and when [Alan B.] Shepard made his first suborbital flight, and [John H.] Glenn made his first orbital flight, and I was not a part of it, it was ripping me apart inside. Everywhere ... the media talked about how you should be happy just making cookies and taking care of your little children. At that time ... I did not see a way in which I could keep my hand active and still stay home.... So it became very difficult for me, because ... I saw a part of history developing through this space program that I wanted very much to be a part of.

"It was not an easy decision," she remembers, "to leave the kids and come back to work." During the three and a half years that Jansen had been away, Lewis "had gone through two generations of computers and had another, a much newer, more powerful, system." When Jansen returned to work in mid-1962, she had a choice of jobs at Lewis, but decided to go "back into the computing world, because that is where I had felt the most ... satisfied — most productive. I never really felt comfortable as an engineer ... doing the research on my own. I had always felt more comfortable when I was doing the math part of it, and supporting the engineers."

"They had gone through two generations of computers. FORTRAN was still the major language that was used.... I had a lot of brushing up to do, and I took ... in house classes.... It wasn't long before I felt very productive, and I was doing real honest to gosh work." Jansen returned to her old computing section, which was supporting Lewis's large wind tunnels. The laboratory had moved into "nuclear fusion and fission investigations, [so she began] developing some modeling of fusion processes, electromagnetic theories. I actually have a report that I coauthored on some electromagnetic modeling." Gradually her work shifted from theoretical calculations "[to] support of the experimental facilities again.... They were still using the 1103 [UNIVAC], believe it or not ... and they wanted to move the support of the wind tunnels and the test cells into the IBM environment." In time Jansen acquired increased levels of oversight responsibility in Lewis's data systems organization, which "provided all the supports, both real time and post processing, for the wind tunnels and for the experimental facilities that are around the center."

While the advent of high-speed electronic computing diminished the need for women computers, "there was never anyone that was pushed out the gate because of it ... ," insists Jansen. "First of all ... a lot of these people didn't stay long; they'd come out of high school, they would work there for a couple of years, and then got married. And when they got their first pregnancy, they would walk out the gates. So gradually there was a diminishing number.... Some of them went back to school, got their math degrees, and ended up being bona fide mathematician computer programmers [working with] the large mainframes." Lewis began to hire people "with math backgrounds and then trained them in the use of computers, because the colleges weren't at that point yet.... This was one of the few areas, back in the '60s, where there was a fairly high percentage of women ... in the math area, and the application and use of computers."

Joseph Totten's road to the space age began in Biloxi, Miss., where he went through basic training in the U.S. Army Air Corps at Keesler Field.[17] "As a kid I always had a fascination for aviation, and I built model plane after model plane. My room was well filled with model airplanes all the time. I'd fly them — not the kind that you have a motor in — but the rubber band kind. In those days, I don't believe we had motors ... other kids that I ran around with, we were all doing the same sort of thing." In 1944, fresh out of high school, Totten enlisted in the U.S. Army Air Corps. A few months after the surrender of Japan on September 2, 1945, he was discharged. He returned to Illinois, where he attended Joliet Junior College and later went to the University of Illinois, finally earning a bachelor's degree in civil engineering in 1954. In between he got married, had his first children, and worked for a public works company, "designing subdivisions, streets, sewer systems, water systems, designing some small bridges and things like that."

When Totten finished college he returned to the same company for a year, largely out of loyalty to the man who had helped finance his last year in college. Restless for something bigger and better, he then cast about for a job as a city engineer or public works administrator. As a fall-back, he applied for a job with Douglas Aircraft in El Segundo, Calif. Douglas offered him a job and turned out to be the only company that "would provide any moving expenses for me. So I decided to take that job. My wife and I ... we had two kids and she was pregnant at the time — we took off, went to California." He was the first Totten to leave Illinois. And that, he says, is "how I got into the aerospace business."

He was soon working on the analysis and design of jet aircraft for the Navy, including "the A3D ... a twin engine attack bomber, carrier based." He also worked "on the A4D ... still flying today (or a more modern version of it), which is an attack fighter aircraft, and the F4D ... a delta wing airplane ... called 'the Skyray.' They looked like a damn stingray — the planform. They had no normal wingshape to it, just a big delta wing." The Skyray was designed for "speed and maneuverability... an aircraft that would be flying over mach 1; at that time, that was a relatively new field." While he found himself working with "aluminum, and things like that" rather than "working with sand and gravel, and cement [Totten] really didn't have to learn new tricks. The fundamental engineering equations ... you can apply almost anywhere. It was just a matter of learning a different language — aircraft language rather than civil engineering language."

Toward the end of the 1950s the aerospace industry suffered a downturn. "Budgeting was pretty low and a lot of programs that had been developed were canceled, like the Eagle missile program, the F10D ... most of the companies were laying people off." Totten decided he did not want to "stay around and get laid off." Besides, the Douglas Aircraft Company had undergone a change in top management which Totten thought was letting the company "go to pot ... there were a lot of us that got very discouraged" with the way the company was being run. So Totten contacted a friend who was working with the Chrysler Corporation, an aerospace contractor in Huntsville, Ala. and the friend put him in touch with Brown Engineering. "The majority of the work that they did was contract to the government providing services in support of the Marshall Space Flight Center." At the beginning of the new year, 1961, Totten returned to the deep South to work for Brown.

The enthusiasm with which Totten began working for Brown Engineering was due in part to his admiration for Brown's president, Milton Cummings, who had interviewed him. "The guy was something else ... a far out looker, you know. He could see things in the future, and he knew how to work things to get to that point.... He was the guy who ... developed the HIC [Huntsville Industrial Center] building complex, which was ... used a lot by NASA in the early days. The HIC was a large cotton mill at one time, and he converted it to office space and laboratories for Brown Engineering and a lot of aerospace companies that were just starting to come into Huntsville.... There were no other large facilities here, outside of the Redstone Arsenal.... Within a year or so, he had the foresight to buy the property."

Totten had foresight too. "After being in Huntsville a while, I saw where the power was and where the control was, with the government. And so I applied for a job with NASA in 1962.[18]... I was a civil engineer, structural ... you're just applying the same laws ... to a different field, that's all.

"Marshall's main work [during the mid-1960s] was the development of the Saturn V," the mighty booster that lifted over 3100 tons — more than a "good sized Navy destroyer" — off the launch pad at Cape Kennedy and nosed the 55-ton combined Apollo command, service, and lunar lander modules into an orbit around the Moon on July 19, 1969.[19] The thundering Saturn was the descendant of liquid-fuel rocket technology foreseen at the turn of the century by Konstantin Tsiolkovski, tested successfully by Robert H. Goddard in 1926, and developed during the 1940s at the Guggenheim Aeronautical Laboratory (California Institute of Technology) and by Wernher von Braun's German Army ordnance group at Peenemuende on the North Sea.

Germany had been stung by the humiliating terms of the Treaty of Versailles (1919), the negotiations for which excluded the German government, and her military leaders ingeniously sought ways to circumvent the treaty's disarmament terms.[20] Those terms forbade Germany to maintain tanks, military aviation, submarines, heavy artillery, or military conscription. At the same time, Britain's use of aircraft and tanks during the Somme offensive (1916) was not lost on the German general staff, which resolved to prepare for the next battle sophisticated, mechanized warfare. These were the seeds not only of the German "blitzkrieg" of World War II, but of the German Army's work, during the 1930s, on rocket research as part of the development of long-range artillery.

Bureaucratic ingenuity played a role as well in the growing importance of the U.S. Army's rocket work at the Army Ballistic Missile Agency in Huntsville, Ala.,[21] to the future space program. In 1955, when a select panel chose the Navy's Viking over the Army's Jupiter C as the launch vehicle for the first U.S. satellite program, ABMA persevered with its work on the Jupiter C, maintaining that it was merely testing nose cones for ballistic missile warheads. Again, when, in 1957, the U.S. Air Force won the interservice battle for responsibility for long-range military rocket development, ABMA decided to "leapfrog" the competition by concentrating on large booster development for space exploration.[22] The strategy was inspired, for Wernher von Braun was a space visionary as much as a master of advanced rocket research. (As fortune would have it, the Navy's first entry into the "space race," designated Vanguard, would culminate in a ball of fire on the launch pad. ABMA emerged triumphant after all as its four-stage Jupiter C, Juno I, took the honor on January 31, 1958 of sending this country's first satellite into Earth orbit.)

Thus it was that in 1957 ABMA began work on a large, advanced booster, dubbed the Super-Jupiter, capable of lifting as much as five tons through Earth's gravitational barrier and placing it into Earth orbit — a feat that would require 1.5 million pounds of thrust. For the Mercury and Gemini projects, the first U.S. manned forays into space, NASA had requisitioned boosters from the military services — the Redstone missile from the Army, and the Thor, Atlas, and Titan missiles from the Air Force. By 1960 NASA was ready for its own super-booster program, and ABMA was ready for NASA. That year, on the Ides of March, ABMA opened its doors as NASA's George C. Marshall Space Flight Center.

When Totten left Brown engineering for the Marshall Space Flight Center in 1962, his "first assignment ... was providing stress analysis support for what we, in those days, called advanced designs ... such things as lunar landers, NOVA[23] vehicles.... We worked on a variety of things in support of the advanced designs of that sort, mostly to do with outer space ... vehicles.... I was working on things that were probably another ten or fifteen years down the road." After working on advanced design projects, Totten joined "a group that worked directly with the Saturn IB," the booster that launched the first manned Apollo spacecraft, Apollo 7, in October 1968 and was used again in 1973 to launch crews to the Skylab orbiting workshop.[24] He "started out in stress analysis and then progressed up.... Stress analysis ... was all we did, analyze the designs to make sure they were strong enough.... [Working in the] structures propulsion area, we were pretty much concerned with design, analysis, thermal, and that sort of thing, where we were actually putting stuff on the paper, checking it to make sure it was strong enough to handle the environments that we'd fly through, and then get all the drawings ready to release and send them over to be manufactured." Then, "during the late '60s, [Totten began working] not only the static side of the house, but ... dynamic and vibration analysis, along with the structural analysis." Totten also worked "in the design side of the house ... the design, propulsion, and structural design lab, where all new engines [were] developed [and] all new structures ... new launch vehicles," payloads, and experiments were designed.

Born in the Illinois farm belt, the son of an auto mechanic, Joseph Totten claims that he can "remember the horse and buggy.... I lived through that as a little kid, and I've seen going to the stars. There are not too many people who can say that they've been there."

Sam Browning also came to the space program by way of the U.S. Air Force, which he joined because he "wanted to fly an airplane." And, he says, "I don't want this to sound trite, but I really felt that people ought to serve this country ... avoiding the draft was not something that occurred to me — another difference between the generation today, and our generation." A native of Birmingham, Ala., the eldest of three boys, Browning was the son of an itinerant carpenter who finally managed to settle himself with the U.S. Army Corps of Engineers in Huntsville. Even though he had had little schooling beyond the eighth grade, Browning's father was "a very talented guy." When the younger Browning declared his enthusiasm for chemistry, his father "pointed out that you have to have a Ph.D to go anywhere in chemistry, and that was long and expensive.... why don't you go into chemical engineering? You'll make a lot more money." And so he did.

Browning's first encounter with the space program was in 1957, when he began working at the Army Ballistic Missile Agency as a coop student while he was studying for a degree in chemistry from Auburn University. "I was in the solid rocket testing area…. The Army group was divided into the solid rocket group and the guided missile development division — which was von Braun's team." After about a year he realized that while he "was able to put my engineering drawing to good use by designing test pictures … and working down on the range with the crews installing solid motors, [he] wasn't getting any chemistry or any exposure to … what I was really going through school after, so I asked for a transfer to GMDD (the Guided Missile Development Division) … and I came over here and worked in the materials laboratory."

In 1959, Browning graduated from Auburn, where he had been in an advanced ROTC program; he then spent three years in the Air Force. To his dismay, he failed his first physical when entering active duty. As luck would have it "there was an outfit in Sacramento that was tagging the personnel folders of people with degrees in chemistry, chemical engineering … engineering physics, I guess. So I got tagged to go into the nuclear development, warhead development testing." Browning did classified work at McClellan Air Force Base for three years, learning "a lot more chemistry there than I had in college. And … a lot of physics.

"We had a few field grade officers … and a laboratory full of second and first lieutenants with engineering and chemistry and physics degrees." Browning's experience at McClellan helped him to "realize that I could compete with people who had degrees from MIT and CalTech and prestige institutions…. Growing up in the South and going to school at Auburn, I had a little bit of an inferiority complex…. These people … were well trained, but … it came down to … whether you got the job done or not. We had one fellow from MIT who was all thumbs … in spite of the fact that he was quite well educated." Browning discovered "these are mortals too. I can hang in there with them."

When Browning's stint with the Air Force ended in 1962, he debated returning to his old ABMA organization at Huntsville — which had, by now, become NASA's Marshall Space Flight Center. "I had a hard time deciding what to do when I got out of the Air Force, because I had a chemical engineering degree and an interest in working in the chemical processing industry. I had … some experience in the nuclear field, and this terrific interest in NASA and the aerospace business…. I didn't want to come back to Huntsville…. Huntsville was a very small town…. One great thing the Air Force did for me was to expose me to California…. Sacramento is a big, big valley. Most of the days you couldn't even see the horizon. The sky just blended into the horizon somehow, because of the smog…. It was almost an alien culture — Marin [County] … yuppie type stuff."[25] But as time went on "I learned that I missed the hills around Huntsville."

Nineteen sixty-two was not a bad time for an engineer to be looking for a job. Browning had offers from Babcock and Wilcox, Brookhaven National Laboratories, Chemstrand, Monsanto Chemicals, Morton Thiokol, and Pratt and Whitney, "to work on the SNAP reactor program up at their Connecticut Advanced Nuclear Engineering Laboratory." His decision not to take the Pratt and Whitney job was fortuitous, for Pratt and Whitney had to close down their SNAP program within a year. Ultimately the "lure of the Apollo program … won out over the rest of it and, like everybody else I guess who's worked for NASA, I didn't take the highest offer

I got.... I came to work for NASA to be part of the space program and to be back in Huntsville." Browning began the year 1963 by reporting to Marshall Space Flight Center, where his first assignment was in the propulsion division. He had been slated "to work on the reactor inflight test stage ... and specifically, the NERVA [nuclear engine for rocket vehicle applications]," but both programs were cancelled the following year.[26] "At that point the section that I was a part of also had responsibility for the RL-10 oxygen, liquid hydrogen rocket engine. And I was simply shifted over to work on the RL-10.... The RL-10 is an engine that was the free world's first ... oxygen, liquid hydrogen rocket engine, [a] very advanced system for its day, and [it] still is one of the better rocket engines around."[27]

In 1964 "a new fellow ... came into the section named J. R. Thompson."[28] Thompson had been working for Pratt and Whitney, and when he arrived at Marshall he was put "to work on the J-2 engine, which was ... still in early development stages."[29] Browning was one of a "pair detailed to work with J.R. developing a math model for the J-2 engine, which was something I had no idea how to go about doing — but J.R. did." Working "in that group through the J-2 engine qualification program" kept Browning busy during late 1965 and early 1966. Once the J-2 engine passed its qualification tests, Browning decided he "didn't really want to get bogged down in tracking paper work on an engine that was now about to move out of the development phase into the flight phase. [He wanted] to stay closer to the new technology part [of Marshall's work], the farther out kinds of things.... There weren't many chemical engineers around, so they tended to assign me to the cats and dogs that came in in advanced propulsion type stuff, which in those days was mainly exotic type propellants." Browning was transferred into the propulsion and vehicle engineering research laboratory, where "we were looking at post Saturn, NOVA class vehicles ... eighteen to thirty million pounds of thrust.... One concept was ... something like two to three million pound thrust engines clustered around a plug nozzle. [Another was the] so-called aerospike nozzle, which has a single annular throat around the periphery of this thing, that might be sixty feet in diameter that, again, had an aerospike nozzle instead of the traditional bell-type nozzle."

Browning's background in chemical engineering had been an "open sesame" to much of Marshall's work in advanced rocket propulsion. For example, he was assigned to a working group investigating the use of fluorine as a rocket propellant to replace oxygen. "We were also looking at new ways to build turbo machinery that would be lower in cost. So I had a couple of studies in low-cost turbo machinery, turbopumps.... We had some contracts out on high-energy propellants, and I monitored those." Before the mighty Saturn V would launch the three-man crew of Apollo 11 on its journey to the Moon in July 1969, Browning was already at work on a NASA venture which actually predated the manned lunar landing mission — a manned orbiting space station.[30]

But even as the crew of Apollo 11 made its epochal voyage to the Moon, NASA was phasing out production of the Saturn in what would become, after the Challenger accident of January 28, 1986, one of its more controversial decisions. In place of the Saturn, the agency began developing a new Space Transportation System, consisting of a winged, reusable orbiting rocket plane or space "shuttle," an external fuel tank, and two refurbishable, reusable boosters.[31] One of the places the Shuttle was expected to go was to an Earth-orbiting space station, which had been a gleam in the eyes of aerospace engineers at Langley Research Laboratory and German rocket engineers working with Wernher von Braun at the Army Ballistic Missile Agency even before NASA was created. Although NASA tried repeatedly — and unsuccessfully until 1984 — to obtain White House approval to begin a space station program, preliminary design and definition studies were an intermittent feature of advanced technology work at both Johnson Space Center and Marshall Space Flight Center throughout the 1960s.

When in 1961 NASA formally embarked on the research and development work necessary to carry a man to the Moon by the end of the 1960s, the agency was able to draw on the cumulative efforts of thousands of engineers who had already been mobilized to solve some of the fundamental technical problems that stood between it and triumph. Important groundwork had been laid during the 1950s in the aerodynamics of high-performance (or military) aircraft, guided missiles, electronic data processing, and advanced aircraft engine and rocket research and development. That groundwork was laid by engineers Bill Cassirer and Joseph Totten and others like them, men and women who began their careers in the 1950s.

The early careers of the ten NASA Apollo-era engineers profiled in this chapter reflect the successful mobilization by the United States of the civilian, technical manpower to wage the Cold War. That war had among its principal weapons not only nuclear deterrence (and the ballistic missiles necessary to make the threat of nuclear weapons meaningful), but the air power thought essential to any successful response to any future military "emergency." The Apollo program provided a peaceful corollary to the militarily inspired work being done along a wide front of technological development.

These early recruits into the new civilian army of the Cold War came, for the most part, from the Northeast or Midwest; one came from Alabama and another from the state of Washington. Half were the sons (and one the daughter) of practicing engineers or scientists. NASA support, through undergraduate coop programs or support for graduate work, was instrumental in the training and initial career choice for at least half of these men and one woman. A majority of them started out wanting to go into aeronautical or aerospace engineering, and all who did moved directly into work in NACA laboratories or the Army Ballistic Missile Agency, with the exception of two who worked for several years with large aircraft manufacturers dependent on government orders before going to work for NASA in the early 1960s. Two of the three engineers in this group who did not begin their careers intent upon going into aerospace research or engineering nonetheless were employed by the federal agencies involved in the research and development work. The one woman in the group began her career with training in mathematics and, except for a few years during which she stayed home to care for a young family, did the same kind of work in the same NASA organization throughout her entire career. (The constancy of her career pattern raises the question of whether, as a woman in a man's profession, once she found a niche she clung to it, or whether alternate opportunities were truly closed to her.)

By the time these engineers were interviewed they had been working for NASA (or the NACA or ABMA) for no less than twenty years, and in seven cases for more than twenty-five years. Did their careers fulfill their initial hopes or expectations? Four had clearly wanted to do research of some kind; only one of those four managed to continue doing fundamental research (in aeronautics) without paying a penalty in "getting ahead." Two gradually shifted into management, moving to NASA Headquarters in Washington, D.C. to carry out administrative or Headquarters staff functions. The fourth also moved into management, but project management that enabled him to remain close to the work in instrumenting spacecraft for planetary missions that had intrigued him when he first joined NASA. All four had risen to the ranks of the senior executive service. Two others achieved senior executive rank during their twenty-plus years with NASA; both had started out as enlistees in military pilot training programs, and both spent several years in the aerospace industry working on optimum engine and airframe designs for high-performance aircraft before coming to NASA. One went into technical management (at Marshall Space Flight Center), while the other moved into program management at NASA Headquarters. All but one of these six, whose NASA careers terminated in senior-level management rather than the "hands on" work that had drawn them to research and technology in the first place, began their NASA careers as NACA or ABMA veterans.

Of the four of these ten engineers who did not advance into executive positions, one was promoted into a managerial track that could lead to a senior executive position, while three remained in technical occupations. Of those three, one became essentially a contract monitor with little further involvement in actual engineering work; one is involved in structural analysis for the Centaur upper stage manufactured by General Dynamics; and one is adrift on a career plateau, passing through a "career development" program and a study of power generating systems for a space station but, by his own account, "pretty much stuck."

-----

[1] A "supersonic" speed is greater than the speed of sound (around 670 miles per hour at sea level, or mach 1); "transonic" describes the range between subsonic and supersonic speeds. "Hypersonic" speeds are greater than five times the speed of sound, or mach 5.

[2] The hydraulics engineer knows that the same friction can determine the pressure loss in a pipe or channel.

[3] Since much aeronautical research was conducted with scale models in wind tunnels, it was important to be able to extrapolate from models to full-scale aircraft. Working in the field of hydrodynamics, Osborne Reynolds (1842-1912) established

experimentally that the range of velocity at which a flowing fluid will become turbulent depends on the fluid's mass density and viscosity, the size or shape of the conduit, and the velocity of the flow. The numerical ratio reflecting this relationship came to be called the Reynolds number. The use of the Reynolds number has enabled aeronautical engineers to extrapolate from wind tunnel tests of models to actual full-scale construction by ensuring that the Reynolds ratio for the full-scale project equals that of the model.

[4] Project Mercury culminated in L. Gordon Cooper's full-day flight of May 15-16, 1963, the sixth flight and fourth orbital space mission for the project.

[5] For a more complete account of H. Julian Allen's work and its place in the NACA's research program in the 1950s, see Loyd S. Swenson, Jr., James M. Grimwood, and Charles C. Alexander, *This New Ocean: A History of Project Mercury*, NASA SP-4201 (Washington, D.C.: U.S. Government Printing Office, 1966), pp. 55-72, and Edwin P. Hartman, *Adventures in Research: A History of Ames Research Center, 1940-1965*, NASA SP-4302 (Washington, D.C.: U.S. Government Printing Office, 1970), *passim*.

[6] For accounts of the research work carried out in the NACA laboratories during the 1950s, see James R. Hansen, *Engineer in Charge: A History of the Langley Aeronautical Laboratory, 1917-1958*, NASA SP-4305 (Washington, D.C.: U.S. Government Printing Office, 1987), and Alex Roland, *Model Research: The National Advisory Committee for Aeronautics, 1915-1958*, 2 vols., NASA SP-4103 (Washington, D.C.: U.S. Government Printing Office, 1985), *passim*.

[7] Apollo 12 was launched on November 14, 1969, toward the second successful manned lunar landing. The mission took ten days.

[8] *This New Ocean* gives a good account of the process of "man-rating" the launch vehicle and spacecraft for the Mercury program.

[9] For an account of the area rule and the design of the F-102, see James R. Hansen, *Engineer in Charge: A History of the Langley Aeronautical Laboratory, 1917-1958*, NASA SP-4305 (Washington, D.C.: U.S. Government Printing Office, 1987), pp. 334-339.

[10] First contracted to Convair/Astronautics Division of General Dynamics in 1958 by the Department of Defense's Advanced Research Projects Agency (ARPA), the liquid hydrogen fueled Centaur was intended to serve as a second stage to increase the payload capability of its host launcher and for versatility in complex space missions. Convair was also the U.S. Air Force contractor for the Atlas missile and launch vehicles.

[11] For a discussion of high-performance aeronautical developments at the end of World War II, see Roger E. Bilstein, *Flight in America, 1900-1983: From the Wrights to the Astronauts* (Baltimore: The Johns Hopkins University Press, 1984), pp. 178-184.

[12] See comments on the growing competition throughout NASA during this period between technology research and project work in chapter 6.

[13] The SNAP program was begun by the Atomic Energy Commission in 1955 to develop nuclear power systems for space vehicles. SNAP-1, designed by the Martin Company, would generate 500 watts of electrical power from the heat of the decaying radioisotope cerium-144. The SNAP series involved the use of both radioisotopic fuel and nuclear fission reactors. The first SNAP power plant launched into space was a 500-watt SNAP 10-Z, placed into orbit from Vandenburg Air Force Base, California, on April 13, 1965. See William R. Corliss, *SNAP Nuclear Space Reactors*, U.S. Atomic Energy Commission (September 1966).

[14] The AJ-2 bomber was a surplus Navy aircraft powered by two reciprocating engines and, for extra speed in combat situations, a J-33 turbojet engine in the fuselage. The J-33 also powered the F-80 fighter.

[15] The UNIVAC, or Universal Automatic Computer, was the first general-purpose commercial electronic computer. Developed by J. Presper Eckert, Jr. and John W. Mauchly, the UNIVAC replaced punched card information storage and retrieval with magnetic tape which, driven on reels past read-write heads, could process alphanumeric information at the rate of half a million characters per minute. The Eckert-Mauchly Computer Company was acquired by Remington Rand in 1950. Remington Rand delivered the first of several UNIVACs to the U.S. Census Bureau in 1951. The American public had its first opportunity to be awed by the "genius" of the computer when CBS television showed the UNIVAC as it forecast Dwight D. Eisenhower's 1952 presidential election victory over Adlai E. Stevenson within four electoral votes.

[16] The IBM 704 was the successor to the 701, an electronic computer capable of doing high-speed repetitive computations for nuclear weapons and aircraft and missiles design. Aggressively marketed to government laboratories, the first 701 was shipped in March 1953 to the Federal Atomic Weapons Development Center at Los Alamos, New Mexico. For a lively and accessible account of the early years of electronic computers, see Harry Wilforst, *Breakthrough to the Computer Age* (New York: Charles Scribner's Sons, 1982).

[17] The U.S. Air Force was created in July 1947, when President Harry S. Truman signed the Armed Forces Unification Act, which established the Air Force as one of three services (the others being the Army and the Navy) under a Secretary of Defense. Primary responsibility for the nation's missile programs was assigned to the U.S. Army's Ordnance Command.

[18] The Army Ballistic Missile Agency (ABMA) at Redstone Arsenal in Huntsville was transferred to NASA and renamed the George C. Marshall Space Flight Center in March 1960. The ABMA itself had been formed, in 1956, from the nucleus of German missile scientists, led by Wernher von Braun, established in 1950 by the U.S. Army at Redstone Arsenal as the Ordnance Guided Missile Center.

[19] The media was fond of pointing out that the Saturn V was taller than the Statue of Liberty and weighed 13 times as much. Roger E. Bilstein, *Stages to Saturn: A*

Technological History of the Apollo/Saturn Launch Vehicles, NASA SP-4206 (Washington, D.C.: U.S. Government Printing Office, 1980), p. 354.

[20] After Adolf Hitler's rise to power in 1933, Germany abandoned all pretense of disarmament.

[21] The U.S. Army established Werner von Braun and his cadre of German rocket engineers as the Ordnance Guided Missile Center at the Redstone Arsenal in Huntsville in 1950. The installation was recreated as the Army Ballistic Missile Agency in 1956 and took the lead role in the joint Army-Navy work in ballistic missiles that resulted in the Jupiter C launch vehicle. It was the Jupiter C that launched the Explorer I satellite into orbit on January 31, 1958, four months after the Soviet launch of Sputnik I.

[22] See Bilstein, *Stages to Saturn*, pp. 11-25.

[23] See footnote 2, chapter 2.

[24] The nomenclature for the Saturn launch vehicles was altered several times throughout the program. The Saturn 1B first stage booster used eight clustered H-1 engines. The H-1 engine, developed by Rocketdyne Division of North American Aviation, Inc., was an uprated version of the original Thor-Jupiter engine, which burned liquid oxygen and a kerosene-based propellant.

[25] In the 1980s the expression "yuppie" (young urban or upwardly mobile professional) came into use to characterize a new generation of salaried professionals who were thought to be unusually aggressive, self-centered, and materialistic in their aspirations.

[26] Nuclear-powered rocket engines were originally proposed for the upper stage of the Saturn and were developed sufficiently for ground testing in the 1960s. The nuclear-powered engine operated on a fairly simple principle: a small nuclear reactor would heat liquid hydrogen which, as it expanded, would produce thrust. A joint NASA and Atomic Energy Commission project, with Aerojet-General serving as prime contractor, the NERVA was never intended to fly and has not flown. However, radioisotopic thermoelectric generators (RTGs), which substitute for batteries, fuel cells, or solar power sources in furnishing nonpropulsive power for spacecraft, have been used successfully on the Pioneer 10 and 11 and Voyager interplanetary spacecraft.

[27] The RL-10 engine was used in the Centaur upper stage and in the Saturn vehicle's upper stage. It was contracted to General Dynamics by the Department of Defense's Advanced Research Projects Agency.

[28] James R. "J.R." Thompson, Jr. arrived at Marshall Space Flight Center in 1963 and remained with the center until 1983, when he moved to Princeton, N.J. to serve as deputy director for technical operations at the Princeton Plasma Laboratory. He returned to Marshall in October 1986, as the center's director. A distinguished rocket specialist, he was project manager for the shuttle main engine and vice-chairman of

the NASA inquiry into the causes of the shuttle Challenger explosion on January 28, 1986.

[29] Borrowing from the technology developed for the RL-10 engine, the J-2 liquid hydrogen engine went into production in 1963. A fully self-contained propulsion system that could be stopped and restarted in orbit, the J-2 was manufactured by Rocketdyne Division of North American Aviation.

[30] For a history of NASA's manned orbiting space station concepts, see Sylvia D. Fries, "2001 to 1994: Political Environment and the Design of NASA's Space Station System," *Technology and Culture* (July 1988), pp. 568-593.

[31] The earliest conceptions of the Space Transportation System (1970-1975) included as well a space tug to move payloads between orbits, a low Earth orbit space station, cislunar space station, shuttle-carried space laboratory module, unmanned large lift vehicle using the external tank and solid rocket boosters, and an unmanned geosynchronous orbiting platform.

Winning isn't everything.
It's the only thing.

Vince Lombardi
Coach, Green Bay Packers
1959-1967

Chapter 4
Journeys

One of the many lessons of World War II was that air supremacy could be the linchpin of military victory. As nuclear warheads emerged as the "ultimate" weapon of the Cold War, the development of guided land- and sea-based ballistic missiles took on a special urgency in the U.S. military establishment. Not yet chastened by the protracted land warfare of Vietnam or the complexities of undeclared local warfare in the Middle East, most strategists assumed that strategic security would go to those who commanded the skies. Impelled by the sheer weight of its role in the allied victory over the Axis powers into an international arena divided into the "free world" and "iron curtain" countries, the United States belatedly entered the race to conquer space.

But what did it mean to conquer space? A nation's ability to send guided missiles into space, or to orbit objects of whatever size and function, served as an ominous announcement to a contentious world that the ultimate penalty for "aggression" might be close to unthinkable. Was there no peaceful purpose to which we might put the capacity to loft objects into space, to view the heavens — and Earth — with unprecedented visual clarity and perspective?

American scientists, too, had a strategic interest in space. Having tasted the brew served up by military patrons during the national "emergency" and the Manhattan Project, the scientific community sought to remain at the table with an ongoing menu of government-funded "basic" research. Yet consciences had been troubled by the uses to which science had been put in "winning" the surrender of Japan; many in the scientific fraternity were eager to explore the next frontier of space under civilian, rather than military, support.[1]

Thus it was that, while the NACA (later NASA) and military engineers began to transfer the new technologies of hypersonic flight and ballistic missiles to vehicles that could lift ever heavier payloads into orbit (even sending some of those payloads on interplanetary trajectories), the payloads themselves were parceled among competing interests. Among those interests, shrouded in ideological assumptions, were the proponents of "manned space flight" and of "space science" — or science in space. The former combined the heroic, romanticized aura of human flight, inherited from pioneer aviation days, with the new romance of space travel into exotic and alien realms. The romance of aviation knew few geographic boundaries, but the romance of space travel was largely an import from Europe, never wholly adopted by a country whose ideology presupposed that its own wondrous land-scapes, its own pluralistic culture and institutions, and its own free-wheeling politics constituted the only last frontier that mattered. The notion that the survival of democracy required an expanding frontier (a notion easily associated with the ignominious attempt of nineteenth century Europeans to extend cultural and political hegemony over the rest of the world) would come back to haunt advocates of expanding the space frontier as opponents of costly manned space programs remained indifferent to appeals to an American "manifest destiny" in space.

Claimants to space as the next frontier for scientific observation had no such ideological difficulty. But they had their own rhetorical problem, which was the alleged priority of disinterested, or "basic" research (science "for its own sake") over applied research, an increasingly costly kind of research which, by virtue of its largely military patronage, could be misapplied. It would be difficult to sequester the disinterested pursuit of science in an organization that had to respond to the mixture of constituencies necessary to sustain a large publicly funded technological enterprise. That there might be powerful sociological tensions at play in the contest between the cloistered secular priesthood of the academic science establishment, and the engineers and technicians who served the country's bidding, whether as industrial or government workers, is also probable. The scientists' handicap — much of what they did seemed arcane to a public relentlessly bombarded with novelties and rarely encouraged to reflect upon them — was compensated for by the fact that most science in space could be accomplished with automated spacecraft, normally cheaper than spacecraft designed to launch and sustain human beings.

The maelstrom of political and ideological interests that surrounded NASA as it broke ground in 1959 and 1962 for its new space centers at Beltsville, Md. and Houston, Tex. would have much to do with the shape of the agency and the careers of the roughly ten thousand engineers who flooded its portals, and those of its contractors, during the Apollo decade. The scientific adventure, riding on the success of the first U.S. satellite program, staked out the initial claim. Although The Johns Hopkins University's Applied Physics Laboratory and the U.S. Army and Navy had both begun to launch sounding rockets[2] during the decade after World War II (the Army using captured German V-2 rockets, the Navy using its more powerful Viking), the Department of Defense in 1954 pronounced the satellite of no military value. In this the department was echoing the Rand Corporation's conclu-sion in a 1946 report that an orbiting satellite was unlikely to be of much military use — but could be useful in meteorology, communications, and astronomy.[3] Rand also noted that the country that launched the first satellite could reap as its reward strategic psychological and political advantages.

As the military services continued their missile development programs, scientists from around the world began to make plans for the Third International Polar Year. The First International Polar Year of 1882 had inaugurated international scientific cooperation in the study of Earth's polar regions; a Second International Polar Year in 1932 continued the enterprise. While the Third International Polar Year would not come due until 1962, the prospect of geophysical investigations during a period of maximum solar activity anticipated for 1957-1958 both accelerated and expanded the scientists' vision. In 1952 the International Council of Scientific Unions gave its blessing to an International Geophysical Year during 1957-1958, inviting all nations to cooperate in the study not only of the polar regions, but of the entire Earth.

Within the next three years the American Rocket Society, the National Academy of Sciences, and the Army and the Navy proposed launching a small satellite during the International Geophysical Year. The White House adopted the idea, and by midsummer 1955 the United States had committed itself. The Department of Defense would launch the satellite; the National Science Foundation (created in 1950) would fund it; and the National Academy of Sciences would decide what kind of scientific instruments it would carry. Each of the services was ready to offer its own rocket: the Air Force its Atlas, the Army its Redstone-derived Jupiter C, and the Navy its Viking. Noting that only the Viking had been developed as a space research vehicle, while the country's nascent ballistic missile program required the Atlas and the Redstone, a Department of Defense selection committee gave the nod to the Naval Research Laboratory's Viking.[4]

The Naval Research Laboratory's successful entry, renamed Vanguard after the addition of its Aerobee second stage (a solid-fuel third-stage rocket) and a 1.5-kilogram scientific satellite, missed its first cue in an unfortunate pyrotechnic display,[5] but the Naval Research Laboratory group prevailed to become the nucleus of the first new space center created after NASA was established in 1958. That center was Goddard Space Flight Center, established in 1958 on land acquired from the Department of Agriculture's Beltsville Agricultural Research Center.[6] Joining the Naval Research Laboratory group were personnel reassigned from the Army Signal Corps' meteorological and communications satellite activities at Fort Monmouth, N.J., as well as atmospheric balloon research from Fort Monmouth and the former NACA Langley Research Center, and the Naval Ordnance Laboratory at Dahlgren, Va.

Twenty years later Goddard's visual character — its low-slung, predominantly red brick buildings settled amid generously wooded, rolling hillsides — suggests, more than any other NASA installation, a college campus. A shaded park for picnics and outings and signs of solicitude for resident Canada geese create an atmosphere of academic repose and collegiality. Goddard's mission focused increasingly on space science, especially after the Space Task Group, assigned to manage Project Mercury, moved from Langley Research Center to the Manned Space Center in Houston in 1962.[7] The institutional separation hinted, correctly, at a cultural separation. NASA would become predominantly an organization that accomplished its work through "out of house" — nongovernment — organizations. Since scientific research has been, in the United States, largely a university enterprise, Goddard's external associations would become, more than any NASA installation other than the Jet Propulsion Laboratory (and notwithstanding industrial ties necessary for the fabrication of instruments and satellites), those of the university science community.

Among the early arrivals at Goddard in 1959 was Henry Beacham, who came from the Naval Ordnance Laboratory in White Oak, Md. Beacham had several years' experience working in the camera research laboratory of the Eastman Kodak company and a master's degree in mechanical engineering from the University of Rochester. During his seven years at the Naval Ordnance Laboratory — now called the Naval Surface Weapons Laboratory — he worked in operations research, or weapons analysis. However, calculating the most efficient ways of destruction held no special charm for him, nor, for that matter, did the space program. What did excite him was the novelty of the engineering research problems that accompanied the emerging satellite programs of the early 1960s.

En route to Goddard, Beacham spent a few months working with the Project Vanguard group at the Naval Research Laboratory at Anacostia Naval Air Station, Washington, D.C., forming associations that may partially account for his early rise in Goddard's management ranks. Upon joining the Goddard group he began work on the environmental testing of satellites, soon moving on to major management responsibilities for Goddard's Nimbus and Landsat programs.

To those critics who questioned the practical value of the Apollo manned lunar landing program, NASA could, in the late 1960s, point to its "Earth applications" programs that placed satellites in Earth or geosynchronous orbit to serve as platforms for global communications and remote sensing instruments to study Earth's surface, weather, and upper atmosphere. The prospect of being able to detect global environmental changes, receive near-instantaneous television broadcasts from abroad, or make reliable and long-range weather forecasts, would become, for the ordinary person, one of the more invisible but important legacies of the space age.[8]

For example, the sophisticated Nimbus series of five meteorological satellites, launched between 1964 and 1972,[9] relayed over 3,000 weather photographs daily. Landsat, a later designation for a series of Earth resources satellites first launched in 1972, allowed worldwide monitoring of land masses from desert to forest, glacier to ocean, as well as accretions and movements of atmospheric pollutants. The first Landsat (Earth Resources Technology, or ERTS-A) satellite photographed the entire Earth with 500 pictures, one-thousandth the number required to photograph Earth by high-altitude aircraft.

Achieving such a dramatic increase in the scale of the world's information about its own environment depended on the reliable functioning of light-weight motors and sensitive instruments far distant from the tender care of terrestrial technicians. The first Nimbus, for example, an 830-pound spacecraft stabilized on all three axes, carried an advanced vidicon camera system, an automatic picture transmission system, and a high-resolution infrared radiometer. The next Nimbus, launched in 1969, carried a SNAP-19 auxiliary nuclear power system.[10] The first Landsat carried a multispectral scanner, return-beam vidicon camera system, two wide-band video tape recorders, and a data collection system.

Ensuring that remote sensing satellites operated as intended required an understanding, earned through systematic testing and an accumulated apprecia-tion of the space environment through data from successive satellites, of the conditions to which each assemblage of instruments — its materials, electronics, and optics — would be subjected. Beacham, his contemporaries from the naval research and ordnance laboratories, and newcomers to Goddard plowed this virgin territory. Beacham's personal progression from satellite environmental testing to systems reliability engineering reflected a logical accumulation of critical technological know-how.

The influx of German rocket research and engineers into the United States after World War II has become the stuff of American space lore.[11] Less well known is aeronautical work done not only in Germany but also in Italy during the 1930s and 1940s,[12] work which laid equally important foundations for modern aerospace technology. In 1911 the romantic Italian nationalist and poet, Gabriele d'Annunzio, took to the Italian skies in a Curtiss aircraft. Twenty-nine years later, Romans craned their necks for hours as two Italians established the world's duration flying record, circling the Eternal City for 67 hours and 13 minutes.[13] A measure of the quality of aeronautical research being done in Italy during the 1930s was the keen interest shown by the U.S. Office of Strategic Services in the Italian aeronautical research center at Guidonia.[14]

During the turmoil of World War II, one of the most bitter struggles for the Italian peninsula occurred at Capua, Italy as the German Wehrmacht fought to hold the Volturno line against Allied forces. In the summer and fall of 1943 the Allies had begun their successful advance northward through the difficult and rain-sodden terrain of the Campania. As British and American troops landed at the Port City of Salerno after the Italian-Allied armistice of September 3, the Germans began a systematic campaign of imprisonment and evacuation to labor camps of Italian troops and Allied prisoners of war. War-time memoirs tell of thousands of Italians and Allied prisoners escaping into the protective hillsides of the Apennines, seeking refuge among frightened Italian villagers, who risked their lives and the demolition of their towns by their defiance.[15]

One of those prisoners was Frank Toscelli. Born in the little town of Vitulazio, near Capua, Toscelli was inducted into the Italian Army in 1943. Seized by the Germans for deportation, he escaped with two of his buddies, was captured, and escaped again. Although one of Toscelli's buddies was wounded during an artillery barrage, the trio managed to find what they hoped would be the Allied line. Initially fearful that they might have stumbled into German hands, they were relieved, remembers Toscelli, when they noticed the "shape of the shoe" worn by one of the strange soldiers: "it was different." They noticed as well "a piece of chewing gum and ... a cigarette paper." They were safe, and they were free.

Toscelli's father had emigrated to the United States in 1907, only to return nine years later when his Italian-born wife became ill with what the doctor diagnosed as an advanced case of homesickness. The elder Toscelli operated a small taxi business in the town of Vitulazio; as he repaired his taxis' engines and the townspeople's bicycles, Frank had watched, captivated by a curiosity about how mechanical things worked especially airplanes. Monoplanes flying overhead fascinated him as well. His father wanted him to be a doctor, but Frank would become an aeronautical engineer. After World War II he went to the University of Naples, earning his diploma in engineering in 1949. Through his father echoed America's siren call. "Go to America," his father had insisted; that "is the land of [the] free." In 1950 Frank moved to Pittsburgh, where he lived with an uncle and worked as a busboy and construction laborer while he attended the Carnegie Institute of Technology (now Carnegie-Mellon University) on a scholarship. By 1953 he had received a bachelor of science degree in mechanical engineering.

Sharing the experience of thousands of former Axis nationals eager to emigrate from war-torn Europe to the land of opportunity, Toscelli played a game of cat and mouse with U.S. immigration officials as he tried to obtain an immigrant visa. Neither a new American bride nor a $1,000 bond posted by his uncle could relieve him of the necessity of traveling to Honduras, Canada, Mexico, or *any* nation bordering the United States where he might get an immigrant visa so he could reenter the United States to stay. Finally, a friend of a friend arranged for him to go to Cuba. With ninety dollars in his pocket, he boarded a Greyhound bus for Key West, Fla. After a few months in Cuba he was broke, but he could get a visa. He managed to scrape together enough money to return to Pittsburgh, where Westinghouse Airbrake (which had first hired him in 1953 as a pneumatic engineer) made a place for him. He remained with Westinghouse until 1960, working with airbrake and switching signals.

By 1960 the space program was gathering steam, and Toscelli became "an enthusiast, like everybody else." Drawn to what he felt was the sheer "adventure" of space flight, he took a job with Westinghouse Electric's Astronuclear Laboratories, where work was under way on the NERVA nuclear propulsion engine. He got "involved then in ... shock and vibration and dynamics." His work gave him an opportunity to see something of America's wide open spaces when he had to accompany a simulated reactor on a train trip to Jackass Flats, Nev. for testing. "I rode the train reserved for us.... We had to measure the forces, the excitation applied to this instrument.... So I saw the country — the vastness of the country.... After we got to Iowa, there was nothing else, although the route was chosen to avoid any place of habitation, any cities or concentration of people." Toscelli also managed to continue going to school at night at the University of Pittsburgh. By 1960 he had his master's degree in mechanical engineering, and when he left Westinghouse in 1964 he had risen to the rank of senior engineer for shock vibration and dynamics.

Toscelli was recruited by NASA in 1964. "They were looking for people to get involved in space [and they were] looking for" engineers with masters' degrees. Toscelli's specialty, gas dynamics, appealed to NASA's recruiters, who interviewed him in Pittsburgh; by the end of the year he had moved to Greenbelt, Md. to work at Goddard Space Flight Center. "I was in the test evaluation area where we have all the equipment testing and the chambers.... I was at that time in ... advanced research and technology because of my considerable experience, and the variety of subjects that I was familiar with." Goddard was in the midst of designing spacecraft that would carry sophisticated instruments subject to damage in the environment of space. Toscelli's work drew him into "the assessment of molecular and particulate contamination of spacecraft" and the auto-effects on satellites' space environment "generated by material outgasing, particulate releases, propulsion, and venting." Of necessity he soon became expert in "vacuum technology [and] internal gas flow" in spacecraft, material outgasing, contamination, lubrication, and propulsion problems. Meanwhile Toscelli remained the restless student, eager to add to his growing experimental grasp of space-induced phenomena an intellectual mastery which, in the European tradition, could only be confirmed through university work. For five years after arriving at Goddard he continued course work at the University of Maryland and Catholic University to complement the thesis work in vacuum technology and gas dynamics and contamination he had done at the University of Naples. In 1969 he traveled to Naples to defend his thesis, returning to Goddard with a doctorate in mechanical and aerospace engineering.

The nature of his work enabled Toscelli to contribute to virtually every Goddard satellite program. For example, as any satellite travels through space, its materials release gases "either because of diffusion through the material or because they are attached to the surface molecules." Satellites had to be designed so that the release of gases and pressures internal to the instruments could be closely controlled to "prevent the problem of voltage breakdown, or contamination of a mirror or other critical devices which may be degraded by environmental conditions which are not appropriate." Those conditions would have to be accurately predicted, and one of Toscelli's accomplishments was the development of a computer program which could "calculate, given several volumes with different gases," the pressures within a satellite. The problems with which Toscelli worked were and remain common to all spacecraft, manned and unmanned alike.

Toscelli speaks proudly of being consulted on the design "parameters" of the space shuttle and the space station, and he remains puzzled that the authority he has earned in his engineering field has not translated itself into more than one promotion since he arrived at Goddard. When he arrived at Goddard in 1964, the center seemed to some to be largely an extension of the Naval Research Laboratory group. "These guys were in the management area already. [They] had the previous experience, [they] knew each other." He has watched, frustrated, as those "with less education, or less production," have been promoted beyond him. "Some ... [get promoted] because of buddy-buddy ... and also, [there's] my age."

"We were young and full of enthusiasm ... the work was interesting ... a brand new facility and all the people, we all had an ambition to move ahead, to do the best we could in this new adventure.... It was very satisfying and very interesting — the prestige, the respect, and of course the fact that we were doing something never done before ... and we all were contributing very much to the field."

———————

From the time he arrived at NASA's Goddard Space Flight Center in 1966 until 1985, when he began working on studies of possible science laboratory modules for NASA's new space station program, Hank Martin worked in the thermal analysis and design of satellites. "That essentially involves making the spacecraft run at the right temperature when it's in orbit, which is an interesting set of problems." He was fresh out of Catholic University when he went to Goddard, with a degree in engineering and, as engineering curricula go, a fairly broad education that emphasized conceptual ability. "I wasn't particularly trained or suited or excited about heat transfer initially. I could have been in the dynamic structures or propulsion or a whole lot of different areas ... but this was what looked good."

Radiation heat transfer was "an emerging discipline.... There had been a little bit of work done in the gas turbine industry because they were dealing with such hot temperatures. But lo and behold, when you get into space that's *all* you've got — there's no air to cool things ... you've got to transfer everything by radiation." Engineers tried various approaches to the problem, "developing computer models ... to predict" heating and radiation, or doing "supporting research" such as investigating "thermal control coatings: you paint something white so it's going to reflect a lot of heat. But it gets out in space and the ultraviolet energy makes it turn brown and the thing gets too hot and you blow out batteries.... We've lost some things because of high temperatures on spacecraft."

Goddard's engineers also explored "different kinds of hardware to control temperatures [like] these louvers, like venetian blinds, that open and close and let heat in or out of a particular system. [Or] the development of heat pipes, which ... are extremely efficient devices for making things run under constant temperature — and various permutations and combinations of heat pipes. Heat transfer technology ... developed some sort of maturity and sort of leveled out in the development area ... within maybe ten years or so.

"I think probably ... why I didn't ... burn out on it was the fact that, working heat transfer for flight projects, I worked in-house programs and out-of-house programs, no manned stuff, but all free flyer scientific type missions. Everybody else who had anything to do with that satellite had some sort of a temperature requirement. The data system guy, he had a radio transmitter, he had some sort of digital onboard computer. If they didn't run at the right temperature, they wouldn't work right. The scientist who was running some sort of energetic particle detectors ... if his experiment didn't run at the right temperature, his data wouldn't be right. The solar cells had to run at the right temperature. The battery ... every single piece on that spacecraft had a temperature requirement. And as a result, I got a little bit of information about what everybody else was doing. And I got very interested in some of the other ... subsystem disciplines ... the power, or the electronics, or the science end of it. If nothing was particularly interesting ... in my particular area of controlling temperature, I'd be finding out, 'What's this guy doing? ... How does his little box work?' ... So there's always something to learn ... some knowledge to accumulate about what other people were doing."

By the nature of his work, Martin was also drawn into satellite flight operations. "I've got all this data coming back from everybody's stuff, and folded in there is this temperature stuff. How do you set up sort of an overview so that I can look at some sort of a computer printout and in a very rapid fashion be able to tell flight control whether something had to be done or not? ... So it was ... this end-to-end approach, which I think I probably only got by being here at NASA, that was extremely interesting. I wasn't really confined into a specific discipline, and part of that was because the opportunity was there, and part of it was because I'm an inquisitive type of person.

"Everything back in those days was kind of an experiment. If it didn't work, at least you learned something. [Whatever it was] in the small project kind of environment ... it was something that needs to be there to develop the kind of overview engineering that I was fortunate enough to have.... In those days ... we had satellites you could carry in the room.... You could get half a dozen guys in a room sitting around a table ... and those half a dozen people knew everything, knew that system inside and out."

Throughout his NASA career the most exciting work Martin remembers doing "was actually working with the satellite that I helped build just before it was launched. I worked the S-cubed [small scientific satellite] which was launched out of San Marco over [west] Africa.... I'm talking about the actual physical hands-on kinds of interaction with the hardware.... A lot of people from top to bottom really get emotionally involved with that sort of thing. I knew people that were responsible for the thermal control coatings, for example.... The satellite would be launched and they'd stand on the beach and watch it go and they'd cry."

When Elizabeth Mueller went to work at Goddard Space Flight Center in 1963, the year she received a bachelor's degree from Emory University, no one had recruited her. In fact, had she not insisted on being interviewed, NASA would have turned her away. Lured by the prospect of working near the nation's capital, Mueller came close to accepting an offer from the Naval Weapons Laboratory at Dahlgren, Va. until, that is, she looked at a map and discovered that it was not (as had been advertised to her) a suburb of Washington. "But Goddard did look like a suburb of Washington, so I came up ... got off the [Baltimore-Washington] parkway, walked into the main gate, and said, 'I'm here to talk about a job.'"

Goddard's personnel people, "with their usual enthusiasm, said 'well, I'm sure you're not qualified, and you can't do this and you can't do that.' And I said, 'well,

I sent you an application and I believe I am qualified.'" As it turned out, "to be hired by NASA with a degree in math you had to have twenty hours, or something like that. And a science other than biology ... physics or chemistry. And I had that in addition to all the math courses that one could possibly take and good grades.... So they took the application. I just insisted that I was there, I was from Atlanta, and I wanted to talk to someone.... So they said, 'all right.' They sent me around to four people and all four of them wanted to hire me ... and I didn't understand one word of anything anyone said to me.... I'd never even seen a computer."

Mueller's career began in high school, where she was a good mathematics and science student. Her mother, a college graduate in mathematics, worked at home doing office work for her father, who was a divisional sales manager for a national shoe retail firm. Mother and daughter had two young women friends, "not long out of college [and] into the early stages of a career [who used to visit and] talk a lot about job opportunities. Apparently at that point in time math — this was ... '57, '58 — math graduates could get jobs anywhere.... So I remember listening to them talk." Mueller's parents had insisted, as she grew up, that she go to college and have a career, even if she never needed to work. They had learned at least one of the depression era's lessons: a woman might have to support herself, not to mention her husband and her family. "You have to eat, and so you have a job because you want to eat. So you may as well get one that gets you a lot of money."

Mueller was so keen on getting out and working that she turned down a graduate fellowship at Emory. "The other thing is that I had made a definite decision I was not teaching. And my parents were going crazy, because they were convinced that was the only thing for a woman to do with a math degree. I took one education course and it was horrible.... My parents couldn't imagine what I was going to do without teaching. And I couldn't either, but I got one of these guide books [that tells] who hires people with certain degrees, wrote a bunch of letters, and the next thing you know, I had all kinds of offers for jobs. IBM at that time was offering one-third less for women than for men. And they had two pay scales — they had it published and that's what they would say.... The federal government was one place where women could get equal pay."

Mueller's first assignment was with an orbital mechanics group, where she worked documenting programs for a large IBM 7094, one of the last large mainframe computers used by NASA before IBM developed its 360 series, available in the mid-1960s. The IBM 7094 provided the initial data processing for Project Mercury, which, with two suborbital and three orbital missions between 1961 and 1963, gave the United States its first manned spaceflight experience. (Goddard had served as the mission control center for NASA's Space Task Group, responsible for Project Mercury, before the Manned Spacecraft Center opened in Houston, Tex. in 1962.) By current standards the machine was as large as its memory was small. Filling the space of several rooms, and with only 64K memory, the IBM 7094 was a noninteractive machine that could only batch process from cards or tapes.

Mueller did not linger long with the orbital mechanics group. For orbital mechanics "you need a lot of astronomy. I'd never taken an astronomy course, and I really didn't like astronomy.... Second of all ... the computers were choked ... you would write a program and submit it and it would be a week before it would come back.... They gave us work to do documenting programs that other people had written. They were using a compiler on the 7094 which didn't allow you to learn much about the machine. Everything was done by the compiler. And I just got bored." Along with two co-workers also frustrated with their work on the large mainframes, Mueller transferred to the Goddard office that was programming a small satellite control computer for NASA's Orbiting Solar Observatory (OSO) series. Between 1962 and 1975 Thor-Delta boosters launched nine OSO satellites during an eleven-year solar cycle, returning unprecedented photographs and invisible spectra observations of the solar corona, and solar flares and streamers, as well as observations of the influence of solar activity on Earth's atmosphere. Six months before the first OSO launch "they didn't even [have] as much as ... a manual for this computer.... In six months we wrote a system and — oh! it was great fun! ... I was single, and I would sleep maybe five hours a day and work all the rest of the time. [Since Mueller was] programming close to the machine ... [with] data coming in, processing in real time ... it was a good way to learn.... You just had to learn how the machine worked."

In time Mueller became so competent at her work that she was chosen to head the control center software group with which she had been working. NASA "was launching about every year" while she and her group developed the control software for each new satellite. "What you would do was develop the software for the new satellite; you'd work in a fury when you didn't have passes to take from the one [satellite] that was up there. So your work schedule would process with the orbit. Then you'd be working around the clock.... But ... after a few years of that, it began to be very old — to work these long extended hours and late hours." In the meantime Mueller met her future husband, who had come to Goddard in 1964 to work on the Orbiting Geophysical Obervatory satellite (six were launched between 1964 and 1969); hoping for something of a normal life, she transferred to Goddard's project to "develop the first flight computer, the NSSC-1 (NASA Standard Space-craft Computer)." The project's aim was to "develop the box in-house.... It was not slated to fly on any particular mission; [their purpose was] just to see if we could develop [what was] originally called the onboard processor." That processor was successfully developed and flown as an experiment in 1972 on the Orbiting Astronomical Observatory-C (Copernicus), which operated for nine years partly because, as hardware began to fail, the processor — actually an experimental computer — could be reprogrammed.

NASA's Standard Spacecraft Computer was inspired by two developments — one particular to Earth-orbiting scientific satellites. By 1966 it had become evident that NASA would be laboring under persistently constrained budgets. Standard-ization and reusability became engineering design watchwords throughout the agency. For instance, the Space Transportation System, with its reusable solid rocket boosters and shuttle orbiters, was initially conceived as a less costly alternative to the "throw away" launch vehicles of the early space program. At the same time, expanding possibilities for scientific satellites in Earth orbit heightened the desire for autonomous controls on spacecraft which would be beyond the reach of direct commands from earth through portions of their orbits. Moreover, scientific satellites would be more versatile — and hence economical — not only if their on-board controls were of a general purpose character which could be reprogrammed for different missions, but also if instructions to their instruments could be changed, during a mission, in response to unforeseen situations.

Unmanned as well as manned satellites had to be provided with devices for attitude, communications (telemetry), and receiving and carrying out commands either directly from the ground or through "stored command processors" which execute certain sequences of commands triggered at regular instants of time. The appeal of developing a digital computer — as distinct from a processor — was that, unlike it's "hardwired" cousin, a computer could be reprogrammed during the spacecraft's flight. NASA's Standardized Spacecraft Computer would also have to draw a minimum of power, notwithstanding memory expansion, and be radiation resistant.

The NASA Standard Spacecraft Computer-1 "was originally called the onboard processor. But ... after it flew on OAO-C ... NASA made it a standard computer and they gave it that name. I got involved," recalls Mueller, "on the ground floor of that [because of] my software expertise. That was the first flight of the onboard computer on a Goddard satellite. And we had to beg for people to give us work to do with that computer." When Mueller completed the onboard processor and advanced onboard processor (earlier versions of the NSCC-1) everyone was afraid to use it. "Now, of course, the problem is how to cut down on the number of requests that you have. They never have enough memory or CPU [central processing unit] to support everything that people want to do." The core memory[16] on the computer grew from 16K in 1972 (for OAO-C) to 48K for the Multimission Modular Spacecraft (MMS), a generic spacecraft developed to service a number of different Earth and stellar observations, and first flown on the Solar Maximum Mission observatory launched in 1980,[17] to 64K for the MMS flown on the Landsat D mission launched in 1982. Excepting changes in the flight software, the Multimission Modular Spacecraft used on the Landsat D Earth observation satellite was essentially the same as that used on the Solar Maximum Mission, proving the concept of a standardized central onboard computer.

"By the time I finished ... the NSSC-1 on the Orbiting Astronomical Observatory, I had both flight software experience, ground software and a lot of engineering type experience, so ... I really could do any kind of work in the software area. And software tends to be very specialized — you find people who program orbit determination ... for life." Mueller was assigned to project management for both the Multimission Modular Spacecraft and the Solar Maximum Mission (which used the MMS), for which she was responsible for flight software as well as ground software. "That was an interesting managerial experience: to work for two project managers, to have budgets for two projects that I had to merge together, to do software that for MMS had to be common and usable for other than just one mission.... I had a conglomerate of contractors and civil service staff."

Once the Solar Maximum Mission with its Multimission Modular Spacecraft was safely launched, Mueller was reassigned to NASA's Large Space Telescope (renamed in 1983 the Hubble Space Telescope after astronomer Edwin P. Hubble).

She was moved "pretty much against my will…. At that time we were a functional organization … the engineering directorate. They had recognized that there … was tremendous amounts of software [talent] on this team that I was managing, so they just said: 'there you go.'" Goddard shared with Marshall Space Flight Center responsibility for the space telescope, and the "not invented here" syndrome may have affected the space telescope's early history at the Greenbelt center. "There was no real team here…. The environment was one in which you were just constantly jerked around…. New management came in and replaced almost everybody. I was about the only one of the people that were here that didn't get sent off somewhere." Mueller toyed with a possible transfer to NASA Headquarters to work in advanced systems planning for the Office of Space Science and Applications. Ultimately she decided the family upheaval would be too great. Besides, a favorite colleague of hers with whom she had worked well before returned to Goddard after his own tour at Headquarters. In 1980 Mueller decided to stay with the Hubble Space Telescope project to work closely with ground systems and operations development, one of the two principal space telescope development areas — the other being hardware development (e.g., instruments, and communications) — for which Goddard has assumed responsibility.

"All the way along the line, even though my background was in math, [I worked] in engineering oriented areas … just learning it on the job as I went along…. I was very fortunate in that I just moved from place to place around Goddard, and at will…. Sometimes I'd have to say 'this is what I want to do,' and if you're good enough, they'll let you move…. [NASA has] not been very good about looking out for people and insuring that people get to try a variety of experiences or move up in an organization. Only a few people — the ones that may be recognized or may be good friends with or otherwise attached to someone else who's moving up — get the opportunities to move around … in a planned kind of way."

The claims made by "manned space flight"[18] on the new space program were more complex. If all we wanted was scientific knowledge of the heavens or cosmic views of Earth, robot spacecraft could provide both. Some argued that space was a new frontier, and mankind would not have breached that frontier unless men themselves physically crossed into it. (The presumption that space was, in fact, a man's frontier persisted until 1979, when NASA saw fit to admit women to the astronaut corps, taking 17 years to respond to the hue and cry raised as the astronaut groups selected for the Mercury, Gemini, and Apollo programs failed to include any women.) Besides, once the United States had set a man on the Moon, to the amazement of television viewers everywhere, and as long as the Soviet Union persevered with its own manned space program, to do less than persist could be perceived as a national surrender — unless, of course, the whole business was dismissed as spectacle.

Others insisted that automatic robotic space systems could not provide the active, onboard "trouble-shooting" frequently necessary to deal with the inevitable glitches that occur with nearly one-of-a-kind, sophisticated technical systems. Less apparent from the rhetoric that surrounded every successful American manned space venture was the fact that two generations of engineers were represented in NASA in the 1960s, many of them schooled in aeronautics and the design of high-performance aircraft. Those engineers (over 95 percent of whom were men)[19] identified their careers with the triumph of human-piloted flight, an achievement which readily lent itself to the view that humans were destined to explore the high reaches of outer space. Designing for all the dynamic possibilities of an aircraft with a man at the controls had been one of the challenges of high-performance aircraft engineering, to which the military experience of combat flight added its own aura of valor. It was not for nothing that the media seized on the first seven American astronauts, former combat or test pilots all, as exemplars of "the Right Stuff."[20] Whatever the mixture of motives that sustained NASA's manned spaceflight program (the U.S. Air Force having opted out of manned spaceflight as a strategic necessity), the continuing venture imposed on aerospace engineers the added challenge of designing for human life support, in-flight human control of space machines, and, most of all, safety and reliability.

Born in the depths of the depression in 1932, John Robertson grew up in Baton Rouge, La., where his father drove a school bus for the high school system. He had had a thing about airplanes from the time he was a boy. "The big interest came ... back when they used to fly airplanes in and land them in the field, and for twenty-five cents you could get an airplane ride." His fascination with airplanes was fueled by the proliferation of aircraft during World War II, and, as would become true of countless other NASA engineers, an early career in aeronautics readily leant itself to the transition to spaceflight. As a youngster Robertson had also been busy with the Boy Scouts and with the Air Scouts, "an old scouting organization that doesn't even exist any longer." While he was in high school he went with the Air Scouts to "summer encampments, where we went to Air Force bases." Robertson's father, a scout master, shared his son's enthusiasm for airplanes.

Robertson's real ambition was to become a manager, and he recognized early that one could enter a career in management as readily from engineering as from a college course in business administration. "I really went to engineering school to become a manager," he acknowledges, "because I knew there was [sic] going to be some years that I had to work as an engineer. [But] the thing that I was interested in, of course, was aircraft. And I decided that I was going to go out and design the world's best airplanes.... I knew I had to go through the nitty-gritty — I had to be an engineer.... But then, I was looking from the standpoint of not always working as an engineer."

At Louisiana State University (LSU), from which he received his degree in 1952, Robertson studied mechanical engineering rather than aeronautics, which was not available as a major program. "The school did that purposely because they [sic] didn't know" how the aeronautical industry was going to fare. Within the mechanical engineering minor field of aeronautics, students could concentrate on design or performance. Robertson chose performance, "developing performance characteristics of the airplane for planform design.... We had a wind tunnel ... made of ... sheet aluminum. Every time we turned it on, it would ... beat like a drum, so we didn't get the chance to use it too often.... But for a school that's just trying to teach engineers how to use wind tunnels ... it was adequate.... We couldn't do any research projects on it, but we used it ... to get some ideas of how you would go about testing different aircraft in the tunnel."

When Robertson graduated from LSU he looked for "the best engineering job [he] could get ... in aerodynamics, rather than in actual designing of hardware, or being on a drafting board." Meanwhile, the United States was again at war, this time in Korea.[21] Robertson knew his draft number could come up any day. Still, he had to go to work. He took a job with Chance-Vought Aircraft, entering the company's training program in aircraft design. That lasted only "two and a half months. The day the course ended and everybody went to their departments, I went out the door to the U.S. Air Force." Robertson had been in the U.S. Air Force ROTC program at Louisiana State University and spent the next two years as an Air Force explosive ordnance disposal officer.

Old LSU connections helped him find a job in 1958 with Convair Aircraft at Fort Worth, Tex. "I enjoyed the work there. To start off with, I was on the B-36 program.... We were working with throttle settings. If a pilot was flying along with a clean aircraft, he would have one throttle setting. But if he came into a combat situation and he started dropping turrets ... then he would have to go to a different throttle setting to maintain the same altitude and same speed [because] dropping a turret into the airstream is the equivalent of adding weight to the aircraft.... I had to ... do some calculations on the weight changes to determine what the different throttle settings would be at different weights and ... at different configurations of turrets into the airstream.... You draw a set of curves so that the pilot would have a handbook in the aircraft with him, and as he got into combat he'd have to go back and find out what his throttle setting would be and change his throttles to maintain his altitude. [We] used Friden calculators. What would take three hours today took two weeks, eight hours a day — once you got to a calculator."

Robertson also worked on an experimental nuclear-powered bomber project: "Jet engines were used for take-off, [while] the nuclear engines were started in the air.... We had a floating, folding wing tip with a droop-snout configuration. The plane ... was so long because you had to have your ... nuclear source further back from the crew.... It had to drop the nose [in order for the pilot] to see the runway coming in." The floating wingtip design was a solution to the need for good cruise characteristics as well as high-speed threat evasion: "Once you got into combat, you'd blow those [wingtips] off and then dash in at mach 3, drop your payload.... When you dropped your payload and got out of enemy territory, you'd fold out what was left ... a small wing to increase your aspect ratio for getting better cruise capability."

When Robertson was working at Convair, the nuclear bomber work "was all in the preliminary dynamic stage.... [Convair] was trying to come up with a proposal for the Air Force as to how it would be built and how it would fly ... [that is,] developing the planform for the aircraft." However, before he had spent three years at Convair, the bomber project was canceled. Convair had to lay off many of the company's engineers after the Air Force discovered that "the aircraft companies were padding their engineering billets by adding more billets than they needed." Robertson was out of a job. But, equipped with the more versatile mechanical engineering degree, he was confident that he could get another job. He considered entering the General Motors Institute. He considered going into safety engineering. Then, while visiting in Baton Rouge he learned that the Army Ballistic Missile Agency was interviewing candidates to work with Wernher von Braun's missile group. He had studied a bit of rocketry at Louisiana State University with a former German Air Force "ace". He had even tried, while still at Convair, to move into Convair's missile program in San Diego, Ca. (but had been turned down because he lacked a master's degree). He had also read, as a matter of personal interest, reports "on the V-2 and, knowing that von Braun and that team had been brought over here ... I thought it was a new ... interesting challenge." Intrigued by the differences between the hardware he had worked on before and missiles — "the fact that you really had only one chance in these missiles we were shooting, because if it didn't go the first time, there was no second chance" — Robertson applied for a job with the ABMA. The ABMA hired him and, because he had done some field service engineering at Convair, placed him in its engine reliability organization.

Robertson's new work — reliability testing — exposed him directly to the engineering for the Redstone, H-1, and Jupiter engines. "We knew that they were using the Redstone as a vehicle for carrying unmanned satellites into space. We knew the Jupiters would later be used if we went into a manned program.... How would you go about testing — put a man on the top ... sitting in a capsule — of a rocket?"

When the ABMA's space-related development programs were transferred to NASA in 1960, "we wanted to go to NASA.... There were people in the Army who kept trying to get into R & D because they wanted to go to NASA too.... We were all looking forward to space travel, and we wanted to be part of it. This was the beginning, and we wanted to be in on the ground floor." Robertson shifted over to the Marshall Space Flight Center along with many others. Ironically, until he transferred again to NASA's Johnson Space Center in 1967, he spent most of the intervening years not at Marshall, but at NASA's Michoud Assembly Facility near New Orleans, La.[22]

The first Redstone, and its derivative the Jupiter, had been built at Marshall Space Flight Center. During the 1950s the federal government (reflecting the political philosophy of the Eisenhower administration[23]) gradually abandoned the arsenal or "in-house" system of military manufacture historically practiced by the U.S. Army. NASA contracted out virtually all of its development and production (see chapter 6). The Chrysler Corporation, which had been manufacturing tanks for the U.S. Army at Michoud, "was given the contract for the Saturn-IB [launch vehicle] and Boeing was given the contract for the Saturn-IC [launch vehicle] ... being built at the Michoud Center Facility." Robertson was sent to Michoud to develop a reliability organization to watch over the contractors' work. There he "had four engineers working for me to do the job — two on Chrysler, two on Boeing.... Our job was just like our government jobs are now — managing what the contractor was doing — but we were managing from the technical standpoint.

"I enjoyed Michoud probably better than any other place.... I had a real good relationship with what was going on in industry as well as what was going on in NASA itself.... One of the interesting things at Michoud [was that] while we were there — more so than here [at Johnson Space Center] — as problems developed that we couldn't work, there was a number of professors at colleges around the country that we could call and get advice from.... They would have a chance to find out what was going on in the space industry, and ... so they were happy to do it.... That gave us a broader view ... an independent opinion.... If necessary, we would send [them] design drawings ... reports — whatever it took.... We ... just made the contacts and talked with them on the telephone and set up a working relationship with them.

"As time progressed ... I was reaching my other goal of being in management.... Working in a reliability organization, we have a broader view of the total program than somebody that's working in an isolated design section.... We have to be familiar with the total vehicle ... we deal with every organization here." By the beginning of 1967 Robertson "could see our program was kind of tailing down. We had boosters stored, enough probably to have completed the total program already, and things were slowing down at Michoud." He looked around for another challenge and found it at Johnson Space Center, then in the midst of a reorganization following the fire in the Apollo 204 spacecraft which killed three astronauts on the launchpad.[24] Robertson was attracted to the enhanced safety, reliability, and quality assurance organization established at Johnson, and transferred to its engineering reliability branch in October 1967. He became "responsible for the reliability of all the major vehicles that we were flying.... At that time we were flying the Apollo and the LM [lunar module]. Then, later on, we went to Skylab and we went to ASTP.[25] I also, at that time, had responsibility for ... electrical, electromechanical, and electronic parts."

Succeeding with his career "game plan," Robertson rose into the management ranks of safety, reliability, and quality assurance at Johnson, where he took part in setting the requirements for the Shuttle (Space Transportation System) program. "We dealt with all the programs. We dealt with the quality aspects of inspection: of quality engineering, of evaluation, of contamination control, of process control — all the gamuts that would cover assuring the quality of the vehicle.... We were responsible for the failure close-out. We didn't do any math modeling because, with just a few vehicles, we don't have the statistical average to do any modeling. So we ran a technique where we made sure that all failures were closed out prior to a flight. And we still do that. Any time we fly Shuttle, we review and make sure that all failures have either been explained, so we have a confidence that they're not going to reoccur on that flight, or that they have been closed out through some design action — or some procedural action."

In 1984 NASA won what may prove to have been an uncertain victory when it received President Ronald W. Reagan's endorsement of a new space station initiative. The idea of placing in Earth orbit a permanently occupied space station had been one of the oldest aspirations within NASA. Various space station concepts had been included in the agency's plans since it was founded,[26] but it took twenty five years for political circumstances to present the agency with a president willing to endorse its vision with a budget request to Congress to begin a program. First Langley Research Center, and then Johnson Space Center (as well as Marshall Space Flight Center), NASA installations dedicated to the development of manned space flight technology, carried out tentative space station design studies intermittently throughout the two decades.

"Before Space Station ever became a program," remembers Robertson, "there was work going on in space station concepts." At the beginning of 1984 he was assigned to a team developing the technical requirements necessary for NASA to issue a "request for proposals" to the aerospace industry to engineer and develop a space station, then configured as a central power-carrying "keel" to which were attached living and laboratory modules as well as instruments for Earth and space observations. (NASA engineers artlessly referred to the configuration as a "power tower;" both configuration and name would change.) "I had a quality, reliability, and safety man colocated with me ... a representative from the Cape [Kennedy Space Center] ... from Marshall, from the SR & QA [safety, reliability, and quality assurance] area, and ... from Goddard. We ... developed a requirements document that identified the SR & QA requirements that would be imposed upon a space station. We took a different tack this time. Instead of writing these requirements down and ... saying, 'this will be it,' I said ... 'the government hasn't built anything in years.'" That inexperience meant that Robertson and his group would have to go back to the aerospace industry, which had been doing most of the actual engineering and building for NASA's program, and solicit its views on the most appropriate safety and reliability requirements.

Thus Robertson remained sensitive to the need of an engineering organization to admit to the need of additional expertise and to draw on that expertise *wherever* it could be found. As one "gets older," reflects Robertson, "you start bogging down with your own techniques.... I think that all over ... people are ... going back to the fact that ... quality, reliability, safety are not the responsibility of a quality, reliability, and safety organization; it's got to be the responsibility of the engineering organization or the designers. They draw from that organization for support and for technical advice.... We look at our automobiles and see them falling apart, while the Japanese cars are still running. I don't know if it's outside quality circles.... But the Japanese are very willing to tell anybody that, when they are asked where they got their quality techniques, they got them from America. We gave away the techniques and didn't follow them, and they did. Now it's coming home to us."[27]

NASA engineers had always been comfortable with hardware. However, designing a spacecraft so that its human occupants could not only survive, but work effectively and return ready to readapt to Earth's gravity and environment, meant that NASA researchers would have to venture into the biomedical realm as well. Biology and medicine — fields which, like mathematics, had attracted somewhat more women than had engineering — became one route through which women with scientific inclinations could find a place in NASA.

Like so many of NASA's engineers, Pamela Donaldson was born in a small southern town, Leesburg, La. Her father was a plumber and pipefitter who did well enough to build a plumbing appliance and contracting business for himself in Leesburg. As a young girl Donaldson had become interested in science — especially medicine and biology — but she rejected the conventional pathway for young women of nursing. Her older sister was a nurse, and Donaldson "didn't particularly like what she did." An alternative that appealed to her was medical technology; when she entered Northeastern State College in Louisiana in 1958 she began a major program in biology. Donaldson was a bright, straight A student in high school, but her father was struggling to keep four children in college. Northeastern State College had the particular distinction of being "the cheapest state school in the United States.... Mainly known for turning out education majors, teachers ... its tuition was $7.50 a semester."

After three years of college classes she entered a medical technology program in a New Orleans teaching hospital. In 1962 she graduated with a B.S. in biology, obtained certification as a medical technician, and traveled to Houston, Tex. to begin work as a medical technician in a hospital. She worked in the hospital's clinical chemistry laboratory for six years. Donaldson worked hard but was still able to find time to take some graduate courses at the University of Houston. She did so well that in 1968 she competed successfully for a National Research Council research associateship at NASA's Johnson Space Center.

1968 was an exciting time to enter the field of space medicine. After the disappointing flight of Apollo 6 (unmanned) in April, when the Saturn suffered "pogo" oscillations, and burn failures on its second and third stages were followed by a splashdown of the spacecraft 50 miles off target, NASA successfully orbited Apollo 7 in October with its three-man crew.[28] Two months later astronauts Frank Borman, James A. Lovell, Jr., and William A. Anders were lofted into lunar orbit from which they confirmed planned manned landing sites, reported that the Moon's surface appeared like "dirty beach sand with lots of footprints in it," and broadcast Christmas greetings to a watching and listening world.[29]

Anticipating the physiological changes to which the Apollo and later astronauts would be subject, and ensuring that the spacecraft that housed them and the suits they wore would adequately protect them was partly the work of biomedical specialists like Donaldson. When she began work at Johnson Space Center, she "started working in ... endocrinology and ... the physiological changes with space-flight." After her research associateship expired in 1970, she stayed at Johnson, where she acquired ever greater responsibility for the biomedical work done for all of NASA's Apollo, Skylab, and Shuttle missions.

"When we started out the man in space program," she recalls, "we picked up ... Army Air Corps flight surgeons. And National Academy [of Sciences] panels ... all predicted that when you go to put people in a weightless environment — shoot them off on top of rockets — you're going to have … a lot of medical problems…. As it turned out, after we flew a few flights, some predictions … just went away altogether. Things like: Man wouldn't be able to swallow in weightlessness. Well, we soon found out they could. They wouldn't be able to eat up there. Well, we found out they could; it could be messy … you had to contain the food, but they could eat…. A lot of things that had been initial concerns … you look back on them now, they seem kind of foolish.

"Some of the things we had not predicted exactly…. One of them was the effects of weightlessness on the physiological responses of the body … some of our Gemini astronauts were coming back from space flight with altered body chemistry…. My own area of interest from my graduate education was in endocrine control mechanisms, and specifically those that control salt water in the body, metabolism." Donaldson was able to develop a number of experiments that were done on the Apollo astronauts, and the results of those experiments, along with some medical data collected during the Gemini program, enabled Donaldson and her co-workers to "put together a picture of what we most often saw with astronauts. It was not normal…. While they came back and sat up and walked and talked and waited and made speeches and all, their chemistry showed that there were still some pretty dramatic things going on in the body. Not pathology … [or] anything that would cause you to medicate them or put them to bed…. But it was … physiological changes, interesting science.

"Other folks were working in various fields with the same issues…. You immerse somebody in water [or] … to bed rest and they have certain changes that look kind of like what we were seeing, but not just like it…. I was able to put together a pretty complete flight experiment for the Skylab missions, looking at the endocrine control mechanisms during weightlessness…. We were able to put the crews on controlled metabolic diets and collect blood and urine and fecal samples throughout the pre- and post-flight [period]. That represents what is the sum total of the … information on man in space in that area. Those [Skylab] missions gave us the foundations that we are now working on.

"Basically what we think is happening [is that] as soon as the human body goes into weightlessness, the blood that we're used to pooling in our lower extremities … is redistributed throughout your body because there's no gravity pull. Your body senses then that it's got too much blood because … the sensors are in your neck and great veins of your chest…. The brain says, 'we've got to unload some of this fluid,'" and the body begins diuresis. In the process, "not only do we get rid of the plasma volume portion of the blood, but we also get rid of our blood cells…. And it occurs pretty fast after you get into space. What else happens? … When you lose water, you also lose salt. And when the body loses salt … we keep pumping up the hormone aldostrontium that controls sodium…. The hormones don't seem to work up there like they do on the ground, and why? We don't know.

"When you land back on Earth … just the opposite happens. All of a sudden blood pools in your lower extremeties you feel faint. You sit down or drink something to make up the volume difference … your heart, great veins, neck sensors are all saying, 'hey! where's all the blood?' So … you retain fluids, you retain salt, and you build back up the blood volume over a two-week period. None of these things ... are pathological.... But they are all interesting, and the mechanisms are particularly interesting.... We need to know about those mechanisms because some of them need to be corrected.... Shuttle astronauts, after being in weightlessness for a week ... had to operate the landing controls. They did not need to have any feelings of queasiness.... We started giving them a liter of salt water before they came back in because you will retain the salt water immediately.... That would build up their blood volume."

Donaldson's studies of the effects of weightless on body chemistry led her into hematology as well as endocrinology, and other biomedical fields as well. "In the early flights we found" the body also loses red blood cells in space "because of oxygen. But we don't use 100 percent oxygen anymore.... So right now we're theorizing that it is sequestration of the cells of, probably, the spleen. It's another way the body has of reducing the blood volume quickly." She also worked in toxicology, exploring the permissible components of a spacecraft's atmosphere as well as what sorts of filters would be needed for its water system.

By its very nature Donaldson's work crossed over the organizational boundaries separating different projects and programs at Johnson Space Center and enabled her to survive the chronic reorganizations which seem to afflict all large organizations trying to cope with changing demands. She enjoys repeating an observation attributed to an ancient bureaucratic sage: "'We got all together and got ready to work and just as we got ready, our job got reorganized.'" As NASA's manned spaceflight program grew, so did Johnson's biomedical program and Donaldson's responsibilities along with it. In time, during the mid-1970s, she realized that she had probably crossed the threshold from research to management — although until 1984, when she was managing full-time, she was "still conducting research, still having projects, planning experiments and everything." She thinks of herself as a scientist and not an engineer, but the work she has done has been an essential part of the subtle engineering necessary to transport men and women safely through space.

Like many NASA engineers, Ronald Siemans began working with NASA as part of a cooperative work-study program. Born and raised in Cleveland, Ohio, Siemans completed a bachelor's degree in chemical engineering at Cleveland State University at the same time he began working during alternate quarters at Johnson Space Center. When he first went to Johnson in 1969 he was assigned to environmental control systems for NASA's manned spacecraft. By the time he settled in on a permanent basis in 1972, Johnson was heavily involved in the development of the environmental system for the Shuttle orbiter of the Space Transportation System. The Shuttle would be the first spacecraft that offered its human occupants an atmospheric environment truly similar to what they normally experienced on earth.

Earlier manned U.S. spacecraft — the Mercury, Gemini, Apollo, and Skylab spacecraft — averaged an atmospheric pressure of around 5 psi (pounds per square inch), similar to the atmosphere of military aircraft. The air circulating in them was also very high in oxygen (the air in the Apollo spacecraft was 100 percent oxygen) which, as many realized to their sorrow after the Apollo 204 fire, was an extreme fire hazard. Pre-Shuttle astronauts had to wear special suits during ascent into orbit and return in order to adjust gradually to the extreme change in environment they would experience in space.

With the advent of the Shuttle program, astronauts could look forward to experiencing an Earth-like atmosphere of 14.7 psi and breathing air with a nitrogen-oxygen mix of about 78 percent to 21 percent.[30] While the Shuttle was in its early design and development phases, about the time that Siemans went to Johnson, "there was an air communication system requirement ... that no one had really thought too much about.... The traditional systems that are available out in industry were quite expensive. They were going to require a lot of power and ... the integration costs would have been terrible to think about." Siemans had done some work in catalysis while he was completing a graduate program at nearby Rice University and was able to design a small air purification system for the Orbiter. "I knew how to do that ... [by] just adding a little cannister onto the side of the environmental control system. It was a comparatively cheap model to make.... That knowledge probably saved the government ... a couple of million dollars."

Human comfort and safety onboard spacecraft demanded not only a proper mix of atmospheric gasses (not to mention carefully controlled temperature and humidity), but protection from toxic carbon dioxide, a byproduct of respiration. During the Mercury flights carbon dioxide had been successfully removed from the capsule's atmosphere with a filter containing lithium chloride. When Siemans arrived at Johnson "we had a fifty percent performance out of the chemicals that we were using." He tried to persuade his superiors that NASA should do some more research to improve the systems that chemically purified the air in manned spacecraft. He succeeded, and to good effect. "On this last orbiter flight [STS-51I Discovery, a seven-day mission launched on August 27, 1985] we had an EVA [extravehicular activity] on there where one of the astronauts put in the same cannister twice by mistake, and we got 90 percent out of that one."

Siemans was able to transfer the know-how he had acquired to improving the environmental controls on the space suits developed for extravehicular activity "which picked up in importance in the Shuttle program and is becoming more prominent in the space program in general." NASA's first extravehicular life support system, used during the Gemini program, was a cumbersome chest pack containing a jungle of hoses and connectors to maintain suit pressure, provide metabolic oxygen, remove heat, and ventilate gases. Astronauts found the suit a real nuisance and stiflingly hot after only a brief amount of exercise. If astronauts were to move about on the Moon, they would need something better. This they received — a more compact backpack apparatus.

"You look at a man out in deep space, you see the arms and legs moving around. But if you look at his back you see a big box. The big box has an environmental control system in it, just like the vehicle has — it's just miniaturized. You've got the same kind of problems that you've got in the vehicle out there, except that you've got the difficulties of vacuum compatibility and deep space environment ... like vacuum

and radiation, solar energy impinging on the fellow, ultraviolet light on the eyes —
a lot of different ... problems because you're outside rather than inside." The Skylab,
Shuttle, and Space Station programs, with their extended stays in orbit, would
further challenge NASA's life support researchers and engineers.

When Siemans first worked with NASA in the late 1960s as a coop student
"there were ... teams looking at Moon bases and Mars missions and Space Station."
He was assigned to "trade studies that were involved in the Space Station — mass
and energy balances, essentially.... You have to evaluate what the benefits are for a
particular system. You select an approach to do a particular job. You go through a
series of evaluations to see what that decision does to you from a power standpoint,
from a weight standpoint, from a volume in the vehicle standpoint. Any one of
those ... can wipe you out by itself. And you look at the collective integration of all
those items and you compare systems to similar systems."

After NASA's Space Station program won the endorsement of President Ronald
Reagan in 1984, Siemans returned to the problems of providing adequate onboard
life support for Space Station crews. "There are a number of research questions
about the Space Station. It's the first time in the history of man that he's going to be
going into space for a long period of time. The Russians are a little bit ahead of us in
this area.... Are you going to live in space for a long period of time, or are you just
going to send somebody there for three months and ... return them? And we'd better
start thinking about leaving people up there forever.

"In the past one crew would go up and do EVAs maybe twice in an ... entire
career. Now we're talking about one crewman doing EVAs three days a week for his
whole career, which may be ten years long. That's a significant change.... A lot of
issues have to be answered in the medical area.... There's lots of research that needs
to be done involving radiation, for instance. [During the pre-Apollo era] everyone
was afraid ... you'd go to the Moon — you can get so much radiation the guys wind
up with cancer." Continued monitoring of the Apollo astronauts seemed to indicate
that the spacecraft's radiation shielding, combined with their limited exposure,
protected them from any long-term radiation damage. "However, you talk about
going up there, building Moon bases, you're going to revisit all that ... all those same
old issues that we just gave a cursory look at back in the old days."

New England — empty of NASA installations save the short-lived Electronics
Research Center[31] — has contributed few engineers to NASA's ranks, notwithstanding the significant role played by the Massachusetts Institute of Technology in
developing the computer and guidance systems for the Apollo program.[32] Bostonian
or "down East" patterns of speech strike odd notes in corridors and offices in which
one hears the laconic voices of Texas or Alabama, where vocal energy is normally
reserved for bursts of temper or enthusiasm. Old Greenwich, Conn. — one of the
enclaves of the Eastern establishment — is even more remote from the restless space
frontiers of the American South. But the space age has been an age of many minor

wonders, and one of them was the migration of Richard Williams, born in 1941 in Old Greenwich, to Kennedy Space Center.

Few NASA engineers, when asked about their parents, mention their mothers first. Williams does. "My mother is a concert pianist, a graduate of Julliard [who played] professionally at Carnegie Hall.... She has two baby grand pianos so that [she and her pupils] can play at the house.... Music made my mother's life." Williams's mother finally despaired of teaching her son, one of three children, to play the piano and settled for basic instruction in the rudiments of music. "I think I had a repertoire of two simple tunes that I could play on the piano." Williams's father embodied the social mobility of many Americans in the early twentieth century. The son of a purchasing agent for the Boston and Maine Railroad, the elder Williams was able to go to engineering school and "worked his way up" from a machinist at the Shick Electric Razor Company to a production management position at Conde Nast Press — publisher of *The New Yorker* and *House and Garden* magazines. An avid sailor, Williams's father crewed regularly for numerous ocean races, among them the Bermuda and Trans-Atlantic races. The family "had boats.... I had a sailboat when I was young, a little Cape Cod knock-about, 16 feet.... We spent an awful lot of time not only on Long Island Sound, but up the Hudson River into Lake Champlain, up into Canada."

From his family Williams inherited not only a love of boats and the water, but a love of all things mechanical. "My grandfather on my mother's side was a Swede.... In Sweden he was a railroad engineer." After he came to the United States "he somehow got in with the Rockefellers and was the head chauffeur for John D. Rockefeller, Sr. They had their home in Greenwich, Conn. And the Rockefeller boys at one time were going to build a U.S. version of the Rolls Royce.... They tried to set up a manufacturing line in New Haven. The first car rolled off the line and it was so heavy that you couldn't steer the thing. It took two men and a boy to steer the thing. And so my grandfather wound up working ... to change the geometry of the steering mechanism. He got it to steer, but ultimately the whole idea folded." Williams was fond of his grandfather, "who lived in the country and had a four- or five-car garage. He had a small shop in there, and I would go and spend time with him."

So Williams grew up working on cars, his own and those belonging to the patrons of the local garage and filling station. When he graduated from high school in 1957 and it came time to go to college, he balked at Old Greenwich expectations and tried to enlist in the Navy. Although he had been in the Naval Reserve, the Navy discovered traces of asthma and sent him on his way with an honorable discharge. He found a job with a company that made electromechanically operated quotation boards for the New York Stock Exchange and magnetic memory devices for airline reservation systems. There he got not only several years' experience in product development and field engineering, but a mentor who persuaded him to return to school, to Clemson College in South Carolina. Four years later (in 1966) with a good bit of mechanical engineering and lots of football behind him, Richard Williams went to Florida.

Williams's Swedish grandfather had preceded him to Florida in 1949, and it was there that the two generations had met during the summers to toy with machinery.

"I saw this area as it was, and how it changed…. My grandfather was the one that talked me into coming out here [to Kennedy Space Center] for an interview while I was in college." A friend and neighbor of his grandfather's had excited him about the work NASA was doing there, and when Williams was given a job offer, he took it. "Pay-wise, it was the lowest offer; it was around $5,200 a year around 1966…. Everybody, including my parents, told me I was absolutely nuts because I had an offer from General Motors that was over $8,000 a year. But it was in Flint, Michigan…. I said, 'aw, I don't want to go to Flint, Michigan.'"

Williams's start at NASA's Kennedy Space Center misfired. He had been hired to work in a new materials test laboratory, but the laboratory was never built, so he decided to go to work for Pratt and Whitney, which had made him a handsome offer to work at a plant in West Palm Beach. But in 1966 "NASA was having so much trouble recruiting people that they weren't about to let me get out without a fight…. Back in those days contractors were coming in and offering whole offices jobs…. Whole offices were leaving NASA one day and going to work for contractors [the next]." Since NASA had paid his moving expenses to Florida, Williams felt somewhat obligated to look around the center for something else, and, just when it seemed that nothing would appeal to him, he paid a visit to the flight simulation organization "housed in the Air Force side [Cape Canaveral Air Force Station, adjacent to Kennedy Space Center]." The supervisor "took me out to the simulator and … gave me a 'ride'…. We went into orbit right there, and it really sent me 'into orbit!' I said, 'Boy, this is absolutely fantastic!'

"It was not a KSC position; it was a Manned Spacecraft Center [MSC; renamed Johnson Space Center in 1973] position. So the government retained me, but KSC lost me, and I joined MSC. [Williams] hired in with that group and trained the Gemini 9, 10, 11, and 12 crews in the simulator. I continued on in that capacity through the Apollo program. [The Manned Spacecraft Center had] built a building on the Kennedy Space Center side, called the flight crew training building, in which we had two Apollo Command Module simulators and one Lunar Module simulator … for mission training purposes. The crews would come down here and by the time they got to this point … they would have been selected for a mission and would know all of the basic systems. Our job was more of putting it into a mission time line and firming up that time line.[33]

"MSC had (and still has) astronaut quarters over in the Operations and Checkout building at Kennedy Space Center. We had the flight crew training building and … use of a beach house out here on the ocean … for R & R [rest and recreation] purposes. It was actually for security as well as … quarantine…. In the earlier days of the Apollo program, the crews would all be down here from Houston, and they would be staying here full time because of the schedules…. We socialized with them. We had, in the afternoons, ball games…. They did come out to parties with us…. We had a group — we called it the 'lucky 100' — of people down here that … had to have close association with the astronauts…. We were asked during this period not to frequent public places, [to] eat at home, stay at home…. As a relief mechanism — the crews, obviously they stayed out there — we got to using this beach house, and we would have after-work parties.

"I worked with the contractors that built the simulators, the old trainers ... some of the early aircraft simulators that pilots used to train in.... We worked with those people quite closely in order to assure fidelity of the simulation. At the same time, we coordinated quite closely with the home base back in Houston.... I spent a good bit of my time [going] back and forth to Houston.... We supported the crews right down to launch.... Any last-minute changes to their procedure they would put in [their books] in pen and ink ... and they carried that whole file of books for those missions.... During the missions we would go, one or two of each group, to Houston to support the mission ... from a console in one of the back engineering rooms off of the Mission Director's center at Johnson Space Center."

Fifty-five hours into the flight of Apollo 13 [launched April 11, 1970], when an oxygen tank explosion in the service module forced NASA to abort the mission, "we were on the consoles that evening ... the crew had just ... bedded down for the evening. This fellow that was with me knew the command module and service module systems very well; [after the tank exploded] he said, 'Gee, you know, things don't look right.' He was actually the one that [sic] pointed out to the front room at the Mission Control Center that 'hey ... something's looking funny here. I'm not getting proper signals back on this flight.' This fellow ... started breaking out systems schematics and what not, looking at things.... We spent the next five or seven days now almost working around the clock. We brought some other people in to help us, working out procedures, and we acted as a go-between. We would work up a procedure out there [in Houston], then I would phone it in to our people back here because this simulator at KSC was in the configuration that that mission was in. It simulated the whole nine yards.... It was fortunate for the crew that Fred Haise was on that mission because he had spent a number of years working with the Grumman [Corporation] people on that vehicle. So he knew the vehicle inside and out and knew what it could do. As it turned out, the Lunar Module served as a lifeboat.[34]

"In December of 1970, at the end of the Apollo program, we shut this training facility down. We were all offered jobs back in Houston. Well, I had spent enough time in Houston during my tenure with the Manned Spacecraft Center that I knew that I did not want to go live in Houston.... I was very well situated here, I loved the area, loved the water, and every time I went to Houston — they have a little lake that's called Clear Lake.... I don't know how they came up with the name Clear Lake; that water is the dirtiest water I have ever seen in my life.... I wouldn't even put my foot in the water down there at Galveston. You'd come out in the morning and the stench from the refineries in Texas City would bring tears to my eyes! ... I refused to transfer to Houston.

"I thought my Christmas present was going to be a layoff notice. The Apollo program was winding down; this area was becoming a very, very tough area in which to find a job because of all the layoffs.... I had several neighbors in the area where I lived ... [who] knew I was NASA and they were contractors, two of them being Boeing people, and they were offered jobs with Boeing in Seattle, in the aircraft end of it, if they could get themselves at their own expense to Seattle. You couldn't give a house away here, and they begged me, 'take over payments, just take the house, do anything with it.' And I said, 'here I have an infant son and my wife wasn't working … and gosh, I'm looking at a layoff too; I can't do anything.' Well, I made the decision to stay here, and it was looking grim."

Williams had the good fortune to have gotten to know many KSC people, and one of them put him in touch with a top-ranking KSC manager who offered him a job in the center's design engineering group. He persuaded the Manned Space Center people to keep him on their payroll for a month until he could officially begin work at Kennedy. In the meantime, he had little to do besides "picking things up and cleaning things out and housekeeping." When Kennedy Space Center closed down the Apollo operations, "the contractor [Singer-Link] literally just walked away and left everything — just walked out of there on a Friday like they were coming back on the Monday. All of the logistics and spare parts, everything, was just left…. The people just walked out and at the work benches the little soldering irons were still plugged in. There was still food in the refrigerator. It was just incredible. So I spent that month trying to straighten up things and figure out what we had left…. There were literally thousands and thousands of dollars of useable parts…. The outfit that I went to work for at KSC [was designing the building for the] launch processing system [for] the upcoming Shuttle program. So I was able to get some people together, and we … were able to salvage a lot of the equipment and the parts and pieces that were left and transformed it into a development laboratory from a simulation facility."

After spending about a year with the center's design engineering group, Williams began to suspect that he had stumbled "off the beaten path into a deadend position." He began to look around and found himself a job in unmanned satellite launch operations "on the Cape side again — a NASA organization — and [I] got back into the spacecraft area," where Williams has remained. "In those days we were called spacecraft coordinators…. We had the Delta launch vehicle program … and the Atlas-Centaur launch vehicle program. And each one of us was assigned various satellite groups that were coming through to launch their satellites on one of these launch vehicles. We would go out and work with the manufacturer, the satellite owner, to integrate their satellite with the launch vehicle. For the most part, a lot of our satellites were built by three standard manufacturers: Hughes, RCA, or Ford Aerospace. It was somewhat routine, but each one required its own changes. It was, once again, dealing with different people and different situations, and it was quite interesting.

"The thing that has kept me here was … that we — about '73 to '77 or '78 — dealt with a number of foreign entities and launched satellites for these foreign countries. The first one that I really had any association with was a French-German communications satellite called Symphonie…. I did spend quite a bit of time in Munich, Germany and Toulouse, France, working with these organizations…. From that we went into an English project called OTS (Orbiting Test Satellite)…. And then there was a number of French satellites. And we got into an Italian one called SIRIO [a microwave propagation satellite]…. Since then we've done a number of trips throughout Europe dealing with various satellite companies…. I've been to India twice now, meeting with the Indian government. We've launched several satellites for them."

However, Williams's new-found pleasure in the increasingly cosmopolitan character of space missions can not erase the dark memories he shares with so many NASA engineers of the consequences of the collapse of public interest in space after the successful flight of Apollo 11 — memories which constitute for him "one of the lowest points in my career…. We had all been so hyped on this thing of going to the Moon. And then, to all of a sudden wake up one day with the realization of 'there's no more'…. Why didn't we plan for something further on? … I was just devastated. Of course, this whole area, with layoffs … was just very [hard hit]…. There was no diversification for these guys that had just finished launching the Apollo launch vehicle, which was probably one of the greatest engineering marvels of its time. They would [end] up on the streets, out of work, with no place to go. I knew a couple of engineers that were actually at the gas station pumping gas…. One of the engineers … got into real estate and has left the area. He said, 'I wouldn't go back for all the tea in China. Just because of the heartbreak'…. If you went around this center and carefully asked everybody what was the most important experience in their careers here, I think they would all agree that the collapse of support, the collapse of the program, the collapse of the money after [the] Apollo period, was the biggest single event.

"One of the highlights of my career," reflects Williams, "has been my association with people from all over the world … with the astronauts…. I wouldn't have missed it for anything in the world…. [But] I look forward to the future with mixed emotions, I guess. I hope that we can come out of this Shuttle disaster, the Challenger accident of January 28, 1986, with some direction. And that direction, I hope, is a mixed fleet…. I hope we can afford to … carry on with both programs…. The people that I talk with throughout the agency feel that we've made our mistake with trying to put all of our eggs into the Shuttle basket."

Throughout the Shuttle era NASA continued to launch spacecraft with un-manned, expendable rockets. The small Scout, with its limited payload of 150 pounds, continued in production and routinely launched small scientific satellites into Earth orbit from Wallops Island, while NASA used its remaining inventory of Delta and Atlas-Centaurs to launch heavier unmanned payloads from Cape Canaveral. During the two years following the Challenger accident, when U.S. space policy and NASA's own programs underwent an agonizing period of reappraisal, the White House modified a decision made during the administration of President Richard M. Nixon that the Shuttle would be the nation's principal launch vehicle and the use of expendable launch vehicles gradually phased out.[35] While the U.S. Air Force began to procure Titan launch vehicles again, the Reagan White House (adhering to its general philosophy of "privatizing" much of the government's activities) directed in February 1988 that "federal agencies … procure existing and future required expendable launch services directly from the private sector to the fullest extent possible," and announced that in the interests of "assuring" national "access to space … U.S. space transportation systems that provide sufficient resiliency to allow continued operation, despite failures in any single system, are emphasized."[36]

———————

NASA's Apollo generation of engineers was, above all else, a generation caught in an era of transition. During the immediate postwar period the country's engineers, working for NASA, the military, and the emerging aerospace industry, mastered the fundamental problems of designing and building the vehicles needed for controlled flight beyond the atmosphere. During the Apollo decade programmatic emphasis, federal funds, and career opportunities expanded to embrace the technical problems associated with the objects that would be sent into space — automated scientific spacecraft and piloted spacecraft to transport human crews to the Moon and eventually beyond. Engineering secure spacecraft environments — whether for delicate instruments or human crews — became as important as flight dynamics and, as a result, men and women with backgrounds in mathematics, biology, and chemical and mechanical engineering were as likely to find careers in NASA as were aeronautical engineers.

The careers of the seven men and one woman profiled in this chapter embraced as well a revolution in engineering in which the slide rule and mechanical calculator were replaced by the high-speed electronic computer, a now ubiquitous and indispensable device that refines the designs of all modern air- and spacecraft, controls telecommunications, and has begun to supplant the intuitive guesswork essential to the creative genius that the engineers brought to aeronautical and rocket research in the first half of this century.[37]

Only two of these engineers began their careers doing work that was a direct byproduct of World War II — John Robertson, who worked on bomber engines before joining the Army Ballistic Missile Agency in 1958, and Henry Beacham, who worked in weapons testing for the Navy before transferring to NASA's new Goddard Space Flight Center (with numerous other Navy personnel) in 1959. The rest, except Frank Toscelli, were born during World War II, and by the time they were ready to seek out careers, the kinds of engineering work offered by NASA had expanded far beyond the initial phase of launch vehicle development. They might have as readily gone to work in other engineering fields, but NASA was where the opportunity was — especially for the young woman, who would have suffered the most transparent discrimination had she sought work with a large private computer firm.

Their personal histories and professional lives embraced as well profound changes in the American social landscape that would unfold after the children of the Great Depression entered college and later joined the salaried middle class, or what sociologists of the 1950s proclaimed the new "organization men." Only three of these eight engineers came from large urban areas, and only two were born in the Deep South; five of the eight were educated in public institutions. Two were the children of salaried professionals; the others were children of either small businessmen or service workers. The institutionalization of both science and engineering, and the increased role of government in the national pursuit of scientific research and technological innovation, for which NASA had become during the 1960s a principal agent of change, would prove to be one of the most pervasive forces in their careers.

---

[1] For the best surveys of federally supported science and engineering, see A. Hunter Dupree, *Science in the Federal Government: A History of Policies and Activities*, 2nd ed. (Baltimore: The Johns Hopkins University Press, 1987) and W. Henry Lambright, *Governing Science and Technology* (New York: Oxford University Press, 1976). The volume on the military and peaceful uses of nuclear energy is enormous; its range is suggested by Vincent C. Jones, *Manhattan: The Army and the Atomic Bomb* (Washington, D.C.: U.S. Army Center for Military History, 1985), Richard G. Hewlett and Oscar E. Anderson, Jr., *The New World, 1939-1946* (University Park: Pennsylvania State University Press, 1962), Spencer R. Weart, *Nuclear Fear: A History of Images* (Cambridge: Harvard University Press, 1988), Richard Rhodes, *The Making of the Atomic Bomb* (New York: Simon and Schuster, 1986), and George T. Mazuzan, "Nuclear Energy — A Subject in Need of Historical Research: Review Essay," *Technology and Culture*, Vol. 27, No. 1 (January 1986).

[2] Sounding rockets enable scientists to obtain vertica l profiles of Earth's atmosphere, as well as measurements of radiation, plasma, and micrometeoroid flux, from above the atmosphere. The sounding rocket's measurements, however, are for brief periods at high altitudes above the launch site.

[3] R. Cargill Hall, Early U.S. Satellite Proposals, in Eugene M. Emme (ed.), *The History of Rocket Technology* (Detroit: Wayne State University Press, 1964), pp. 74-79.

[4] For varied accounts of the U.S. inauguration of the space age, see Homer E. Newell, *Beyond the Atmosphere: Early Years of Space Science*, NASA SP-4211 (Washington, D.C.: U.S. Government Printing Office, 1980), Bilstein, *Stages to Saturn* (loc. cit.), and Constance McLaughlin Green and Milton Lomask, *Vanguard: A History* (Washington, DC: Smithsonian Institution Press, 1971).

[5] See chapter 3. The first successful American satellite in space was Explorer, developed by the Jet Propulsion Laboratory of the California Institute of Technology. The Jet Propulsion Laboratory was also responsible for the fourth stage of the Army Ballistic Missile Agency's Jupiter C rocket, which launched Explorer into orbit on January 31, 1958.

[6] The installation was originally (January 15, 1959) designated the Beltsville Space Center. On May 1 it was renamed Goddard Space Flight Center in honor of American rocket pioneer Robert H. Goddard. See Alfred Rosenthal, *Venture into Space: Early Years of Goddard Space Flight Center*, NASA SP-4301 (Washington, D.C.: U.S. Government Printing Office, 1968).

[7] The Space Task Group was located at Langley Research Center, but administratively it was assigned to the Manned Satellites Directorate at Goddard Space Flight Center under Robert R. Gilruth. Until the first permanent buildings were occupied

at Goddard in late 1960, the Center existed more as an organizational entity than a physical location, its components housed largely at Langley Research Center and the Naval Research Laboratory. The Manned Spacecraft Center was renamed for Lyndon B. Johnson in 1973.

[8] NASA's Earth applications satellite programs promptly embroiled the agency in controversies with other federal agencies such as the Department of Defense (with its military interest) and the Departments of Commerce, Interior, Agriculture, and State. The agency would discover again and again that demonstrating the technical feasibility of any space venture was only half the battle. See Pamela Mack, "The Politics of Technological Change: A History of Landsat," University of Pennsylvania Doctoral Dissertation (1983) and, for a brief overview, Newell, *Beyond the Atmosphere: Early Years of Space Science*, chapter 19.

[9] The Nimbus series served as the second generation of U.S. meteorological satellites, following the Tiros series, first launched in 1960, which provided weather images from above Earth's cloud cover.

[10] See chapter 3, footnote 13.

[11] See Frederick I. Ordway, III and Mitchell R. Sharpe, *The Rocket Team* (New York: Thomas Y. Crowell, 1979).

[12] For recent accounts of early aerodynamic and engine research, see Robert Schlaifer, *Development of Aircraft Engines and Fuels* (Cambridge: Harvard Business School, 1950), Edward W. Constant II, *The Origins of the Turbojet Revolution* (Baltimore: The Johns Hopkins University, 1980), and James R. Hansen, *Engineer in Charge: A History of the Langley Aeronautical Laboratory, 1917-1958*, NASA SP-4305 (Washington, D.C.: U.S. Government Printing Office, 1987).

[13] The feat was accomplished in 1930 by Maj. U. Maddalena and Lt. F. Cecconi. See *World Aviation Annual, 1948* (Washington, D.C.: Aviation Research Institute, 1948).

[14] See chapter 3, footnote 7.

[15] G.A. Shepperd, *The Italian Campaign, 1943-1945: A Political and Military Reassessment* (New York, 1968), pp. 67-156.

[16] For a history of the computer hardware and software developed for NASA's manned and unmanned spacecraft, see James E. Tomayko, *Computers in Spaceflight: The NASA Experience, Encyclopedia of Computer Science and Technology*, Vol. 18, Supp. 3 (New York: Marcel Dekker, Inc., 1987).

[17] The 5,000-pound Solar Maximum Mission satellite was launched into a 354 mile high Earth orbit to take continuous observations of the Sun in wavelengths ranging from visible light to the highest-energy gamma rays during the current sunspot cycle. Its attitude control devices were disabled by the failure of undersized fuses six months into its mission, and the satellite was placed in a "survival" one degree per second roll around its solar-pointing axis by the reprogrammed NSCC-1. During the

1984 mission of Shuttle flight 41-C, the satellite was retrieved, repaired in the Shuttle's cargo bay, and lifted into orbit, where it resumed operations.

[18] During 1988 the gender neutral term "human space flight" began to appear in some NASA pronouncements and publications.

[19] See table 7, appendix C.

[20] The expression came into popular usage after it appeared as the title of Tom Wolfe's trenchant account of the Mercury Seven, *The Right Stuff* (New York: Farrar, Straus, Giroux, 1979).

[21] North Korean troops crossed into South Korea on June 25, 1950. Three years later, on July 27, 1953, an armistice ended hostilities in a war that resulted in over 54,000 American troop deaths, almost as many as the War in Southeast Asia, which claimed the lives of slightly over 58,000 American servicemen.

[22] NASA selected the unused government ordnance plant at Michoud in 1961 for the industrial production of Saturn launch vehicle stages under the direction of Marshall Space Flight Center. (The facility was called Michoud Operations until 1965.) The Michoud Assembly Facility was later used as the manufacture and final assembly site for the large external tanks for the Space Transportation System.

[23] See Hans Mark and Arnold Levine, *The Management of Research Institutions: A Look at Government Laboratories*, NASA SP-481 (Washington, DC.: U.S. Government Printing Office, 1984), chapter 3.

[24] The fire occurred on January 27, taking the lives of the three-man crew for NASA's first manned Apollo spaceflight: Virgil I. Grissom, Edward H. White II, and Richard B. Chaffee. For details, see Ivan D. Ertel and Roland W. Newkirk, with Courtney G. Brooks, *The Apollo Spacecraft: A Chronology, Vol. IV, January 21, 1966-July 13, 1974*, NASA SP-4009 (Washington, D.C.: U.S. Government Printing Office, 1978).

[25] Project Skylab (Apollo Applications Program), which flew in 1973, and the Apollo-Soyuz Test Project, a joint American and Soviet on-orbit rendezvous and docking mission, which flew in July 1975, used Apollo-Saturn hardware. See W. David Compton and Charles D. Benson, *Living and Working in Space: A History of Skylab*, NASA SP-4208 (Washington, D.C.: U.S. Government Printing Office, 1983), and Edward Clinton Ezell and Linda Neuman Ezell, *The Partnership: A History of the Apollo-Soyuz Test Project*, NASA SP-4209 (Washington, D.C.: U.S. Government Printing Office, 1978).

[26] See Sylvia D. Fries, "2001 to 1994: Political Environment and the Design of NASA's Space Station System," *loc. cit.*

[27] Robertson was interviewed in September 1985, four months before the Challenger accident, which occurred on January 28, 1986.

[28] Walter M. Schirra, Jr., Donn F. Eisele, and R. Walter Cunningham. For summaries of all the Apollo missions, see Courtney G. Brooks, James M. Grimwood, and Loyd S. Swenson, Jr., *Chariots for Apollo: A History of Manned Lunar Spacecraft*, NASA

SP-4205 (Washington, D.C.: U.S. Government Printing Office, 1979), Appendix C, Apollo Flight Program.

[29] Not everyone watched and listened willingly. Two thousand viewers called into television networks in New York City, complaining about the interruption in the broadcast of the day's football game. (*The Economist*, December 28, 1968, p. 112.)

[30] At, or near to, the surface of Earth, the air contains about 78.09 percent nitrogen, 20.93 percent oxygen, and very small amounts of other gases such as argon, carbon dioxide, neon, helium, krypton, hydrogen, xenon, and ozone. For an account of this and other biomedical issues during NASA's manned spaceflight programs, see John A. Pitts, *The Human Factor: Biomedicine in the Manned Space Program to 1980*, NASA SP-4213 (Washington, D.C.: U.S. Government Printing Office, 1985), p. 20-23 *passim.*

[31] Established in 1964 in Cambridge, Mass., the Electronics Research Center (ERC) assumed the functions of the NASA North Eastern Office, which had administered NASA contracts for electronics research and development in the northeastern United States and served as a liaison with the electronics industry in the region. The center conducted programs in aeronautical and space-related electronics research. Because of budget reductions, NASA closed the ERC in 1969 and transferred the facility to the Department of Transportation.

[32] See James E. Tomayko, *Computers in Spaceflight: The NASA Experience*, NASA CR-182505 (Washington, D.C.: National Aeronautics and Space Administration, 1988).

[33] For an intimate account of astronaut simulation training (although for the later Shuttle program), see Henry S.F. Cooper, Jr., *Before Lift-Off: The Making of a Space Shuttle Crew* (Baltimore: The Johns Hopkins University Press, 1987).

[34] The crew of Apollo 13 (Fred W. Haise, Jr., James A. Lovell, Jr., and John L. Swigert, Jr.) relied on the Lunar Module's systems for power and life support for their return to Earth. See Henry S.F. Cooper, Jr., *13: The Flight That Failed* (New York: The Dial Press, 1973).

[35] In a letter to NASA Administrator James C. Fletcher, written two days before President Nixon's resignation on August 9, 1974, Deputy Secretary of Defense William P. Clements, Jr. assured Fletcher that "the Department of Defense is planning to use the Space Shuttle ... to achieve more effective and flexible military space operations in the future. Once the Shuttle's capabilities and low operating cost are demonstrated we expect to launch essentially all of our military space payloads in this new vehicle and phase out of inventory our current expendable launch vehicles" (NASA History Office) Defense Department policy became national policy when the Reagan White House announced on July 4, 1982, that the Space Transportation System "is the primary space launch system for both United States national security and civil government missions." ("United States Space Policy, The White House Fact Sheets, 4 July 1982." NASA History Office).

[36] "The President's Space Policy and Commercial Space Initiative to Begin the Next Century," White House Press Release, February 11, 1988. (NASA History Office)

[37] For some reflections on the implications of the computerization of engineering design from a veteran engineer, see Henry Petroski, *To Engineer is Human* (New York: St. Martin's Press, 1982), especially chapter 15, From Slide Rule to Computer: Forgetting How It Used to Be Done.

Chapter 5
Scientists, Engineers, Managers

The good natured and cosmopolitan historian Plutarch tells how the Roman consul Marcellus, during the Second Punic War (bc 218-201), was foiled in his assault on the coastal city of Syracuse. Marcellus, writes Plutarch, "reckoned without Archimedes." Marcellus had approached the city walls of Syracuse with a formidable "fleet of sixty quinquiremes" bristling with "many different kinds of weapons and missiles," and a massive "siege-engine which was mounted on a huge platform supported by eight galleys lashed together." But the philosopher of Syracuse, in his role as military engineer, would not be outdone. Once so confident of victory, the Romans were horrified by a

> tremendous barrage … of missiles, including a great volley of stones which descended upon their target with an incredible noise and velocity. There was no protection against this artillery, and the soldiers were knocked down in swaths and their ranks thrown into confusion. At the same time huge beams were run out from the walls so as to project over the Roman ships: some of them were then sunk by great weights dropped from above, while others were seized at the bows by iron claws or by beaks like those of cranes, hauled into the air by means of counterweights until they stood upright upon their sterns, and then allowed to plunge to the bottom, or else they were spun round by means of windlasses situated inside the city and dashed against the steep cliffs and rocks which jutted out under the walls…. Often there would be seen the terrifying spectacle of a ship being lifted clean out of the water into the air and whirled about as it hung there, until every man had been shaken out of the hull and thrown in different directions, after which it would be dashed down upon the walls.

The Romans were so alarmed by the sight of "so much as a length of rope or a piece of timber" over the Syracusan fortifications that Marcellus was forced to abandon his assault and to attempt to reduce Syracuse by a blockade.

However great may have been the legacy of Rome's eventual triumph over Carthage and its allies, Plutarch's account of the struggle for Syracuse preserved an equally enduring legacy from antiquity. That was Archimedes' contempt, inherited from Plato, for those who devote their lives to "the solution of practical problems" encountered in "the needs of everyday life." Plutarch's Archimedes "did not regard his military inventions as an achievement of any importance, but merely as a by-product, which he occasionally pursued for his own amusement, of his serious work, namely the study of geometry." In this Archimedes is made to echo the Greek philosophers' prejudice against the "celebrated and highly prized art of mechanics." Plato had been "indignant" at the efforts of those who used mechanics "to illustrate geometrical theorems, and to support by means of mechanical demonstrations easily grasped by the senses propositions which are too intricate for proof by word or diagram." Plutarch — schooled in philosophy in Athens and Delphi — thus conveyed Archimedes's prejudice to two millenia of readers:

> As for Archimedes, he was a man who possessed such exalted ideals, such profound spiritual vision, and such a wealth of scientific knowledge that, although his inventions had earned him a reputation for almost superhuman intellectual power, he would not deign to leave behind him any writings on his mechanical discoveries. He regarded the business of engineering, and indeed of every art which ministers to the material needs of life, as an ignoble and sordid activity, and he concentrated his ambition exclusively upon those speculations whose beauty and subtlety are untainted by the claims of necessity.

In the end victory went neither to abstract theory nor to engineering, but to guile. While negotiating with the Syracusans a ransom for one of their errant number, Marcellus chanced to notice a poorly guarded tower. As he parleyed with his opposition, his men measured the tower and prepared "scaling ladders." Patiently waiting for a feast day when the Syracusans would be preoccupied with "drinking and other festivities," Marcellus's men crept over the tower. Before the Syracusans fully grasped what was happening to them, Marcellus stood weeping (so Plutarch tells us) on the heights over "the great and magnificent city below" as he contemplated the plunder that would soon consume it. "But what distressed Marcellus most of all," writes Plutarch, was the killing of Archimedes. Accounts of Archimedes's death at the hands of Marcellus's soldiers vary, Plutarch acknowledges. But "at any rate it is generally agreed that Marcellus was deeply affected by his death, that he abhorred the man who had killed him as if he had committed an act of sacrilege, and that he sought out Archimedes's relatives and treated them with honour."[1]

The classical education Frank Toscelli received in Italy, in the region where Roman legions defended the empire two millennia before, was an education rare among American engineers. It had evolved from the Renaissance ideal of liberal learning, a process which cultivated all aspects of the human intellect, physical attributes, and creative sensibilities. "In *my* time," he remembers, high school students studied philosophy, Latin, Greek, two modern languages, and ancient and modern history. "We had to study Italian literature, European literature; we read Shakespeare" and "took courses in translation." Electives were unheard of: a liberal learning and a full science curriculum "provided that background which would permit" students "to reason, synthesize, to analyze a problem, and *then*," with such tools, to become an engineer. The Renaissance text for the worthy life submerged the harsh distinction perpetuated by Plutarch between men who work with their minds and men who work with their hands, men who understand nature and men who manipulate nature for practical ends. Through the slow and intermittent deterioration of legal class distinctions in Europe, the nature of one's work would persist as a more subtle means of announcing one's standing in the world.

For Toscelli engineering represented not the subordinate alternative to science imagined by Archimedes, but the culmination of scientific understanding in a sequential evolution of mental capacity. "There is not really much of a difference between" scientists and engineers. "If you want to be involved, if you have the background of math and physics, then you can be either one." The business of education, his own experience had taught him, is to "provide the foundation" on which you "build yourself." One can become an expert in an exotic field like materials outgassing in space, but only after one has become well grounded in the basic sciences and mathematics. He is disturbed by the impatience of the engineering he sees around him, the haste to calculate without fully understanding what is being calculated.

Frank Toscelli, with his catholic education, his "love of learning," and his conviction that problems must be fully understood before they can be solved, stands out among his peers. Few things unite American engineers trained in the 1940s and 1950s so much as the narrowly technical focus of their education.[2] Time and again NASA's Apollo era engineers confess to having tried to avoid curricula that required grappling with literature, or philosophy, or history. A narrow technical curriculum, already pressured by the rapid growth of sheer technical information to be absorbed, became separated from the study of the natural and physical sciences as well. Thus the relationship of science to engineering would be burdened by institutional — and inevitably sociological — demarcations having no necessary relationship to what actually occurred when a handful of engineers puzzled out the ways to achieve a smoother airframe or a more efficient aircraft engine. Absent the catholicity of a traditional European or liberal arts education, attempts to unite science (broadly conceived) with engineering would become as much a matter of rhetorical contrivance as of substance.[3]

When the crew of Apollo 11 landed on the lunar surface in July 1969, conventional wisdom had it that successful technology was a linear byproduct of scientific research: engineers apply what scientists discover. Such a view, of course, helped scientists at universities (where most "basic research" was done) make their appeals for federal funding.[4] NASA (no doubt unwittingly) yielded to popular perception in its own accounting of the professional personnel the agency employed throughout the Apollo decade by placing scientists and engineers in a single category.[5] (In doing so, it followed the example of the federally funded National Science Foundation.) Granting the problematic character of personnel statistics, organized as they must be into artificial categories,[6] only one-fourth of the 9875 scientists and engineers who joined the agency between 1958 and 1970 (and were still with NASA in 1980) consisted of persons whose field of highest degree was in mathematics or a basic science[7] discipline rather than engineering. The proportion of trained scientists increased to one-third among those "scientists and engineers" who joined NASA between 1966 and 1970 (see table 2).

NASA's occupational classifications (or "codes") changed between 1960 and 1985, so the numerical results of the effort to distinguish NASA scientists from NASA's engineers *by the nature of the work they did* should be treated as estimates, based on the merging of similar occupational categories (see table 3). Those categories, however, are similar enough to enable one to distinguish between persons in primarily engineering occupations (research and development, design, testing and evaluation, facilities operations and maintenance) and occupations in the space or life sciences. As a measure of the kind of work that was most probably being done by these "scientists and engineers," NASA scientists were outnumbered by NASA engineers 26 to 1 in the agency's first two years. By the end of the decade the ratio had declined dramatically — with NASA employing one scientist for every eight engineers — but the large preponderance of persons working as engineers during the agency's formative years was most certainly a powerful factor in its organizational ethos.

If aggregate NASA personnel statistics during the 1960s failed to distinguish between scientists and engineers, NASA's leadership cadre did not. When asked who among NASA's "pioneering generation of aerospace engineers" most reflected the "characteristics which have typified NASA during its first quarter century" (see Appendix C), NASA's top managers in 1984 more clearly identified "scientists and engineers" who had, in fact, been trained in engineering. Moreover, in identifying exemplary Apollo era engineers, they were no less certain: the engineers were not scientists; the engineers were the men who had been doing either engineering or technical work — or had risen into NASA's management ranks.[8]

NASA engineer Joseph Totten (who began working in stress and structural analysis for launch vehicles at Marshall Space Flight Center in 1962 after eight years in private industry) has some difficulty deciding where science stops and engineering begins. Of himself, he says simply: "I'm not a scientist. I'm just a practical engineer." But he credits a good bit of creativity to both occupations. "Engineers, to me, are the ones who do the designing and analysis of things. The scientists are the ones that dream up experiments, that develop new systems, if you will, and they go through the development part.... They'd be the research part of it. They would diddle with experiments, or what have you, to develop some kind of a system. Once they got that to a point where they think it would be worthwhile to make [it] into an experiment for flight, why then they would turn [it] over to the design people. That's when the engineering takes place, because then you've got to worry about ... getting the thing such that it can be manufactured.... So often we get into the manufacturing process, and the parts won't go together."

Men and women younger than Totten, engineers who came to work for NASA well into the Apollo program, could have similar difficulty differentiating between scientists and engineers. "People in science and engineering," offers systems analysis and integration engineer Fred Hauser, "do either one of two things: they work on what's called space research and technology, which is kind of independent, or maybe they work with a contractor on the development of [a] technology that may ... be used in the future. Or the other thing that those people in science and engineering do is, they support a project." Engineers like Hauser, who do not question the assumption that scientists and engineers are fundamentally different, locate that difference in the realm of intellectual ability, where (as he perceives the matter) scientists reign and engineering is a practical derivative of science. "Scientists work on things that engineers will use in ten years," explains Hauser, adding, "space scientists, these guys are really smart guys. They are Ph.Ds.... I have a little bit of an intellectual shortcoming there, so I don't have ... the ability, I believe, to develop the background for that."

One of NASA's older Apollo era engineers, Joe Lipshutz, is a native of the midwest, son of an erstwhile electrical engineer turned furniture manufacturer. He has been working in the wind tunnels at NASA's Ames Research Center since before NASA was created. Assigned in the early 1970s to a computerized aerodynamic analysis group, he grew restive and unhappy with the abstract character of computerized analysis. "I got tired of it.... It's not the real world.... It's [more] fun to run a test and see what's really going on. You lose sight of what goes on with a computer, because after a while, if the computer said so, therefore it's right." In a few years he returned to wind tunnel work. The abstract quality of theoretical work is mirrored in his own distinction between scientists and engineers. "The scientists, to my mind, are still the Oppenheimers, the Einsteins — those kind of people ... the truly theoretical, I might call them a scientist, and not an engineer.... I don't consider myself a scientist. I don't generate ... really original type theories compared to people with Ph.Ds." What Lipshutz might do as an engineer is "take what other people use and maybe make it so that they can use it more quickly, more efficiently."

Bill Cassirer has also been with NASA since the NACA days, also in aeronautical research, in this case at Langley Research Center. Holder of bachelor's and master's degrees from Cornell University's program in aeronautics, Cassirer thinks of himself as a "research scientist" for the same reason Lipshutz thinks of himself (with a tinge of self-deprecation) as an engineer: "To me," declares Cassirer, "an engineer is somebody that takes handbook stuff and applies it ... he can look up and get a formula and then plug the formula in. He accepts what comes out.... A scientist is somebody that is working ... to develop the handbook stuff, is working on new ideas and theories." He identifies himself as a scientist: "I've got patents.... I've published original theories.... That's how I differentiate between engineers and scientists."

Trained in mathematics and physics, Sarah McDonald began her NASA career at the Army Ballistics Missile Agency (transferred to NASA in 1960) where, in 1946, she began work during her junior and senior years in college as a science assistant for Saturn mission operations. She has been working in computational trajectory analysis, "developing the equations of motions to write the software programs ... to integrate these trajectories" for most of her NASA career. McDonald shares with Lipshutz and Cassirer the perception that engineers exist to apply the original ideas conceived by scientists to concrete problems. "When I was in school, majoring in mathematics," she reflects, "my math advisor wanted me to just do research, 'pure mathematics,' he called it. That was more science oriented." But she found the environment at ABMA during the early 1950s so exciting that she accepted her German-born mentor's invitation to return permanently after she graduated from the University of Alabama. Her mathematics professor would have been disappointed. "I was utilizing knowledge that's available in textbooks ... and synthesizing those things that we could utilize to work a problem that we had. I don't think that is research at all ... research is doing something that has not been done before, discovering new things." In fact, McDonald and her co-workers were heavily involved in doing research that "had not been done before." Embedded in her distinction between science and engineering is an effort to discriminate between unprecedented deeds involving new knowledge, and the acquisition of that knowledge.

Joe Lipshutz, Bill Cassirer, and Sarah McDonald, who entered college before the end of World War II, are members of the same generation. Their similar and somewhat crudely drawn distinction between engineers as essentially mechanics, and scientists as theorists who define the natural world, is a distinction that echoes from antiquity. This distinction, one that relies heavily on the perception that the former are cerebral while the later are not, seems to have provided numerous NASA "scientists and engineers" a means of occupational differentiation. Hank Smith, a facilities engineer at Kennedy Space Center, knows (at least in retrospect) why he did not choose science as a career: "I'm too practical for that ... [I] like to go kick tires. [I'm] hands-on.... I just enjoy doing things.... I can't stand a brain. I think they have their place, and I think we should have experts like that — scientist — absolutely.... But not for me. Never, no."

For some NASA engineers, the choice of engineering as a career was less a matter of temperament or intellect than of relative occupational security. When Isaac Bloom started college on the eve of World War II, foremost in his mind was making a living. Son of an immigrant East European tradesman living in New York City, Bloom wanted to take up the "nearest thing to a trade" in order to make a living. When the registrar at Brooklyn College told him that the curriculum offering closest to "a trade" was engineering, he began to study engineering. Unlike Bloom, Derek Roebling might have gone into science, had he been more certain that a scientist could earn a decent living. Although interested as a boy in astronomy, he "lacked an understanding of what a scientist was." Moreover, "in those days a scientist was not always assured of a job.... I was thinking, well, I would really like something where I would not have to be worried, you know, about making ends meet. And in the 1950s it was not always apparent that a scientist could do that."

The occupational choices of young men like Derek Roebling, who were the first generation in their families to aspire to college educations but whose families could not afford to send them, were especially susceptible to the influence of the federal government on higher education opportunities. The special attraction of engineering was that if one's college (undergraduate) expenses could be largely met, an engineering career could be launched after four years in a baccalaureate program, while a young man with other professional ambitions could face more years of graduate, medical, or law school. A scientist's career prospects encompassed a greater possibility of unemployment (or underemployment) than the engineer's. At the same time, a demonstrated ability to do original research was one of the criteria for an advanced degree in the sciences; significant original research experience could only be had in the universities that awarded the coveted degrees through their graduate programs. Thus an aspiring scientist faced the necessity of yet more years of education expenses and part-time work for all but the well-to-do. (The cost could be mitigated if the student found work on a federally supported project at a university in whose graduate program he might enroll.) No less daunting, the cost of a good graduate education in science was not only high, but was incurred at the same age at which the scientist's father had been expected to support himself and perhaps a family.

Public policy favored the would-be engineer. During World War II the U.S. military's reserve officer training corps (ROTC) programs had enabled engineers to study while they did military service. After the war, the GI Bill (Serviceman's Readjustment Act of 1944) and its Korean War successor (Public Law 550, 1952) enabled veterans in all areas to return to college. Moreover, between 1950 and 1960 the federal government, motivated by the cold war preoccupation with a strong national defense, more than doubled the amount of money it spent on contract research at American colleges and universities. Nearly half of all federal research funding went to engineering research and development typically connected with large technology projects. The principal exception was the infusion of funds for basic scientific research that came from the Office of Naval Research, created in 1946 and predecessor to the National Science Foundation, established in 1950.[9] Thus, between 1940 and 1950, a young person had a better chance of obtaining a federally subsidized education leading to salaried industrial or government employment if he or she chose an engineering field than if he or she chose to work in the basic sciences.[10]

The need to compete for university grants and scholarships (unless one had other means) may have reinforced among scientists the notion that they possessed superior intellects by virtue of their involvement with abstract ideas and theories (which Platonists through the centuries have regarded as purer forms of knowledge). Those who were able to finance their advanced scientific education themselves could benefit from another well-established source of status: in previous centuries the disinterested study of nature had typically been a gentleman's occupation. The scientist's presumptive social standing thus sprang from class as well as philosophical origins, while the engineer's supposedly inferior standing likewise could be traced to the newness of his middle-class position as well as philosophical prejudice.[11]

When attempting to distinguish themselves from scientists, NASA engineers frequently suggest that the difference has mostly to do with "status." Ed Beckwith, who worked his way up from an apprenticeship in the sheet metal shop at Langley Research Center, where he began his engineering career over 30 years ago, insists that the only true difference between a scientist and an engineer is "in the perception of management somewhere." The people who go "out and run experiments" [as technicians, not investigators] are "second class," while the people who sit at desks, the scientists, are "first class." William McIver, who earned a doctorate in aerospace science in 1959 and has spent some of his NASA career in the agency's Office of Space Science and Applications, also sees any distinction between scientists and engineers largely in terms of status. Scientists in NASA are "as violinists are to an orchestra or as physicists are to a college campus. Scientists are the *creme de la creme.*"

Some NASA engineers experience the putative superior standing of scientists less as a management bias than as the manner in which engineers are treated by scientists. "Engineers tend to be more organized," reflects Jack Olsson, a 25-year veteran of aeronautical engineering at NASA's Ames Research Center. "They're prompt. At a meeting, we usually show up on time." The scientists "never show up on time…. We have personnel problems associated with engineers working for the scientists. If you're not careful, they want the engineer to become more of a gofer."[12]

Engineers at Goddard Space Flight Center, one of two NASA installations that has evolved primarily into a government space science laboratory, have had greater opportunity to ponder the differences between scientists and engineers than have engineers at other NASA installations. A 25-year veteran at Goddard asserts that most NASA scientists look upon NASA's engineers as existing to serve them in a relationship seen much the same way by those engineers. "I think that the vast majority of engineers, ninety-five percent," observes Henry Beacham, "view themselves as serving the science program…. We don't fly satellites for the fun of flying satellites; we fly satellites because there is science that somebody in their wisdom has judged … worth spending the many millions of dollars on — hundreds of millions, now." This notion is echoed by Paul Toussault, who began working for NASA in 1969 after 10 years of a checkered career in graduate school and the aerospace industry. "There's a lot of prima donnas in the science area … and we have a lot of them here at this center…. Scientists think that the whole world is run for them. They think NASA is being run for them."

Scientists "seemed to be much more peer conscious," reflects one of NASA's oldest and most productive surviving engineers, Robert Strong. "I've had physicists insist on calling 'em 'Doctor.'" A materials research engineer for over 20 years at Langley Research Center puts the matter of status succinctly: "I live in a little town called Suffolk, Virginia [with] 50,000 people in the core of the city. I'm one of two NASA scientists over there. Because we are scientists, we are in the upper crust of the social scheme; everybody likes to say they know [us], especially back in the '60s, when we were really hot items — hot stuff."

———————

Sensitivity to the relative status of scientists and engineers is more common among the older engineers interviewed for this study. It may be that status claims have made themselves felt in NASA's internal politics — an aspect of organizational life to which veterans are best attuned — as well as decades of social experience. Although members of all professsions harbor stereotypes of each other, popular notions of scientists held by engineers do not, in and of themselves, tell us much about those who hold them. Whether (and how) engineers differentiate themselves from scientists is important primarily if popular stereotypes of scientists affect how engineers think of themselves and go about their work. NASA engineers see themselves as inferior — by virtue of lesser intellect or status — members of the "scientist and engineer" coupling in the space program; or they assert that, in fact, they are *really* scientists; or they conclude that distinctions between the two are artificial, dissolving in the crucible of "research."

Pamela Donaldson shares with Bill Cassirer the outspoken view that whatever use is made of her work, she is *really* a scientist. Donaldson began her career in 1962 as a medical technician with a bachelor's degree from a small southern state college. After college she worked for a hospital in Houston, Texas and began her affiliation with Johnson Space Center through a National Research Council resident associateship in the biomedical laboratories established by the center to support NASA's manned spaceflight program. By 1968 she had earned a doctorate from the University of Houston in physiology and biochemistry; her work in Johnson's biomedical laboratories continued.

Despite the fact that all her research at NASA was undoubtedly "applied," when talking about her work she returns to her identity as a scientist, revealing considerable ambiguity (and ambivalence) in the process: "I could never envision myself, even back in early graduate school, working on projects that I didn't see a need to answer.... Here our scientists — and I certainly have been one of them — have been given certain latitude to explore [the] weightlessness [in space] situation and its effect on man. But certainly, the main reason we're here ... is because of man in space.... We've been accused of doing observational research ... but it's something that you can get terribly committed to." She acknowledges that "lots of people" do biomedical research without any practical purpose "at universities and medical centers." But "I don't." When asked whether she has done any significant biomedical research without a particular application, she replies, "You have to understand, first of all, that here at the [Johnson Space] center there aren't a great deal of scientists.... I was doing scientific research at the same time I was running operational laboratories."

As engineers who made their careers with NASA articulate their notions of science and engineering, their sense of themselves wanders among competing sources of vocational identity. Engineers and scientists are what they are for internal (psychological or intellectual) reasons, for functional reasons, or for external (social or political) reasons; their identities may be shaped by a combination of all three. By far the most penetrating commentary on the nature of science and engineering comes from those engineers who give extensive accounts of their own work. The more detailed or reflective their account, the more likely they are to conclude that commonplace distinctions between scientists and engineers lose their meaning when both are involved in research, and that the boundaries between "applied" and "basic" research have become untenable in the universe of post-World War II government-sponsored aerospace research and development.

When he was young, muses David Strickland, he thought scientists worked only in the abstract while engineers worked on concrete problems. But as he accumulated years of engineering research in both industry and NASA, he concluded "that there really isn't that much difference between the way a scientist thinks and the way an engineer thinks." William McIver's observation on the supposed differences between science and engineering is that such distinctions are "silly" because "what you are is what you do." And what persons trained in science or engineering and involved in aerospace research and development typically do is work that could be called, by most conventional definitions, both science and engineering. McIver's model engineer is not someone "who simply learn[s] how to use a handbook and look up a package solution.... You want more creativity; you want people who can go from an abstract concept or, in fact, who will come up with abstract concepts. And then, more importantly [people who can] figure out creative, innovative ways to reduce those abstractions to practice." McIver illustrates his model with the "eminent earth scientist [who can be] an electrical engineer and knows about antennas and radar patterns.... So he's an earth scientist and an engineer and he does what you do to get this program done." Or, there's the case of physicists who, "in order to do their experiments ... are having to learn about circuitry and instrumentation and this and that," while there are "engineers ... having to learn about quantum effects in diodes and lasers."

Charles Stern, who began his NASA career working in aeronautical research at Langley Research Center when it was still a part of the NACA, also believes that the conventional separation of science and engineering is "another one of these weird dichotomies that doesn't always make sense." For Stern, science, like beauty, "is in the eyes of the beholder." Science embraces "mathematical and engineering sciences.... I don't draw the line until I come to worrying about how do you design a piece of hardware. And that's another matter." Before settling into his work at Langley in the 1950s, Stern had spent two years with the AVCO Corporation, then builders of aircraft engines and refrigerators. There was a difference between the engineering he did at AVCO — work he refers to as "applied research" — and the engineering he did at Langley: "I think the Langley work was probably ... more closely associated with basic research.... At Langley ... I wasn't interested in this engine or that engine. I was interested in the [engine inlet] flow phenomena and how does one alter them so that unsteady flows don't occur.... We used a fairly high level of mathematics in our theoretical research. We used fairly esoteric facilities, wind tunnels, shock tubes and the like, in experimental research. But we weren't attempting to design any particular thing, or even a general thing."

Engineering research, argues Stern, involves not only systematic experimentation but habits of thought which are above all else "orderly, beginning from zero and working carefully to the end in ascending or descending [order], as the case may be, trying to associate cause and effect, trying to think through logically, not emotionally.... A physical scientist or an engineer [is someone] who starts from zero and moves ahead in a logical cause and effect relationship, trying to find the explanation to behavior in mathematics or in physics." Had he been a scientist, Stern would "have done the same thing ... but ... not had I been a musician." An engineer, he argues, "is one of the genus scientist." If distinctions must be made, they should be made between engineering research and "drawing board engineering."

Stern's older colleague from the NACA days at Langley Research Center, Robert Strong, also sees little fundamental difference between engineering research and science, ascribing to both vocations the essential intellectual activity of relating cause and effect. "In engineering ... [when] you design an airplane it's more than just an architectural sketch of a vehicle. You've got to analyze structure, the forces and moments ... the fatigue." Strong's own "bent" in engineering "was more in the theoretical direction — understanding, applying analytical techniques." And he, too, contrasts engineering with "other fields, like education," in which "it might take a generation to find out whether ... the kid ought to be taught phonetic English." Most important, the engineer has "to ask the question, 'what happens if I do this?' ... You have to apply that kind of logic, rather than emotions, to the solution of problems."

The melding of science and engineering in aerospace engineering research appears as well in Ed Collins's account of himself and his work. Collins is another Langley engineer, but one who began his career in the early 1960s; his work has been primarily in radiation damage research and integrated optics. His college major was nuclear engineering, and he went on for a master's degree in solid-state physics. "I was a scientist.... I crossed fields and my ... work description has changed. I was listed as a physicist and ... I was [a] laboratory type.... I did research. I had to come up with ideas of trying this thing and that thing.... Once I moved into the electrical engineering slot I take [sic] that device that is already built and put together for me by the scientist and I test it, analyze it, and plug it in my system, try to make it play with the other things and, if I get an improvement out of it, that's wonderful."

Trying things out — experimentation — remains essential to both the scientist's and the engineer's work. Where they differ, in Collins's view, is in the degree of anonymity and the relative remoteness of the scientist's work from its consequences. "In science we're doing research [that] you may work on all your life and never really have anything you can hand to someone and say, 'here's ... what I made.'" Remoteness from its consequences inheres as much in the anonymity of the scientist's work as in its motivation. "In the isomer field you can go on forever in making new materials ... by different combinations." But only 10 percent "accomplish a significant discovery in their research." Commenting on the accidental discovery of a commercially successful artificial sweetener, Collins adds: "A lot of it is just pure luck." More commonly "the research people are faceless. You could go in and pick out Joe Blow and say, 'what have you done the last 20 years?' And he may feel very bad about that because he may say, 'well, I've worked on 52 different development projects, but I can't show you a gizmo or a chemical, or whatever'.... The guy that ends up putting the sum total together is the one that gets the glory."

The terms "research," "engineering," and "technology" swim together in Sam Browning's explanation of what he has seen and done during his thirty-year career as a chemical engineer at the Army Ballistic Missile Agency and then the Marshall Space Flight Center. "Technology" to him means research in the interest of innovation. As the Saturn's J-2 engine on which Browning worked progressed through its flight qualification tests in the mid-1960s, he wanted out. "I didn't really want to get bogged down in tracking paper work on an engine that was now about to move out of the development phase into the flight phase, that I'd like to stay closer to the technology part of it — the farther out kinds of things."

Unlike Collins, who is sensitive to the disjointed and anonymous nature of much research, whether in engineering or science, Browning perceives an orderly sequence of research, technological innovation, and development. "Research would be, say, the chemist in the lab who's looking for how he can put a couple of elements together like chlorine and flourine to make a really high-performance oxidizer ... and characterizing the physical properties, the chemical properties.... The technology begins to take over. Now, when he's done that, he calls it chlorine triflouride.... And you can use that with several fuels as a rocket propellant.... It's laboratory-scale testing in a real sense, not the traditional chemistry lab, because you've got to go outdoors on a stand to do it, but that's technology to me. Development, now, is when you take that and say, 'OK, we've done enough on this, we understand it, we're going to fly a mission that uses that. So we will go into full-scale development of an engine system that employs chlorine triflouride.'" Browning's own identity wanders through the artificial differences. "I'm trying to get the laser propulsion project going again.... It's almost more research than technology, because we had to establish that you *can*, in fact, sustain a stable plasma in hydrogen supported by a high-powered laser. And there's an awful lot of high-temperature physics, and computational fluid dynamics, and a lot of other good stuff I don't know much about involved there."

What Sam Browning refers to as "technology" is similar to what John Songyin, who spent the Apollo decade at Lewis Research Center working on nuclear propulsion, calls "applied research." Describing his 1960s work on nuclear power and thermodynamic engines for space vehicles, he recalls "we were doing the basic spadework for a mission we thought would be coming.... Our aim there was not tied to any particular schedule leading to launch and takeoff of this mission. We were ... [trying to] answer the technological questions so that when the mission would be identified and schedules scheduled, that these technological answers would be there for the system people to put it all together for the mission.... I would say [it was] applied research and development ... where you're one step toward a product development or toward ... an airplane or ... food or something like that." Songyin compares his early Lewis work with "basic research," which he considers "getting down into the very basics of nature — almost like gene splicing … you're just trying to understand nature."

NASA's engineers have been dispersed among the agency's several far-flung installations, and the installation in which they have worked tends to influence their perceptions of themselves and their work — whether they are scientists at heart, lowly engineers in fact, or represent the union of both in the experimental and logic-driven process of causal explanation called "research." Langley engineer Marylyn Goode observes: "There are certainly a lot of engineers that [sic] work a lot more with their hands and building things than I do, because I work very much sitting at a desk and writing papers…. I think what a lot of us here at Langley [Research Center] do is sort of more in between the pure scientist and the pure engineer than maybe somebody who works at Kennedy [Space Center], who really works with the hardware…. But, by the very nature of Langley and Lewis [Research Center] and Ames [Research Center], our work is more into the basic research and things that some engineer is going to use probably ten years in the future … rather than working on something, some immediate product." Intersecting such elusive distinctions are status differences within aerospace engineering itself: rocket engineers may disparage aircraft engineers, and both may disparage "facilities engineers."

Whether or not sharp distinctions between science and engineering, or between "basic" research and "applied" research are tenable any longer may also be a function of historical time. The NASA engineers who spoke of the melding of science and engineering in the crucible of research commonly allude to a breakdown in the stereotyped perceptions they had of each as young men first making career choices. What their changing view reflects is the emergence of a class of engineering which has passed through a phase in its own historical development that necessarily required a high degree of research in the fundamentals of its medium, namely, aeronautics and space technology.

Hank Martin, one of the younger engineers interviewed, made an unusual effort to understand historically the vocational identities of scientists and engineers. He, too, as a high-school student, "pictured a scientist as someone who works in a laboratory." What has changed since then has been the profession of engineering and our understanding of it. "Engineering," he suggests, "back in the '50s … was an emerging profession…. Engineers, I think, at that time were stereotyped … as the sea of white shirts who were doing the mechanical drawings in the aircraft factories and laying out the steel trusses for the bridgework…. It did not appear at that time as a very exciting profession, because I think it was stereotyped as something fairly routine. You look up the specifications in the book and you get the right formula and you apply the numbers and you put it on a piece of paper and you do the same thing again the next day. In fact, with the advent of what we would call aerospace engineering today … [we have] a more realistic view of what was going on in the fields of automobile development and electronics design and things like that, even back then. There's as a lot more … to it, and there was a lot more interesting type work than one would be led to believe if you had read the papers and watched the televisions and the books at the time."

The story that Plutarch tells served to reinforce the ancient platonic philosopher's prejudice against mere mechanics, whose work was caught up in the "practical ... needs of everyday life." The epistemological and functional peculiarities that allowed such a prejudice to survive no longer have much meaning for post-World War II engineering in the realm of advancing technologies. The federal government, now the dominant "client" for both science and engineering, has never been able to distinguish successfully between the two. Where distinctions *do* persist is among professional associations and the academic milieu, which distributes the credentials for the modern professions — along with the notion, at once antique and academic, that those who traffic in knowledge and ideas have a higher claim on society's deference than those who traffic in things. NASA's Apollo era engineers have inherited the notion, and struggled with it, and many have concluded that it has outlived its time.

The question of whether someone working in advanced technology research is a scientist or engineer is complicated by the fact that each designation is burdened by perceptions of social status and philosophical prejudice. Objective or measurable distinctions are also difficult because, at heart, they involve a question of vocation, or "calling." Personal satisfaction in work comes from a sense of being called to that work and is ultimately a subjective thing. Vocation should not be confused with occupation, what men and women have done for millenia to put food on the table. Conventional wisdom suggests that the fullest rewards of a careeer are reserved to those whose occupations are vocationally satisfying. Whether seeing themselves as engineers, caught up in solving practical and concrete problems, or as researchers unraveling the mysteries of the man-made world in its ongoing dialog with the laws of nature, NASA's Apollo generation of engineers profess pride in, and affection for, the work they do — or used to do. Their vocational choices were made early in their lives, and their vocational identity is largely faithful to those youthful choices. For most of them, however, occupation diverged increasingly from vocation as they began to spend more of their days doing work for which they had little natural inclination.

The occupational reality most widely shared among engineers is their employment by hierarchichal organizations, whether in private business or in government, with relatively large numbers of technical underlings at the bottom and fewer managers toward the top. Authority and responsibility (if not power) for ever broader line or staff functions increases toward the apex of the organizational pyramid; and because most personnel systems (certainly that of the federal government) are designed by management to reward the assumption of increasing managerial responsibility, to "get ahead" or "move up" in the modern organization is to move into management. This fact has faced all Apollo era NASA engineers. To the extent that the ethos and pragmatic necessities of management conflict with the vocation and technical necessities of engineers, that fact has been a ubiquitous source of discontent.[13]

As career employees in the federal government move upward in rank and salary through the GS (general schedule) system, some supervisory or management responsibilities begin to encroach upon job descriptions at the level of GS-13.[14] At GS-15, under the federal government's personnel classification system instituted in 1979 during the presidency of Jimmy Carter, NASA engineers typically face entering the senior executive service or staying at GS-15, contenting themselves with periodic cost-of-living and performance-based raises. In those rare cases in which the "dual track" (parallel technical and management grade and salary sequences) has been effective, an engineer could rise to the level of GS-16 without moving into management. Generally, however, an engineer who declines to shift into management can expect his career, measured by rank and salary, to end at GS-13 — and to forsake a roughly 25 percent increase in salary potential.

Thus, when one talks with NASA engineers from the Apollo era, one typically talks with men and women who are no longer working as engineers. More than four-fifths of them have gone into management positions, and, among the older engineers who were employed with NASA by 1960, over 90 percent are in management positions. Sharply confirming the managerial destiny of "successful" engineers is the fact that more than 85 percent of the engineers selected by NASA's top management in 1984 as representative NASA engineers were in fact working as managers; over four times as many of those "engineers" were in senior executive service positions as the average Apollo era engineer.[15]

One of a small minority of twenty-plus year engineers who did not go into management, Joe Lipshutz expressed as succinctly as any why the greater status and salary rewards in a large organization should be reserved for managers. "No employee should make more than his boss." And a "boss" is, by definition, a manager. "If the person is responsible, with a lot of people under him, directing everything, and he is a GS-15, then an engineer, who is working independently — why should he be a GS-15? He has no responsibility." As for himself, Lipshutz's career path came to a stop at GS-13 — willingly, he insists: "Anybody that goes into management has got to be crazy. The headaches are not worth the money ... the paperwork that flows out of [NASA] headquarters and the requirements ... would drive me up the wall." Thus he implicitly accepts the hierarchical nature of rewards and responsibility in the large organization for which he, an engineer, works. He regards efforts to reduce the loss of engineering talent to managerial ranks through dual (technical and managerial) career ladders as bound to fail.

Ames Research Center, where Lipshutz works, introduced the dual career ladder "in theory." However, in his view, the notion never went much beyond theory. "We were told that engineers could reach the GS-15 level. In twenty-eight years I have known it to occur once, and that's just recently." Someone to whom it did occur, Jack Olsson, evidently displayed enough talent to be promoted to a GS-15 staff engineer after resisting the temptation to seek a division-level management position. Nor has he succumbed to the lure of the Senior Executive Service. "I'm at the top of the grade; they can't give me any more money." The increase in salary, a few thousand dollars, he might get by entering the Senior Executive Service would be paltry compensation for the "headaches." A temporary stint as an assistant divisional manager taught him that the "intellectual" rewards of "research" far outweigh being mired in work that he "wasn't enjoying."

Time and time again, whether they moved into management or settled for GS-12 or GS-13 positions, NASA engineers declare the "twin-track" (dual career) ladder a myth. A very senior level NASA engineer turned manager, David Strickland, is accustomed to circumlocution; he observes: "The two-track [career ladder] — we haven't fostered that particularly well." George Sieger at Johnson Space Center supposes that the technical career ladder does not work at his center because, unlike Ames, Johnson is not an R & D center. He attributes the failure of the dual-career concept at Johnson not only to his center's relative emphasis on human spaceflight operations, but on the federal government's civil service structure, which is embued with the same hierarchical structure of management responsibility, rather than personal professional achievement, found in more traditional organizations. The government, too, bows to the "organization man."

While ordinary engineers with no special talent or inclination for management could expect to move upward into management positions in NASA (as we shall see), the technical career ladder seems to have eluded all but the most exceptional engineers. John Songyin, who "got pretty much stuck at the GS-13 level" at Lewis Research Center, thinks that the dice were loaded against the technical career ladder when it was first instituted at Lewis. It "was set up such that it was very difficult to go up the technical side of the ladder … you had to be at least [a] nationally recognized expert in order to go up that way, whereas it was much easier to go up the supervisory ladder." John Songyin's colleague Robert McConnell rose to the GS-15 level by earning a doctorate in chemistry and becoming attached to a major research division at the center. He has managed, however, to avoid accumulating supervisory chores. Had he attempted to advance on a technical career ladder, "it would have been far tougher…. For years they've been talking about dual ladders, and every time they had a grand meeting of people in the auditorium somebody brings [sic] up the subject … and the comment is, 'we're working on it.' [But] to become a GS-15 without having been a supervisor is nigh impossible."

About half of the handful of research GS-14s and GS-15s who McConnell can recall have had doctorates; but probably more important than a doctoral degree is whether an engineer has "something to show … some finding … an [industrial research] award, or a patent." At Marshall Space Flight Center "there is," according to propulsion engineer Sam Browning, "not really a technical ladder." The chances of moving beyond GS-13 in a nonsupervisory position are miniscule, "no matter how competent you are … unless you've got a Ph.D." But getting a Ph.D. while holding down a job is tough and requires "a lot of spadework, a lot of cooperation from management on up the line to get it." He ponders: "If I could go back to the middle or late '50s," when he began his career, "and know what I know now … [I would] probably go for a Ph.D."

Only at Goddard Space Flight Center did an engineer we interviewed vouch for a successful dual-career ladder. The ladder "works" at Goddard, where there are "a fair number of GS-14s" in technical positions. But the "standard's pretty high," adds Henry Beacham; "if the journeyman is a GS-13, a GS-14 should have a national reputation, and a GS-15 should have what amounts to an international reputation. That's very much harder for an engineer to do than a scientist.... At the GS-14 level, if a person has worked on projects where they [sic] get to challenge contractors like TRW or General Electric — all of those — and they turn out to be right more often than not, I think that counts."

Bill Cassirer of Langley Research Center, one of those rare engineers who managed to ascend to GS-16 as a research engineer, remembers a time when the technical career ladder was not even an option — however elusive. A well thought of research engineer, Cassirer struggled to keep up with his research while progressing to section head and branch head. "As a section head ... I could do research almost 75 percent of the time. When I got to be a branch head it reached the point where sometimes I had to get my secretary to lie and say 'Bill's not here.' On the guise of working on highly classified information I had some frosted glass put on my doors so I could be in there working." Describing himself as a "research scientist," Cassirer is quite explicit about what establishes one's standing as an exceptional engineer: "patents" and "original theories."

There is, as Songyin's and Cassirer's observations suggest, another force at work in the failure of the dual-career ladder in NASA besides the hierarchical nature of conventional bureaucracies. Professions attempt to control behavior "standards" and economic security not only by limiting access (typically through awarding credentials), but also by regulating upward movement through definitions of "success." Notwithstanding their many differences, management and engineering share with all professions an inclination to attach status to the degree of remoteness from the practical and the particular. In this they echo a long-standing prejudice. For management, increasing remoteness from practical and particular concerns inheres in the hierarchical and typically centralized structure of power; headquarters is "where the action is." One's status is a function of where one is located, and where one is located determines what one does. Barriers to upward movement are as likely to be structural as they are to be personal.

In the learned professions, which include science and by extension research engineering, professional standing is largely independent from one's location within an organization. "Achievement" is defined and acknowledged by professional peers, and it is the judgment of peers that controls access to the "top" of the profession. Ascent on the technical ladder was, and probably remains, difficult for NASA engineers because the measures of achievement that signify whether they are worthy of ascent derive from a profession — science — that places a premium on novelty, for example, "patents" and "new theories," which is understood to be the result of intellectual rather than manual — or practical, or particular — preoccupations.

A GS-12 with a Ph.D., Derek Roebling at Kennedy Space Center argues that "the way of advancing" in NASA "is not technical knowledge so much, or management knowledge so much, as [being] the man on the white horse, the leader, the hard-charger, the friend of management who gets things done.... I have a doctorate ... but I do not mention it. I do not want some guy who is a bachelor of science in mechanical engineering and cigar-chomping saying, 'God Damn! We don't want any Ph.D. professors or anything like that here!'" Robert Ostrand has a bachelor of science degree in mechanical engineering. He works at Lewis Research Center, where he willingly moved into management, believing that his best years as an engineer were numbered. He has what he thinks is a "minority opinion" on the dual-career ladder: "Here," at Lewis, the "dual ladder is ... grossly overdone.... If there are certain very talented engineers, if they can show me that they can walk on water, [that] they're that good, I'll get them a GS-15. [But] in a center like this, that's one or two guys ... a small percentage of guys." To be an engineer talented enough to ascend to the same heights as a manager is to be part of a very small percentage — almost as small as those who "walk on water."

The care and feeding of the managerial hierarchy has limited opportunities for one of NASA's (and any similar organization's) essential resources — technical talent: "Our people," observes George Sieger of Johnson Space Center, "once they get to the journeyman level — there is no outlet for them except to become a manager or a flight director or move out of the organization. And that is unfortunate, because we need those steady-state GS-12s and GS-13s ... they are still the core of any organization. We have no advancement potential for those kinds of engineers."

Just how deadening thwarted aspiration can be when engineers realize that they can only "move up" by going into management — but that there are many fewer management positions than upward moving engineers to fill them — surfaces in the lament of one frustrated Langley engineer: "In January (1986) I'll get my last step of a GS-13. I have nowhere to go. If I can't go on the management side or something doesn't change for promotions on the technical side ... something has got to change. I'm just typical. There's hundreds of me. That's my last salary increase. I don't count the cost of living raises because everybody gets them. Other than incentive awards, I have nowhere to go for another 19 or 20 years. You either leave, or you pull in and say, 'OK. If I've got nowhere to go, I'm just going to put my feet up on the desk and do what I have to do.' You know, you can't live that way if you really care."

When organizations complain of "brain drain," or of being unable to compete for good talent, they typically cite the inability to offer competitive salaries. But upward mobility — or lack of it — can be shaped as much by the kind of work attached to career advance as by the kind of money earned along the way. "A lot of the young guys," explains Richard Williams, a Kennedy Space Center engineer turned manager, "will ... stay around for four or five years and then they'll go to private industry where they really can design and can do real engineering. We're seeing this now — guys who have twenty years are applying for an early out and going to work for contractors, so they can be engineers again."

The perception that NASA loses valuable engineering talent when engineers move into management in order to get ahead assumes that the failure of the technical career ladder stunts otherwise productive and continuously creative engineering careers. Some of NASA's Apollo era engineers, however, have been aware of the problem of obsolescence in engineering, and consider management a legitimate and productive alternative for engineers who have, perforce, accumulated some understanding of how technical programs work. Even if they are no longer in command of the details, they are, so to speak, ready to move from the particular to the general. Robert Strong, who experienced a successful career as both a research engineer and a NASA program manager, put it this way: "After you've been involved with technical problems for a long period of time, you find you get stale." He had observed that "when we started running projects ... [there] were people who kind of got bored and reached the end. They couldn't see any more progress they were making in their own field. They wanted a change. Well, these people had enough technical depth and, with a little help, were able to manage projects and parts of projects very, very well when they were [with] people who knew enough about the ... project so that they could keep track of the main thrust of the effort."

There was a special reason for Philip Siebold's sensitivity to the time clock that shadows the modern engineer. Now at Johnson Space Center, Siebold began his career without benefit of an engineering degree. He paid his dues as a draftsman for the Martin Company and eventually, by going to night school, earned a B.S. in engineering at the age of 40. By that time, however, he realized he "couldn't compete technically with the 20-year-olds who were coming out of college with either masters or doctorates in technical fields. I had been spread out too long. What they needed is someone to direct them, to manage them." Recognizing that engineering management was the most likely alternative to the wasteland of obsolescence, Siebold entered a night school program in management; by the time he entered NASA in 1964, he was prepared for a second career. Richard Williams, who made the shift from engineering to management at age 30 when he left flight crew simulation for a unit coordinating domestic and foreign spacecraft manifests at Kennedy Space Center, is open and unassuming about his engineering abilities. Having left "hands-on" work, he misses it: "I do, and at the same time I don't.... I thoroughly enjoyed getting out in the field and being around the hardware.... I can go back and ... look at the hardware, which is still interesting to me. But from an engineering standpoint, I don't know that I could engineer my way out of a paper bag anymore."

Obsolescence is undoubtedly a difficult subject for those whose career fortunes depend on a profession that thrives on the accretion of knowledge. That may account for the fact that far more engineers complain that the lack of a true dual-career ladder frustrates careers than acknowledge the possibility that management offers a second chance for most engineers who — under the press of daily work —

simply cannot keep up. Whether technical obsolescence sets in before or after engineers shift to management is a difficult question to answer. More pertinent to understanding the organizations in which engineers work, not to mention the quality of their own second careers, is the question of how well they fare as managers.

NASA engineers experience management in two ways — as technical managers (managers of projects and tasks having little continuous involvement with the same people), and as managers of people (or of organizational units having the same personnel). Those who have spent some time in organizational management recognize that there is a qualitative difference between "good" engineering and "good" management, and that a system that rewards good engineering with a promotion into a management position risks promoting ill-equipped managers. The qualities these engineers cite as important to good managers all require a high degree of insight, empathy, and selflessness in dealing with others — the gift of dealing well with people. "Good managers are people oriented," insists Ed Collins at Langley Research Center, "and not all technical and research people are people oriented. Many of them are loners.... Many of the managers that are in line now ... should be back in the lab. And some of them came up through the buddy system.... They were very good men technically, but it was overlooked ... [whether] they could work with people and really handle people and inspire. I think a manager should be able to inspire his people to work for him." A good manager is "kind of like a teacher," observes veteran NASA engineer and manager Robert Strong.

"What I learned," reflects George Sieger, "from the people who were ... good managers — I can go back to high school: a teacher in high school ... taught me that if you develop positive attitudes, things are going to happen." When, as a young aircraft flight data analyst, Sieger had no idea whether his work was good or not, his boss "made me think it was beautiful," and thus gave him confidence to try new things. Sieger remembers every good manager he has had. One taught him "precision." Another taught him "to use your mind, to not accept the obvious as the solution." And another taught him "finesse." Imagination, courage — "all of these things ... are part of this puzzle every human being represents." Good management is also "leadership ... being able to ... anticipate ... to mobilize resources, to move into a posture where you're always looking to find a way to end this job in the belief that there's another one downstream that's equally interesting, more challenging.... Management is turning people on." The qualities that make for a good teacher can require a lifetime of learning. Good managers "evolve," echoes Fred Hauser at Marshall Space Flight Center; "I don't think you can teach them to be a manager ... by trial and error, the leaders just come to the surface."

However, the components of "leadership" are open to debate. Those with a genuine sympathy for people tend to see leadership as a matter of creatively "drawing out" (the literal meaning of education) the inherent potential in others, while NASA engineers whose own career goals have stressed technical achievement measure leadership by the extent to which one can induce others to work to preestablished organizational goals. The difference is subtle — the latter view both drawing its energy from and reinforcing greater anxiety over organizational control.

Joseph Totten has a confident, creative attitude toward management similar to that of George Sieger. "I'd like to think that I have some unique managerial capabilities that have gotten me where I am. I seem to be able to get along very well with people.... I don't have too much trouble negotiating things. People find it easy to work for me, and I find it very easy to get people to do things that need to be done.... What I try to do is make sure that they understand that I'm not going to be hard on them every minute of every day.... They're in a position where I give them responsibilities and I expect them to go ahead and practice that responsibility ... stay out of their hair, give them what they need. If they have any problems they can't handle, then I'm here for consultation."

Sieger's and Totten's views of good management contrast with that of Jack Olsson. For Olsson, the manager's role is essentially instrumental: it is to help his people succeed by the organization's rules rather than to develop personally and professionally per se. Each individual has a "limited growth path," he explains, and the good manager has "to try to develop that path for that person and point out to him where he's deficient and how he needs to write more reports ... or something in order to get the kind of recognition that's necessary to move up the ladder, both professionally and financially. So there's a lot of counseling of people and appraising their work." From Robert Ostrand's perspective, effective management is largely the same process: since (he claims) 20 percent of the people "make 80 percent of the significant accomplishments," a manager needs to know who they are and "take care of them." (Ostrand is not clear about what he should do with the other 80 percent.) Like so many of NASA's engineers turned managers, he had not been "planning on being a manager. It used to scare the hell out of me whenever I thought about it.... When I became a manager for the first time, I had all these guys, and I said to myself, 'All these guys are sitting there and they're waiting for me to tell them what to do....' It was terrible. But I soon learned to tell them." Werner Posen at Marshall Space Flight Center believes that management requires, most of all, "leadership talent." This, he thought, he had: the "talent to make people *like* to do what you want them to do ... that was a reinforcing process, which led me more and more into management." A twenty year plus veteran like Posen, Bill Cassirer agrees: "What makes a good manager is to recognize the type of ... people he has working under him and then do whatever is necessary to get the best output out of his whole people."

However, virtually every engineer we talked with insisted that engineers, by inclination and experience, are not natural managers. And, because most of those interviewed have become managers, that they think so suggests that "moving up" has meant a struggle to adapt to careers for which they have little interior motivation other than the desire to get ahead. First, the reason some engineers are chosen for management is one of the principal reasons they have difficulty as managers. "We have a tendency to reward our highly capable technical people by putting them into management," comments Marshall engineer Joseph Totten, who has happened upon the "Peter Principle" (organizations tend to promote people to their levels of incompetence).[16] Unfortunately, a gift for the concrete particulars of a problem does not necessarily translate into the general outlook managers need to flex with the unpredictable, the persistent fact of life in organizations. "That's a very tough adjustment, going from an engineer … to a manager," concedes Robert Ostrand, who moved between several engineering and supervisory jobs while working his way to the GM-15 level at Lewis Research Center. Ostrand shifted "from a very detailed — I was working, you know, a one-inch square a mile deep as a researcher…. All of a sudden I'm in a great area where I'm working a mile square a millimeter deep. And that's what you do." "Sometimes" managers are "not as well rounded as they ought to be," echoes another Marshall engineer.

The trouble with managers who were once engineers is that "once an engineer, you're always a tinkerer," offers John Robertson at Johnson Space Center, another GS-15. A younger colleague of his in the same center explains: engineers "can't get away from the engineering side; they've got to do all the details." A proclivity toward meddlesome management — an inability to delegate — does not, however, seem to be the largest problem facing engineers as prospective managers. The problem that casts the largest shadow over these engineers turned managers is the problem of temperament, about which they are both explicit and articulate:

"Engineers got into engineering because they didn't like to deal with people. They like to deal with things that have definitive answers which you could reach by a fairly clear set of processes…. They make lousy managers."[17] Or "Quite often your engineers … wouldn't recognize an emotion if it hit them in the face … some of them are not people oriented at all."[18] Or "I'm not really convinced that engineers make the best managers. Engineers tend not to be the kind of 'people persons' who good managers should be."[19] Or "I don't believe a successful engineer necessarily becomes a successful manager." … Technicians "really don't interface with outside people…. A manager has to be prepared to do that."[20] Or "I know people" who "just are not people persons. They get along with people, but they can't hardly manage their own time, or selves, let alone other people and an organization."[21] Bob Jones, a GS-14 rocket engineer assigned to Kennedy Space Center, is the most succinct of all: "Engineers — like I said of myself: I related to things."

Whether these engineers and others like them have absorbed a stereotype of engineers or truly experience a profound awkwardness with the more intractable universe of personalities and feelings is hard to say. But the consequences are likely to be the same. Common experience tells us that those who feel confident about what they do are more likely to enjoy their work, and to be adventuresome in their work, than are those who are haunted by a fear of making mistakes. "You can tell the technicians who have become managers by the fact that they are probably … the few people wearing white shirts and ties," remarks Ed Beckwith at Langley Research Center. Being at ease with people is an essential ingredient in the fine art of persuasion, without which few managers succeed for long.

It is not only the NASA managers themselves who suffer from the lack of confidence with which they, former engineers, appear to have moved into management. The engineers they leave behind as their subordinates suffer, denied the personal skills and sympathies of the good supervisor upon whom their own success partly depends. "We're so science, technology, engineering oriented that we have forgotten the human side.... Engineers are kind of selfish people. Their projects come first. And the people themselves are kind of pushed off to the side." Bettylou Sanders, a Johnson Space Center engineer in a GS-13 managerial spot, reflects a bit further: "I'm not sure that we always get the best product, because we have unsatisfied people."

NASA, like most large corporations, offers management education programs with varying degrees of emphasis on "sensitivity training." Yet the engineers we interviewed tend to agree that the qualities that make for a good manager of people cannot be taught (although they may, through experience, be acquired). Periodic instruction in management philosophies and techniques does not appear to compensate for an organizational culture that has difficulty identifying and promoting good managers. Yes, many engineers may not be "natural" managers, even though management is the principal upward career path open to them. And yes, there may be some confusion about what "good" management is, as NASA engineers turned managers commend management styles that range from the highly permissive to the manipulative. But there are also aspects of management (probably not unique to NASA) that appear to make it just plain unappealing.

An engineer who remained an engineer, Ed Beckwith has avoided the predicament of the middle manager. Once a NASA engineer goes into a management job, he can expect to spend the rest of his time "checking budgets ... defending what we are doing" and enduring the "frustration involved [in] dealing with ... upper management.... The red tape involved in doing this and the red tape involved in doing that ... the frustration of a lot of wheel spinning." The problem with management is "we've got to take all this crap!" At Lewis Research Center it is not much different: "Our branch chiefs and section heads," complains Robert McConnell, "don't know what's going on.... They're much too interested in getting money from here to support [them], and money from there, and getting this report in every week and every month."

The dissipation of energies into paper-shuffling and mendicancy (even more necessary as NASA budgets declined after 1968) may be intensified by the fragmentation which threatens any large organization that, like NASA, attempts to sustain a multitude of programs, projects, and installations. Charles Stern has been a division-level manager at NASA Headquarters for much of his career. If the agency has a unified sense of purpose, it will be communicated outward from Headquarters, or not at all. While Headquarters attempts "oversight and coordination ... management in the broad sense," he reflects, "the degree to which the plans of the various organizations are [truly] coordinated, the degree to which they all seem to be oriented to a common future ... is usually nil." Part of the problem is that NASA, unlike a large private corporation, is constantly poised between the competing interests of government: competing contractors, competing political constituencies, their surrogates within the federal bureaucracy, the White House on one hand and the Congress on the other. Administrator James E. Webb, a veteran of the Bureau of the Budget who stood at NASA's helm for much of the Apollo decade, made a virtue out of necessity. He resisted efforts at centralized, long-term planning in the agency, arguing that NASA's purpose in life was the legitimate business of the political process and thus always subject to change. Adaptability, and not single-minded attachment to purpose, should be the hallmark of a well-managed federal agency.

Struggling against the centrifugal tendencies caused by limited resources and bureaucratic particularism, and pulled at the periphery by competing political constituencies, managers may be tempted to retreat into the niceties of organization charts and chains of commands. When asked to talk about management in NASA, Pamela Donaldson, one of the few high-ranking women managers in NASA, described at great length who reported to whom in an elaborate hierarchical mix of line and staff positions. Most NASA managers, however, seem to recognize that effective managing in any organization depends on the ability not only to reinforce good managers and the qualities that produce them, but to transmit those qualities to younger staff "on the way up."

The temperamental unsuitability of many engineers for work that requires constant and effective interaction with others, and the centrifugal tug and pull that act on an organization like NASA, translate daily into a shortage of time and attention for the "drawing out" that George Sieger described as he talked of how he learned to be a good manager from other good managers. At Ames Research Center, Herman Sabado has spent a year or so managing an interplanetary probe project. But he laments that he has not had the kind of mentoring from a senior manager that would enable him to feel more prepared for the work he is now doing. What he means by mentoring is help in mapping out a career that takes account of stages of preparation and ability, and then some help in following the map. "To some extent," he confides, "I feel a little uneasy that I really don't know what I'm doing in management." NASA did send him to some management courses, "but I really felt that I should have done that before I got the management position." Notwithstanding ample amounts of paperwork, "even now, I really do not consider myself a real manager in the sense of 'I have my own project, and I'm going to manage it.'"

"Because we are all engineers and not humanists," speculates Bob Jones, "there hasn't been a focused, concerted effort to ... develop a new generation of good second line management." Joseph Totten, who speaks from the experience of a senior executive, echoes Jones's observation: "We have done a fairly poor job of developing real managers." If Jones and Totten are right, everything they and their colleagues have said about the problems that face NASA's engineers turned managers would be explanation enough. Still, they work at managing, and some evidently take managing as a new profession very seriously — perhaps too seriously, as if to justify severing their roots in their technical origins. "Now, in the recent history of NASA," reflects NASA veteran (and manager) at Ames Research Center Abraham Bauer, "there's been a movement toward ... managers who almost take pride in not being technically [involved]." He contrasts this trend with the "early history" of Ames, when the center was managed by "technically oriented managers" who understood and cared about decisions that had technical aspects to them, such as "whether a laboratory should engage in certain areas of work." Bauer attributes the change to "modern management" ideas in vogue during the 1970s, and especially the influence of management schools which thrived on the notion that good managers could be trained by studying "management" practices and principles detached from the content of the enterprise they would be expected to manage. He deplores this notion, insisting that "if you want to have a strong research laboratory, you want to have strong technical people running it." His conviction reinforces the promotion of engineers to management positions and defies the conventional wisdom that engineers do not naturally make good managers. "*Enough* do," he counters, recalling the career of E. O. Lawrence (for whom the Lawrence Radiation Laboratory in Berkeley, Calif. is named), inventor of the cyclotron and a 1939 Nobel laureate in physics. "I'm sure that the man had the ability to work with other people, because there was a whole generation of disciples of his who became famous physicists."

Ultimately, believes Bauer, good management in technical institutions amounts to "leadership by example." Good managers in laboratories like Ames Research Center exemplify "resourcefulness, creativity." When he began working at Ames as a younger man, "there was a resourceful, creative person at the top. And his ideas kind of trickled down to others so that people ended up doing important research who, if they were just thrown out on their own, would never have done extremely important research.... Right now, individuals are being called upon to be these things [resourceful, creative] on their own.... I do not see present managers as being mentors. Period."

Abraham Bauer's somewhat unconventional view raises the interesting possibility that, in fact, engineers are neither more or nor less suited to become managers than are lawyers, physicians, or members of other "learned" professions. Given the subjective character of most notions of "good" management — relying, as they do, on accumulated, anecdotal experiences that are difficult to objectify, perhaps NASA's engineers do themselves a disservice. Perhaps they have accepted more than they should a stereotype of the engineer that portrays him (and occasionally her) as incompetent in a world of personalities, feelings, and the technically intractable. Some NASA engineers have gone into management, liked it, and succeeded at it; as Bauer suggests, perhaps "*enough* do."

One out of five of the NASA managers we spoke with confessed to enjoying management (and one can assume that if they enjoyed it, they were successful at it). The reasons they gave for liking managing mirror the range of notions they and their peers have about what makes a good manager. Just as notions of good management in NASA vary in emphasis from permissive to manipulative roles, those who enjoy managing do so for reasons that range from an apparently genuine pleasure in the creative challenge of working effectively with people to the psychic and monetary rewards of managerial power and status.

Elizabeth Mueller came to Goddard Space Flight Center with a background in mathematics and worked her way up as a computer software specialist for various unmanned satellite projects. She distinguishes between project management and "line management," or managing organizational units, for which she has declined "many jobs." "If you're in a line organization, you're generally ... managing people, but you're not doing quite so much of the technical work.... You're not outside the organization interfacing; I have never been interested in doing that." In contrast, she enjoys project management because "I like to find [technical] requirements, deal with the outside world, the experimenters [and] the contractors." Although she seems to shrink from the unremitting interpersonal aspect of line management, clearly "interfacing" — where the solution to a complex technical problem is at stake — is something she relishes.

Mueller's colleague, Henry Beacham, finds management rewarding for a similar reason: he likes "trying to make a contribution, trying to figure out what people want to do and fitting that into what needs to be done — trying to make people *want* to do what needs to be done." The challenge involves both people and technical experience: while working with people is "what you *do* do ... you have to have the outline of it [the technical problem] in your own mind pretty clearly before you want to ask people to do it." What motivates Beacham is the creative aspect of managing people doing technical work. A similar kind of creativity is the source of the satisfaction John Robertson has gotten out of his work managing engineers in a line organization at Johnson Space Center. Having chosen an engineering career to begin with in anticipation of moving into management later, he relishes what he experiences as "an interesting and very challenging job." What is interesting for him is "trying to get all of these people talking together and trying to reach a consensus." He agrees with a NASA Space Station Freedom project manager who observed: "Our job is ... to be missionaries."

The satisfaction Joseph Totten gets from his own work in line management — the satisfaction of working easily with people who seem to find it easy to work with him — is no doubt partially a function of his view of what constitutes good management. That view is a permissive one, one that sees the manager as an enabler of others' talents and development. There are other NASA engineers turned managers who share Totten's outlook. At Kennedy Space Center, for example, Richard Williams talks of the "rewards that go along with" meeting the "challenge of people, how to keep people meaningfully employed.... I'm extending myself to my guys that are out in the field. I have seven NASA fellows and three support contractor guys. The support contractor fellows are all young, fresh out of school engineers, and I look at them and it just amazes me, because ... none of them had any field experience up until the time that they joined my group here.... It's a whole new world for them, and they thoroughly enjoy it." Hank Smith, who oversees contractors doing facilities engineering, gets some of the same satisfaction out of his work. "I enjoy managing engineering.... I love it; I really do. I've taken short courses [in management], attended schools here and there on management.... I've always enjoyed people. And it's a people business now."

If management offers the satisfaction of working creatively through others, it also offers some relief from the powerlessness often felt by those who are typically at the receiving end of an organization's directives. Top executives will dispute whether they have much real power over events, but it is the perception of greater authority and status that matters. Although Ed Collins never did achieve his ambition to enter management, he has found some compensation in the fact that, as a project engineer, "I do have a title now." Working in her center's central administrative organization, Eleanor Finch at Kennedy Space Center likes management because "I have more options now. If I really don't want to do something, I can always delegate it to somebody else." After fifteen years in engineering, Werner Posen made a shrewd assessment of where the power lay and began his own shift into management. "You are part of a system," he explains; "you see who is calling the shots, and you see [that] sometimes you work under people who make decisions that you would do differently.... Who is calling the shots? Do you just want to do your thing? How about money? How about prestige?"

Because the authority that an engineer has depends as much on the currency of his or her technical knowledge as on simple talent, that authority declines with the onset of obsolescence (unless, of course, an engineer manages to remain current while working). However, a manager's authority is cumulative, and authority for the manager typically increases the longer he (or she) manages, learning to "work" an organization's administrative procedures, personalities, and clientele. Robert Ostrand seems to have grasped this intuitively early in his career, when he realized that the day would come when (as an engineer) he would face his own obsolescence and would have to go into management if he wanted to continue to "get ahead." "I'll tell you something I learned ... the hard way," he says, reflecting on the misery of the "reduction in force" Lewis Research Center had to institute in the late 1960s. "Forty-year old engineers, or older, are very difficult to sell because usually they've worked for twenty years.... It isn't that they aren't competent; but a company can ... go and get a young kid out of school and after two years they'll be able to do the same thing as that forty-year-old engineer.... If you're an engineer and you're doing pure engineering and you're over forty years old, you're in a high-risk profession.... That's not true of managers. Hell, I can go out and — you know, I'm sixty years old — I can go out and get a hell of a good job today if I want to."

―――――――――

For all the creative excitement that surrounded the early years of the U.S. space program, NASA's engineers have been and appear to be still men (and women) caught in the middle. They have seen public accolades, influence, and status conferred upon scientists, whose ideology scorned the "material needs of life" to which engineers devoted their "art." Yet scientists have not been bashful about claiming the practical results of engineering as mere applications of their own abstract speculations, "untainted [as Plutarch wrote] by the claims of necessity." The ambivalence and confusion with which American institutions deal with science and engineering is enormous, and it has become internalized by many engineers, resulting in a true problem of vocational identity. Institutionalized "research" has offered the engineer a role that is less fraught with ideological biases and generally understood to be both cerebral and practical; "research" has crossed the chasm that

Archimedes cut when he pronounced engineering "ignoble and sordid," but the speculations of science full of "beauty" and "subtlety."

Most of us do not live by vocation alone; aspirants to the salaried middle class must work and transform a vocation into a career. When NASA's engineers mapped out or stumbled forward in their careers, they discovered that they could not normally make much of a life-long career out of engineering — even engineering as "research." The hierarchical organization in which they have worked (and in which most engineers work), has managers, not engineers, at its apex. For most of them neither temperament nor education equipped them for the daily stuff of management. Their peers at private research and development organizations like MITRE Corporation and RAND Corporation, which benefit from federal funds without the burdens of federal personnel rigidities, no doubt experience greater career mobility.

Haunted by technical obsolescence, tempted by the relative status, monetary rewards, and the power of management, most NASA engineers have willingly "moved up" in the organization only to experience a good bit of frustration. The "technical career" ladder seems to have offered some hope — but not much. There seems to be enough apparent ambivalence about whether engineers really have much creative ability left in them after mid-life to sap the support for a viable alternative to management as the culmination of an engineer's career. A few engineers adapt, and adapt quite well, finding that they can operate in the human dimension effectively, and with considerable personal satisfaction. But in the end, the fact remains that they are neither true scientists nor true managers. They are engineers. NASA's Apollo era engineers can take some consolation from the fact that the factors that contribute to their situation — the ideological prejudice that venerates science while exploiting the works of engineers, or the hierarchical organization that reserves the top for managers (owners of all modern enterprises having become so remote as to be virtually invisible) — affect, to a greater or lesser degree, the working lives of salaried engineers in every modern research and development organization.

----

[1] Plutarch, *Makers of Rome: Nine Lives by Plutarch*, Ian Scott-Kilvert, translator. New York: Viking Penguin, 1986, pp. 96-105.

[2] Donnell W. Dutton, "A Brief History of Aerospace Engineering Education and Curriculum Changes," January 1982 (NASA History Office).

[3] See Edwin T. Layton, Jr., *The Revolt of the Engineers: Social Responsibility and the American Engineering Profession* (Baltimore: The Johns Hopkins University Press, 1971, 1986 ed.); Peter Meiksins, "The 'Revolt of the Engineers' Reconsidered," *Technology and Culture*, Vol. 29, No. 2 (April, 1988), 219-246; Thomas P. Hughes, ed., *Changing Attitudes Toward American Technology* (New York: Harper & Row, 1975); Daniel S. Greenberg, *The Politics of Pure Science* (New York: New American Library, 1967); Don K. Price, *The Scientific Estate* (Cambridge: Harvard University Press, 1965); Amitai Etzioni and Clyde Nunn, "The Public Appreciation of Science in Contempo-

rary America," *Daedalus*, Vol. 103, No. 3 (Summer 1974), 191-205; Theodore Roszak, "The Monster and the Titan: Science, Knowledge and Gnosis," *Daedalus*, Vol. 103, No. 3 (Summer, 1974), 17-32; Richard R. Nelson, "The Economics of Invention: A Survey of the Literature", *The Journal of Business*, Vol. 32, No. 2 (April 1959), 101-127; Chalmers W. Sherwin and Raymond S. Isenson, "Project Hindsight: A Defense Department Study of the Utility of Research," *Science*, Vol. 156 (June 23, 1967), 1571-1577; Illinois Institute of Technology Research Institute, *Technology in Retrospect and Critical Events in Science*, Report to the National Science Foundation (Chicago: Illinois Institute of Technology Research Institute, 1968); Sylvia Doughty Fries, "Expertise Against Politics: Technology as Ideology on Capitol Hill, 1966-1972," *Science, Technology & Human Values*, Vol. 8, No. 2 (Spring 1983), 6-15; and Sylvia D. Fries, "The Ideology of Science during the Nixon Years: 1970-76," *Social Studies of Science*, Vol. 14, No. 3 (August 1984), 323-341.

[4] See Sylvia D. Fries, "The Ideology of Science During the Nixon Years: 1970-76," *Social Studies of Science*, Vol. 14, No. 3 (August 1984).

[5] NASA summaries of its civil service workforce during the 1960s included, within the general category of "scientists and engineers," "occupational codes" 200 (general scientists and engineers), 700 (aerospace scientists and engineers), and 900 (primarily life sciences). The remaining occupational codes were 300 (technical support), 600 (professional administrative), 500 (primarily clerical), and 100 (trades and labor).

[6] Common experience tells us that a job classification or title does not necessarily reflect the actual content of the work being performed, or the training and skills being brought to that work.

[7] Physics, chemistry, biology, biochemistry, physiology, zoology, astronomy, geophysics, earth sciences, "other science."

[8] NASA's Apollo era scientists and engineers (those who remained with the agency) were overwhelmingly white males (see table 8)]. The "nominee" group would undoubtedly have reflected the virtually uniform racial and gender composition of the larger population had it not been for the fact that the number of nominees from NASA's Office of Equal Employment Opportunity (52 names) was twice the average for all NASA's organizational elements combined (25 names).

[9] J. Merton England, *A Patron for Pure Science: The National Science Foundation's Formative Years, 1945-57* (Washington, D.C.: National Science Foundation, 1982). By its last year of operations, 1949, the ONR was spending about $20 million on 1200 projects in 200 institutions benefiting nearly 3000 scientists and 2500 graduate students. Committee on Science and Public Policy, National Academy of Sciences, *Federal Support of Basic Research in Institutions of Higher Learning* (Washington, D.C.: National Academy of Sciences — National Research Council, 1964).

[10] The amount spent by federal agencies on contract research at American colleges and universities increased from $150 million in 1950 to $450 million in 1960. John S.

Brubacher and Willis Rudy, *Higher Education in Transition: A History of American Colleges and Universities, 1636-1976* (New York: Harper & Row, 1976); Frederick Rudolph, *The American College and University: A History* (New York: Vintage Books, 1962); *Federal Support of Basic Research in Institutions of Higher Learning*, Ibid.; Committee on Science and Technology, U.S. House of Representatives (99-2), *Science Support by the Department of Defense: Science Policy Study Background Report No. 8* (Washington, D.C.: U.S. Superintendent of Documents, 1986), chapter III; *National Patterns of R&D Resources: Funds & Manpower in the United States, 1953-70* NSF 69-30 (Washington, D.C.: National Science Foundation, 1969).

[11] See chapters 1 and 2.

[12] "Gofer" is a euphemism for an errand boy or girl.

[13] For commentary on management as a dimension of the careers and professional identity of engineers, see Edwin T. Layton, Jr., *The Revolt of the Engineers: Social Responsibility and the American Engineering Profession*, 2nd ed. (Baltimore: The Johns Hopkins University Press, 1986), especially chapter I; and Robert Zussman, *Mechanics of the Middle Class: Work and Politics Among American Engineers* (Berkeley: University of California Press, 1985), pp. 151-154, 140-145.

[14] An alternate "merit pay" series, GM-3 through GM-15, encompasses management and supervisory positions for which promotions are based on periodic performance evaluations rather than automatic serial pay increases.

[15] See table 4.

[16] Laurence J. Peter and Raymond Hull, *The Peter Principle: Why Things Always Go Wrong* (New York: Morrow, 1971).

[17] Henry Beacham, a senior executive at Goddard Space Flight Center.

[18] Hank Martin, a GS-14 at Goddard Space Flight Center.

[19] Jack Olsson, an engineer at Ames Research Center who opted out of management.

[20] Ed Beckwith, a non-supervisory GS-13 at Langley Research Center.

[21] Richard Williams, a GS-12 at Kennedy Space Center.

The little fishes of the sea,
They sent an answer back to me.

The little fishes' answer was
'We cannot do it, Sir, because-'

Lewis Carroll
"Through the Looking Glass,"
Chapter 7

Chapter 6
Changes

As more than 13,000 NASA engineers worked at their daily routines during the mid-1960s, pursuing the "moral equivalent of war" to which President Kennedy had summoned them, the solid ground of common national purpose had already begun to soften under their feet. In 1962 Kennedy dispatched American "military advisors" to Vietnam to help shore up the regime of Ngo Dinh Diem. Before the year was out, the Soviet Union boldly installed bases for nuclear missiles targeted at the United States in nearby Cuba, removing them only after Kennedy called the Soviet bluff and threatened to quarantine Cuba if the missiles were not removed. A year and a month later Diem was overthrown and murdered, and Kennedy lay buried, victim of an assassin's bullet. As civil rights protests began to spread in 1963, murder took one civil rights leader, Medgar Evers, and stalked another, Martin Luther King Jr., finding its mark in 1968. The President's brother, Attorney General Robert F. Kennedy, would fall to an assassin that same year as he was about to celebrate his victory in the California primary for the Democratic nomination for the upcoming presidential election.

American violence at home, as race-related riots spread from urban ghetto to urban ghetto, was matched by American violence abroad, as air raids ordered over North Vietnam in 1965 escalated into intensive bombing campaigns and massive U.S. troop deployments. Television, which had been acquired by 94 percent of all American households by the mid-1960s, rendered these scenes of violence common-place and provided a world stage for an outpouring of public protest against U.S. military involvement in Vietnam. The "Counter Culture," "hippies," and the radicalism of the "New Left" underscored the disintegration of the simple bi-polar world of the 1950s, a world of easy contrasts between freedom and communism, rectitude and sin, success and failure.[1] In March 1968, President Lyndon B. Johnson — so tough in the battle against the North Vietnamese, so tough in the battle against poverty and race discrimination — formally abandoned any hope of reelection.

Raising the specter of runaway inflation as costs for the war in Vietnam and the social programs of the "Great Society" mounted, Johnson's economic advisors persuaded the President in 1965 that the budget for the space program would have to be contained. For an ambitious space program to follow the Apollo adventure, there was diminishing enthusiasm outside NASA. In fiscal year 1966 NASA's budget began its downward slide (although actual expenditures for 1966 were the highest of the decade).[2] The prospect of national abandonment was only one of the ominous dimensions of the disintegration in the midst of which NASA's Apollo era engineers found themselves.

One of the most momentous changes in the technique of engineering—a change that would have been experienced by these scientists and engineers had they spent their careers with private firms or government agencies other than NASA — has been the development of high-speed electronic computation and data processing devices — the modern computer. NASA's Apollo era engineers agree on the importance of the computer revolution to the changing character of their work as much as they agree on any other single facet of their careers. "The power that a computer gives you in doing design is phenomenal," observes Michael Goldbloom, who spent the 1950s and 1960s working in private industry before joining NASA in 1970. "There are things that you can do in a day today that you used to not be able to do in four or five, six or seven months — things like ... optimizing a given design ... looking at various alternatives.... And the thing that's made it that way is the tremendous revolution that's occurred in microelectronics."

Philip Siebold, who began his career as a junior draftsman for the Martin Company and stayed with the aerospace industry for twenty years before going to work for the Johnson Space Center, remembers engineering when its principal tools were the drafting board and the slide rule. When he began working in 1942 "everybody started on the drawing board. Five years ago you got an engineer out of college and he didn't know what a drawing board was and didn't want to work on one. What he wanted to do was sit at a desk. Now, with CAD/CAM[3] coming in ... [drawing] is becoming a big thing again because ... it's not the laborious thing of a big drawing board and pencils ... you're sitting there with a little light probe, and you can make the changes a lot easier. You can play much [sic] more games of getting a picture and twisting it around rather than all the labor of putting it [on paper]. So now people are getting more oriented back to drawing." As for the slide rule Siebold first used, "young people today don't know what one looks like.... Fifteen years ago we went from slide rules to little hand calculators we carried around.... You don't even see those any more. Everybody has a big computer sitting in their office.... You can do a problem today on a computer or a calculator that you couldn't do thirty years ago; it would take me a lifetime to do it."

One of the computer's effects has been a high degree of intermarriage among the subdisciplines of aeronautical engineering and design. Armed with their light pens and instantaneous drawings on computer screens, present-day aeronautical engineers work with designs that instantly merge changes throughout an aircraft. "Designs are being more and more blended," remarks Joe Lipshutz, another NASA veteran of an era (at Ames Research Center) when research into aircraft design concepts was largely a matter of drawing board, slide rule, and models mounted in wind tunnels. "It's getting kind of hard to determine where the wing stops and the fuselage begins…. You are not going to build an airplane now just because it is aerodynamically efficient … from an aerodynamicist's point of view." The introduction of computer-assisted design "means that your chances are that the numbers you get out of the wind tunnel and extrapolate … to the actual flight conditions will get closer to what the final airplane is going to do."

The computer revolution has influenced more than aircraft design; combined with the laser,[4] it has created a new generation of experimental instruments for measuring structural tolerances and dynamic forces.[5] The computer has also brought about an enormous increase in the speed and sophistication with which things like spacecraft trajectories, for example, can be projected and analyzed. Someone like Sarah McDonald, who began working at the Army Ballistic Missile Agency in 1946 before she had even completed her college work in mathematics and physics, has especially clear recollections of the impact of the computer on her own work because she began her career using electromechanical calculators to determine trajectories for the rockets that would culminate in the first manned Moon landing of 1969. "We didn't have much data to establish those trajectories with," so she and others began "some of the first work in … defining the methods that were going to be used to land on the Moon." In the beginning "all we had was a Marchant and an old Friden calculator; the most it could do was take a square root, and [the machine] occupied much of a table."

McDonald's colleague at Marshall Space Flight Center, Joseph Totten, who began his working career in the mid-1950s, still keeps his old slide rule in his desk drawer. "I still use it…. I grew up with it and I still like it." But he readily acknowledges the changes that high-speed electronic computation have wrought in engineering. When he first came to work for NASA "the only computers we had were the 'hand cranks' [analog electro-mechanical calculators]," on which he did all of his calculations. "In the middle '50s the computer was something that was in about nine rooms and you couldn't see the end of it. I can remember the first mobile computer that we had. [It] was something about half the size of my desk and it had a bunch of boards … and it had a lot of pin holes in it and you put in your pin, worked up your program and then put the pins in to repeat the program on the boards. Then you put the boards in the computer and it could probably run a very simple program."

As Totten and his co-workers labored over stress and structural analysis for the more powerful Saturn booster required to deliver the Apollo spacecraft to the Moon, "anything we had to do had to be done quick. And to do it on the computer meant that you had to take time out to write a big program and then you had to go and get that thing into the computer and then you had to check it out before you could make sure that it was going to run properly…. We were using computers, but you only used computers on really big programs. On the little stuff, we just hand cranked it out…. Now, hell, you've got hand calculators; you've got programmable memory in them." As he has shifted into managerial work, Totten mostly uses a computer, on his desk, as a word processor and information management device. It is the younger engineers fresh out of school who "are so computer oriented…. They get in here and they can start designing on a computer right away."

How NASA's Apollo era engineers assess the role of the computer in changing the nature of their profession depends somewhat on what kind of engineering they do. For engineers like McDonald, so much of whose work involved crunching numbers, the computer has been absolutely liberating. "You can walk up and down the hall and look at engineers working and a larger percentage of them are sitting at a terminal … they have tools available to them to make some of the menial parts of the job a lot easier, so you're able to do a lot more and broaden your scope." Another of NASA's few female engineers of the Apollo era communicates some ambiguity in her recollection of the progress brought about by the computer. Sandra Jansen began her work at Lewis Research Center in 1947 as one of NACA's small armies of women "computers." Trained, like her co-workers, in mathematics, Jansen spent her early working days reducing data that flowed in from testing facilities and wind tunnels.

While NACA's female computer pools were something of an occupational ghetto, they provided, at the same time, an occupational haven for women with a taste and talent for engineering trying to make a go of it in a male-dominated profession. With the coming of the electronic computers in the 1960s came men with mathematics degrees, men who gradually began to displace the older women. "Those of us with the math, who were trained then to move into the computer field, were not discriminated against," and "there were also new younger women that were hired, too." Nevertheless, between the mid-1950s and 1960s the "almost totally female" computing sections were transformed into organizations employing about the same proportion of men and women. Jansen does not speculate about whether the women could have been retrained to adapt to the new technology. It may be that the computer did much more than transform the reckonings that make up much of an engineer's work. Once considered a repetitive, routine chore to be relegated to women, computing — the "high technology" of the 1960s — promoted the emergence of a proto-scientific profession requiring degrees in mathematics for admission. Whether that requirement arose out of the technology itself, or out of the aspirations of a socially mobile generation, is debatable.

The computer revolution, for all its benefits, has left many Apollo era engineers uneasy. Obsolescence is one of their concerns. Notwithstanding its marvels, the computer remains an "appendage of your own brain," reflects Michael Goldbloom. "You have to be completely facile in both designing software and programming it, as well as using it." Only then does it become "a tremendous help." Unfortunately, "most engineers of my age, or even younger, that don't become fluent in the use of the computer become obsolete very rapidly." Now even people "who … know how to program — are used to using a computer — are not anywhere near as versatile or capable with those systems as a kid that starts playing with it when he's ten or eleven years old."

Even though NASA's Ames Research Center has been at the forefront of NASA's efforts to develop advanced computational capabilities, some Ames engineers "were slow" to welcome the introduction of computers into their work. "There were some branches that really dragged their feet," remembers flight researcher Jim Davidson; they "didn't encourage anybody to take programming classes and these sorts of things." Some of these veteran engineers worry that the growing dependence of modern engineering on the computer is depriving its practitioners of that conceptual training and facility essential to theoretical and experimental creativity. Goldbloom recalls trying to help one of his children with calculus. He realized that "what can happen is you learn the rules so well that you know what to do, but you just don't understand the theory behind what you're doing. And it is very important that you understand the concept and [only] then use the computer as an aid, rather than use the computer and pure clip book method to do a job without understanding the process of what you're doing."

Although Frank Toscelli at Goddard Space Flight Center shares the general amazement at the change in engineering brought about by computers, he too has doubts. Toscelli can remember working on the first Orbiting Astronomical Observatory (OAO, launched in 1966), when "we were supposed to have a computer but decided it would be too complicated, that instead they'd put in some memory device, and this memory device could memorize two hundred thousand bits. We thought that was terrific. Now the memory has trillions of bits and bytes." Nonetheless, Toscelli doubts that computers have done much to advance engineers' conceptual grasp of the phenomena they are designing or operating. "Young people ... are very competent on the computer," he agrees, "but they ... sit in front [of it] all day long and play.... They throw numbers ... in the computer, and they provide a lot of numbers. But there is no connection with the real thing.... Older people know what's going on — the analysis — and the approach to take to a problem." "Engineers coming out of college now ... can leverage themselves by a tremendous amount," echoes Robert Ostrand at Lewis Research Center. "They've got to get some judgment by doing their own work. [Experience] is the only way you can get it."

Jack Olsson, who has remained an active and productive researcher throughout his career, cautions that "you have to be very careful to realize that the computer gives you only what you put in. There's a real tendency to believe that simply because it's in the print-out that it somehow has validity.... The particular area that I was most interested in when I started [boundary layer theory] ... would never have developed if the computer had been there, because people would have just thrown the Navier-Stokes[6] equations on the computer and found out the solutions numerically.... There are certain ... simplifications to the differential equations which allow them to be integrated in closed-form solution that you can write out on a piece of paper and you don't need a computer; those would never have been developed." Yet "from those equations ... you get real insights into the problems that you never would get out of a computer.... So the computer is OK to fill in the last detail and get very accurate results, but understanding is not enhanced by the computer."

The computer has become an essential tool of technological change; it is also — as a few of NASA's Apollo era engineers acknowledge — an instrument of human obsolescence as a younger generation of engineers competes for authority and occupational space with older engineers. Whether those older engineers are otherwise threatened by the young is not wholly clear; probably, as in most walks of life, some are and some are not. German-born Werner Posen, who grew up in a culture that readily cast the mantle of scientific authority on engineering, finds the younger generation of engineers "not better and not worse." But Joe Lipshutz, who, during his 30 years working in Ames Research Center's wind tunnels, has seen the computer compete with the wind tunnels, as the arbiter of what will fly, is much more sensitive to the danger of personal obsolescence. Younger engineers, he speculates, are "probably ... a lot smarter than I was twenty-five years ago.... They're a lot sharper. It's scary." But then, he surmises, "we probably scared the old engineers too with what we were taught in school that they were never taught."

Sarah McDonald agrees that the younger engineer has survived a more demanding curriculum, one in which computer proficiency is an essential part: "I wonder," she marvels, "how kids ever pass everything." "We've got some sharp kids coming out of college these days," observes Dan O'Neill, McDonald's co-worker at Marshall Space Flight Center; "I don't know if they are brighter, but I think they are exposed to a lot more knowledge and information than I was, and the older people were."

———

As one listens to these engineers ponder the changes they have seen, one easily recognizes the fairly obvious ones — the computer's inroads and the inevitable hazards of age in a profession that lives on cumulative knowledge. But they think they detect more subtle changes in the content of engineering not only as a technical occupation, but as a profession. "One of the fundamental things" that differentiates his generation from the current generation of engineers, thinks Dennis Whitebread, is that his generation was "rooted with a fundamental concept of engineering.... Today engineers don't ... really perceive their activities as a profession in the same context as doctors, lawyers, and so forth." Professional identity, it seems, has been replaced by careerism. What Whitebread remembers is a profession — perhaps somewhat romanticized over time — in which "there was once more of a humanitarian kind of ... engineering.... The engineer was here to produce for mankind"; engineers worked for "the enjoyment of what they are [sic] doing." Professional cohesion has dissipated, in Whitebread's reveries: younger engineers "don't see the need for pursuing professional licenses"; instead, they "only work in engineering for a period of time and they look forward to coupling this with an MBA" and moving ahead in management — which, to him, means abandoning the engineer's ancient calling.

If careerism has replaced the sense of a common calling in engineering, it may be that the circumstances under which engineers work has changed. Several of the Apollo era's engineers detect larger forces at work than differing internal motivations between younger and older engineers. Careerism may, in fact, be a reasonable response to a decline in the opportunities and rewards for independent, creative work. When William McIver first went to work at Lewis Research Center in 1957, the year the Soviet Union opened the "Space Age" with its launch of Sputnik I, "you could come to NASA ... with a bachelor's degree and get involved in a research program right away." At Lewis, "we had very small groups of guys working on really big projects [and] each person working on a project had a significant part in it. I was involved [in] ... free flight rocket experiments.... We actually had to design the rocket engine. We had to do the instrumentation. We had to figure out the fuels. We had to design the burners, the combustion ... the whole shooting match, from beginning to end, reduce the data, do the calculations — everything."

McIver doubts that similar excitement awaits the new engineer today, one like the "youngster" he met on her way to NASA's Jet Propulsion Laboratory after graduating from a southern university. "She's involved in doing the software for the probability matrices associated with look-up tables and analyzing some data.... The project she's working on is extremely important," but this young engineer has little way of personally appreciating "the magnitude or the importance" of her work. Even if she and other newly minted engineers like her did have an opportunity for more comprehensive involvement in a particular project, McIver is not sure that they could make the best of it because of the fragmented and specialized nature of the education they have received. That is because he thinks they do not "receive the training which would orient them toward research and innovation and conceptualization," the aspects of engineering intelligence that, in McIver's view, make for the most creative and rewarding engineering.

Implicit in William McIver's doubts that modern engineers are adequately prepared for creative work is the notion that the most rewarding kind of engineering is research engineering. The premium he places on research derives at least partly from the research culture he entered when he went to work at Lewis, one of the original laboratories of the pre-NASA National Advisory Committee for Aeronautics. As the complex technological challenges of the Space Age shouldered aside the relatively more familiar problems of aircraft design, the amount of creative research that could be pursued comprehendingly by any single engineer — or indeed, encompassed in a basic engineering curriculum — diminished. Jim Davidson began his engineering career at Ames Research Center, another NACA laboratory, in 1944, after a year's stint with North American Aviation. "Aeronautical engineering, when I took it up," he remembers, "was airplanes — subsonic airplanes. And education had to change completely ... for supersonics and space dynamics." As Jack Olsson (whose NASA career also began at Ames before it became a part of NASA) looks back on the past 30 years, the most important change he has experienced has been just this change in emphasis from aircraft to space mission design. A contemporary of McIver's, Olsson remembers the 1950s as a time when "airplanes [were] as close as you could get to the engineering of what was then almost "science fiction." And "suddenly, the opening of the space era made a great deal of difference for me because I went from airplanes — hypersonic vehicle design — very quickly ... into reentry system design and then, from there, into mission and system analysis."

Not only research, but all aspects of aerospace engineering, have been consumed by complexity. The change that has most impressed Bob Jones, who has spent his career since 1958 working in propulsion systems for launch vehicles at Kennedy Space Center, is how "relatively simple" the original propulsion systems — like that of Centaur — were "compared to the complexity, redundancy and sophistication of today's systems." Initially "you used to be able to look at an engine schematic and start the engine. Prevalve opens, main fuel valve opens, et cetera…. The H-1 engine [on the Saturn 1B stage] was beautiful. All it needed was a 28-volt signal to the turbine spinner; [it was] solid concrete from then on; it relied on its mechanical [parts]. It didn't need any electrical stuff to operate the machinery." Now "I look at the schematic of the Shuttle Main Engine and I think, God, what a dinosaur [I am]. I didn't even recognize the main fuel valve…. The plumbing has gotten more complex, and there's more of it, and the pressures are higher." Nonetheless, the old engineer's touch still has its place: "You still, in many cases, go around with soap solution looking at soap bubbles as a way of leak checking; that's what we were doing in the '50s. They have mass spectrometers now, and they've got ultrasonics; but the fundamental tools are the same — pressure gauges, soap checks. Notwithstanding the fact that "there's orders of magnitude [of] differences in electronics … we'd say in the old 'propulsion bucket' that 'I don't trust nothing with a wire tied to it.'"

The extent to which the technical requirements of the nation's space program can be blamed for the fact that the romance of engineering has been displaced by the complexity, fragmentation, and specialization that accompany the sheer magnitude of modern engineering enterprises is an interesting historical question. When Michael Goldbloom began working for the Sperry Gyroscope Company in 1949 in the automatic controls field, "the way the company was organized, the same group of engineers that did the actual mathematical analysis, what an autopilot should look like, was involved in the circuit design, was involved in systems testing, followed the system out to the field, was engaged in flight testing — in effect, you saw the product, your creation, from womb to tomb." Goldbloom and his fellow engineers experienced "a tremendous feeling of satisfaction in seeing a missile fly with your design built into it." Since those early days of the 1950s, engineering has become "so specialized," argues Goldbloom, "that I don't believe there is any company that has an organizational structure that will allow you to do that. Either you're in analysis, and do the original mathematical, conceptual design of the system; or you're involved in system testing; or you're involved in flight testing in the field. And you don't follow your designs completely through from womb to tomb…. Just like in the medical profession, the field has become so complex that it's just more efficient for companies to specialize." The problem is that "for an engineer working in that area I don't believe it's anywhere near as rewarding as the experience that I had when I first started." If Goldbloom had his career to do over again, he would get a doctorate so he could either teach or do research; he would not work for a large company.

Thomas Swain, a colleague of Jack Olsson's and Jim Davidson's at Ames Research Center, also recognizes that complexity and specialization are partly endemic to modern engineering. When Swain's generation "went to high school, there was just a word called engineering ... that was a respected field to go into." But now, he asserts, "there's such a huge variety of technologies that people learn about at quite an early age ... there's this tremendous choice out there," and "when kids go into college they are aware of the greater variety of things." At the same time, Swain sees a factor at work within aerospace engineering itself which has contributed to the perception of deteriorating opportunities for significant creativity that can be experienced within an individual's career. That factor is the waning importance of single "breakthroughs" necessitated by serial plateaus in our understanding and command of fundamental technological problems in aerospace research and development.

In retrospect, Swain detects three such plateaus: the first was reached after NACA, with the military as its principal client, mastered the problems of transonic and supersonic flight. By the mid-1950s "the power controls and aerodynamic shapes and so forth" to master "supersonic flight had been conquered." Then came what Swain calls "the doldrums. There was some good routine work going on ... in the wind tunnels. But in the flight research end of it, there was just sort of a plateau, sort of like waiting for the next set of problems to show up." Then the rapid growth of commercial aviation, which has relied heavily on technological developments for military aircraft, generated a significant market for aeronautical research in its own right. Interest in a supersonic transport, vertical- and short take-off and landing (VTOL, STOL) aircraft provided "the next set of problems.... So, all of a sudden there were these new areas" that stimulated a "resurgence of the aeronautical technology development" that occurred "when the NACA became NASA." A third new set of problems arose when Ames found itself part of a rapidly expanding new space agency and part of "a much bigger organization" which was "suddenly a source of funds." And NASA meant, once again, "exciting times," prompting many of Swain's colleagues to shift from aeronautical research to space science — as, for example, when Ames was given responsibility for the Pioneer series of interplanetary spacecraft in 1962.[7]

Abraham Bauer's ruminations also lead to a sense of passages and plateaus. His perspective is undoubtedly broadened by his early years as a chemical engineer and physicist for the Tennessee Valley Authority and Oak Ridge National Laboratory before moving to Ames in 1948. "There are always eras of golden opportunity," he reflects; "we had one, I lived through one ... working on the atom bomb ... ballistic [missiles] ... manned spacecraft ... planetary exploration. How often does a set of opportunities like that come up within one career?" Engineering is partly shaped by "the set of opportunities that are available.... But I can't foresee right now a string of developments of the kind that we've seen in the last thirty years coming along in the next thirty." NASA's Space Station Freedom program, initiated in 1986, will offer "lots of opportunities for carrying out things," but as Bauer sees them, they won't be "quite as bold and challenging and new as sending a man to the Moon."

Indeed, the event that most unites the memories of NASA's engineers is the mission of Apollo 11, the successful effort to land men on the Moon and return them safely. The event signaled the United States' initial preeminence in space. It was a technical and managerial achievement of high drama and the first such achievement of the new age of television, one that enjoyed extraordinary visibility. Granting the drama, the unarguable technical accomplishment, the global visibility of that achievement — one must measure the Apollo program, if it is to be measured by any way other than its actual monetary cost, by its consequences. The Apollo program is a prime example of an effort by this society to buy knowledge — the "hard" knowledge of science and engineering — for an urgent national, and largely political, purpose: to demonstrate to a world divided by the Cold War that the "free world," and all the ideological and institutional habits with which it was associated, would prevail over communism. Here, too, was the great opportunity for those visionaries, especially among the European emigres, who dreamed of crossing the last frontier of space.

The full historical measure of the Apollo program must be taken not only by the extent to which it realized the aims of both politicians and visionaries, but by the extent to which it improved this country's ability to acquire and use knowledge for broad public purposes in general. Measured by this standard, the processes put in place or solidified in order to achieve the Apollo triumph are as important, for the long run, as the event itself and the undeniable technological "spin offs" frequently used to justify public "investments" of new science and technology. The technological boundaries that had to be crossed before Neil Armstrong could step on the Moon were the simpler ones. (Wernher von Braun is said to have quipped, "We can lick gravity, but sometimes the paperwork is overwhelming.") It was the managerial solutions that were the tough ones, for NASA's Apollo era administrators did not have *carte blanche* to operate as they chose. A formidable host of accumulated incentives and constraints normally obscured by the innocuous term "public administration" determined the larger consequences of the Apollo program, especially for the men and women who brought their knowledge, and developed that knowledge, to make it happen.

The incentives and constraints that determined the processes by which NASA could and did operate were both inherited and externally imposed. One was the culture of the *decentralized in-house research organization* inherited from NACA, with laboratories scattered from Hampton Roads, Va., to Moffett Field, Calif. The transfer to NASA during the early 1960s of former Army missile facilities at Redstone Arsenal and Air Force facilities at Cape Canaveral, Fla., and the creation of new NASA installations at Houston, Tex. and Beltsville, Md., ensured that federal administrative centralization (see Introduction) would have to compete with decentralized laboratories (or "centers") for administrative control of the new space agency. However, an in-house research culture and a decentralized institution were not the only inherited constraints that decided how NASA would go about its work — and thus determine the shape of its engineers' careers.

Another of those constraints stemmed from the widespread public distrust, clearly translated into presidential and congressional politics during the 1950s, of "big government." Coupled with general misgivings about a large government establishment was the deeply rooted American faith in private enterprise which, through the mechanism of a free market, was thought the best guarantor of economic security and a free society. On this usually bipartisan ideological foundation, and partly in reaction to the alleged excesses of the New Deal, as well as a weariness with the massive mobilization required to emerge victorious from World War II, federal policy (enforced by the Bureau of the Budget and its successor, the Office of Management and Budget, established in 1970) required that the government acquire its goods and services from the private sector. What became known as federal acquisitions policy was translated into the dense forest of regulations and procedures governing "contracting out."

Thus was added a third constraint (or, in the eyes of Congress and OMB, incentive), on the way NASA would conduct the Apollo program and its other activities. NASA would do its work not by amassing a large complex of federally owned engineering and fabrication facilities or civil servants (over which NASA had little managerial latitude in any event), but by contracting for the bulk of its hardware and R & D work, as well as support services, to the private sector. (One NASA installation, the Jet Propulsion Laboratory of the California Institute of Technology in Pasadena, Calif., would be wholly a "contractor" operation.) Doing so had the obvious advantage of enabling the civilian space program to harness talent and institutional resources already in existence in the emerging aerospace industry and the country's leading research universities.[8] Contracting out had the additional advantage of distributing federal funding, which was funneled through NASA's centers, around the country and, as a consequence, creating within Congress a political constituency with a material interest in the health — and management — of the space program.

The military services had had the most experience with contracting, since they had acquired equipment and logistics support from the private sector since the early 19th century. More recently, it was the U.S. Army and the U.S. Air Force, which was created out of the U.S. Army Air Forces under the Defense Reorganization Act of 1947 that created the Department of Defense, that had the most experience with contracting to the private sector. As a result of the Army's Manhattan Project and the ballistic missile programs managed by the Air Force's Research and Development Command, both services came to rely on private contractors for advanced engineering and development work — the Air Force going so far as to create the Rand and Aerospace corporations. In 1959 the General Services Administration authorized NASA to use the Armed Service Procurement Regulations of 1947, which contained important exemptions, tailored for research and development work, from the principle of making awards to the "lowest responsible bidder."

The practice of contracting out and associated acquisitions procedures were not the only body of administrative processes NASA acquired from military experience; equally important was the role of the *program* as the managerial device for executing the agency's broadly framed mission to explore space and advance aeronautical and space technology. Conceptually and administratively the NASA program was the umbrella under which projects were identified and planned, Congressional authorization and appropriations obtained, private sector sources solicited and evaluated, contract awards made, and contracts administered. Thus the interests of NASA program and project managers became closely intertwined with the interests of actual and prospective contractors. In turn, because programs and projects were managed through NASA's centers, the institutional health of the centers became intertwined with the interests of program managers and aerospace contractors. And, because Congress necessarily attended to constituent interests that included the communities in which NASA's centers and contractors were located, Congressional interest in NASA's programs reached well beyond the degree to which they might meet broad national aerospace policy goals.

Decentralized NASA *centers*, most with strong in-house traditions, NASA *programs*, and *contracting out* together constituted a tightly interwoven triangle of interest that could frustrate the ability of the agency's central managers at NASA Headquarters to forge a single coherent strategy for the civil space program. Most of NASA's Apollo era engineers did not, of course, experience directly the executive frustrations faced by NASA's senior managers during the 1960s and the 1970s. What they *did* experience was the bureaucratic and political consequences of the center, program, and contracting triangle.

NASA's older engineers — those who transferred to the new space agency between 1958 and 1960 from NACA laboratories, the Army Ballistic Missile Agency, and the U.S. Navy Research Laboratory and Ordnance Laboratory — share memories of working in in-house (civil service) facilities whose essential mission was research. The NACA veterans predominate among this older group, and they measure the character of today's NASA against the remembered qualities of "the old NACA."

Robert Ostrand remembers Lewis Research Center, the NACA's aircraft engine research center in Cleveland, Ohio, during the 1940s and well into the 1960s, as a place whose primary work was technological innovation through research and testing. Ostrand went to work at Lewis in 1947, fresh from the University of Michigan. While at Lewis, during the 1950s, he did graduate work at Case Institute of Technology to earn a master's degree in engineering. The research emphasis of neighboring Case Western's graduate engineering program undoubtedly reinforced the notion, for Ostrand, that the best engineering was research engineering. Like Ostrand, William McIver had been able to obtain his graduate science and engineering degrees from Case Western while he worked at Lewis. During working hours he was able to do the same kind of original research expected of him by Case, an opportunity offered to numerous other Lewis engineers. NACA, observes McIver, was intended to "promote the aeronautical capability [of the country].... We did the esoteric research and we transferred the technology to the commercial community."

Long-term support for basic research, whether in government or industry, is an act of faith, for it has to compete with more tangible and immediate claims on an institution's budget. It is not surprising, then, that basic research organizations tend to exist on relatively lean diets. "Before 1958," recalls Robert McConnell, a contemporary of McIver's at Lewis, "you never bought anything. If you had to experiment on something, you would cut something out of a blade and experiment that way. [If] you went to buy a 70 dollar item, you'd have to hock your right arm." Even so, working for the NACA at Lewis seemed special; it seemed special because of what McIver remembers as the *"esprit de corps* and reputation associated with the NACA.... A NACA [Technical] Report was divine; nobody argued with it." And the reason those technical reports seemed so authoritative was that they had been scrutinized and concurred in by NACA's other two laboratories, Ames Aeronautical Laboratory and Langley Research Laboratory. NACA was "just a very proud, very conscientious research outfit."

NASA's older engineers, who shared the experience of working with the NACA at the Ames and Langley laboratories have similar memories. The older they are, the more likely they are to believe that the end of NACA's innocence was brought about not by the creation of NASA in 1958, but occurred during and shortly after World War II. Jim Davidson went to work for Ames in 1944, when, as he recalls it, Ames was full of "people who were very dedicated ... working for very low pay, and there weren't many amenities.... You had this small core of really excellent, dedicated people who were doing work that was quite advanced." Thomas Swain has been at Ames almost as long as Davidson, having arrived there in 1946. The NACA Ames Aeronautical Laboratory he remembers was a place that "was very young.... The average age ... was about 30. Even the management was quite young." There was "a lot of enthusiasm, lots of spirit, a wide range of kinds of people. There were a number of the real scientists involved [in Ames's work] and a lot of practical engineers," and the laboratory was "100 percent civil service." One of the advantages of the young organization was that its "levels of management" were "shallower; there weren't nearly as many steps between the working level and the top level."

Davidson thinks NACA changed with the war; "a lot of people came in who maybe didn't have high academic backgrounds, and there were a lot of ... bureaucrats running it.... We were on a pretty tight budget. Congress would spend money for expensive wind tunnels, but for other things — even instrumentation — they didn't budget" at adequate levels. There were "days [when] we had to sign in when we arrived in the morning and sign out when we left. Nobody could have coffee machines in the buildings. The building I was in ... they had one telephone in the hall and the secretary would tell you when you had a telephone call."

As the aviation industry matured in the 1950s, it began to compete, along with universities, for the NACA's more creative talent. Swain attributes the gradual softening of the NACA's research edge to the widening pay differential between private sector and government. At the same time, universities like Stanford were able to offer successful NACA research engineers academic careers, with "opportunities ... that are above money." Davidson believes that the NACA itself was partly to blame; he had become dissatisfied by the mid-1950s as he came to realize that "a lot of new developments and research were being done in the industry and in the academic community." The change, he thinks, was due partly to "the personnel involved ... what their directions, motivations were," and partly "the money Congress would spend on developing ... flight research vehicles" that NACA would test and develop for the U.S. Navy or the U.S. Air Force.

Nonetheless, there were compensations. Some of the intimacy and unspoiled atmosphere of Ames survived through the 1950s. When Joe Lipshutz began working there in 1957 on a cooperative U.S. Army / NACA program, "we were on the frontier at Ames. There was nothing north of us, and very little east of us.... The whole Santa Clara Valley was desolate compared to what it is today." One could "go to the top of the San Mateo mountains and see all the blossoms in the valley.... You could have a nodding acquaintance with everybody. You could go to certain individuals — these would be very sharp people — and pick their brains quite a bit.... You'd walk up and ask them, 'I've got a problem'.... And now there are as many contractors as there are civil service people on the field. Before ... for all practical purposes, it was all civil service."

Langley Aeronautical Laboratory was the grand doyen of the NACA. What some of Langley's veterans came to call the "Langley tradition" (and their junior colleagues came to understand as the Langley tradition) was virtually synonymous with the NACA. The Langley laboratory that Bill Cassirer went to work for in 1949 to do supersonic aerodynamic research was a place known for "a kind of bare bones living, but ... almost everybody working to try to solve good research problems, and doing a good job — and the publications that came out of here were high class." Research, not engineering and development, was the organization's principal mission — a mission that, in Cassirer's opinion, became compromised as the NACA began, for survival's sake, to work on "some of the so-called research airplanes, or project airplanes — the X-1 and so on."[9]

Because it was a research institution, remembers Robert Strong, Langley's "product" was not a particular aircraft, but research reports and technical conferences. The quality of the NACA's reports and conferences was what the NACA's work was measured by, and the organization fostered a keen competition among individuals and groups of researchers, as well as NACA's centers to produce the "best." That meant a certain amount of duplication, as more than one research team or laboratory tackled a problem; the duplication, in the eyes of Strong and another Langley veteran, Charles Stern, was a small price to pay for the competition that stimulated the NACA's creative energies.

The NACA's emphasis on original research could be sustained because good researchers were reinforced by their environment and rewarded with increasing status and authority. While aeronautical engineers working on design, development, and manufacturing in the aviation industry during the 1950s might find themselves working in "bullpens," or rows of drafting tables, Langley aeronautical engineers, remembers Stern, could be spared such an indignity. Private or shared offices lent to one's work the atmosphere of an individualized, professional, and original enterprise. What's more, "everybody in the whole chain of command from me up to the director," recalls Cassirer, "had been a rather outstanding scientist.... It used to be that ... most promotions were made from within, which meant you went from a branch head to a division chief, then from division chief to associate director, and then finally, director."

The NACA's culture was more than a research culture, however. Its ethos was broad enough to embrace the technicians who could not claim to be involved, except in a supporting role, in the fundamental work of the professional research engineer. Ed Beckwith, a technician who came to Langley in 1953 as an apprentice in the sheet metal shop, laments the passing of NACA with as much energy as his co-workers who were professional engineers. "We had people that you respected. You might not agree with them and they might really tongue whip you, but you respected those people.... Back then," insists Beckwith, "you had big people, [people like] John Stack[10] — hard, tough, he knew what he wanted and really went after it." The Langley tradition, for someone like Beckwith, was "competence, respect, and assertiveness — leadership; things that we don't see now."

The perception that what distinguished the NACA was a unique in-house research culture, one that fostered individual creativity and independence of mind, persisted into the post-NASA years, when it continued to be idealized by NASA's younger engineers. Although the nature of Lewis Research Center's work had already begun to shift to more applied, project work by the time John Songyin moved there from General Electric in 1961 (Songyin started out at Lewis working on the development of nuclear electric power systems for space vehicles for the Atomic Energy Commission), this younger NASA engineer imbibed Lewis's NACA identity as a fundamental research laboratory: "It's my perception that, during the NACA days, right up to the time when the NACA became NASA, there was a different kind of atmosphere here, they were more interested in pretty basic phenomena.... It would be looking into the phenomenon of shock waves, whether it be wing foils or shapes of fuselages or around propellers or things like that."

Marylyn Goode, Richard Ashton, and Ed Collins all joined NASA's ranks after 1960, going to work at Langley Research Center. For Collins, the NACA culture persisted well into the 1960s, at least during the period that Floyd Thompson served as director of Langley Research Center (1960-1968). Under Thompson "we had a very research-oriented center." Thompson "was interested in research and wanted researchers to get their due share and notice.... As the other directors came in they were more hardware oriented, more program oriented; research ... they couldn't understand it." Goode and Ashton also acknowledge the "Langley tradition" — only they do so with some ambivalence. That tradition, to Goode suggests "a very, very dedicated engineer who has very little love of material things, but is wholeheartedly interested in his project and his science, and he's the kind ... who walks around looking like a 'nerd,' very intent on his project.... There's some of them still out there." Richard Ashton, a black Langley engineer with an advanced degree in engineering physics, after 19 years had not progressed beyond a GS-12. Although he insists that he is glad he made his career with NASA, his comment on the Langley tradition strikes a sour note: it's "arrogance," he says; "the attitude that we're the best in the world and no one is better than us ... the feeling that we're superior to everyone else."

Ritual celebrations of the NACA culture — however warranted — might have receded into the backwash of NASA's own institutional life had it not been for the fact that others who completed NASA's initial complement of scientists and engineers came largely from the Navy's research laboratories, from which they brought institutional values similar to those extolled by the NACA group. Transferring directly in 1959 to the new Goddard Space Flight Center, they remember, like their new colleagues from NACA, an intimate, rough and ready, in-house research organization that survived into the 1960s. "I still have the boots that they issued me so we could get to the building if we were first in down the road here," remembers Henry Beacham; "the mud was pretty deep." The first Explorer satellite built at Goddard "went from the building it was built in ... to the test facility ... on a little hand-pulled cart." Getting things done was relatively easy: "It used to be possible to say, 'Gee, this is what we want to do. Let's get together after work and figure out how to do it, propose a new building and get it in the budget in a week's time instead of four years.... We used to take risks, personal risks.... We were bending the rules, but [if] it was the right thing to do and ... we got called on it, we'd just explain it was the right thing to do and we'd go on from there."

Entering Goddard fresh out of college in 1966, Hank Martin has similar memories of problems solved informally by heads bent over a table, or satellites that could be carried in one's hands. "There was a time at Goddard," muses Ernest Cohen, who came to Goddard in 1960, when "if you got an idea, you could run with it. You could build an instrument, or you could do a lot of bootlegging ... getting experiments pushed through that you'd like to see done."

One of the things that makes it easy to get things done in any organization is familiarity and common purpose. That was brought to Goddard by the Navy people was apparent to those who, like Cohen and Frank Toscelli, were not among the original NRL or NOL group. Toscelli remembers Goddard being run by the former Navy people, who quickly moved into the new center's management positions; they "had the previous experience" and "knew each other." At first Toscelli did not mind being something of an outsider because "the work was interesting ... and we were young, and full of enthusiasm." As at the former NACA laboratories, so also at Goddard: the newer staff soon learned to venerate the culture of their predecessors' memory. "I wasn't here in the early years of Goddard," explains Paul Toussault, who did not arrive until 1970; "but talking to people, I can see that it was an exciting time and things got done in a hurry.... The first spacecraft that went to Mars, the first planetary spacecraft, which was *Mariner 4*, from the time of the first concept to the time it actually flew was like a year ... amazing!"

Whether an organization is a private corporation or a public agency, it must market a wanted product or service in order to flourish. Investing in knowledge for its own sake is a long-term proposition, and the conviction that increases in knowledge are desirable is not widely or demonstrably shared in a democratic society suspicious of the "high culture" claims of intellectuals.[11] Historically the federal government has given modest funding to the pursuit of "pure" knowledge through the Office of Naval Research, the National Science Foundation, and the National Endowment for the Humanities; however, not withstanding the claim of disinterestedness with which pure knowledge is distinguished from useful knowledge, even government support of science and the arts and humanities is utilitarian: at the very least there is the expectation that the nation will be somehow enhanced by art, by literature — and very much by science, which conventional wisdom holds to be the wellspring of technological progress.

Advanced technology for national defense has, perforce, dominated the federal government's support of research and technology, and it was the military's approach to managing weapons research and development that led to the managerial device of the R & D "project" and "program." The project (the development of a single entity or system) and the program (a cluster of interrelated projects) became, in effect, products and product lines marketed by the military to Congress and the White House. As the NACA was transformed into NASA, the NACA's more modest aeronautical research role — the "service" it provided the military and aviation industry — was rapidly replaced by the need to direct its research and development know-how to specific projects or programs, in particular, the manned sequence known as the Mercury, Gemini, and Apollo projects leading to the landing of a man on the Moon in 1969.

The effect of this reorientation of the NACA's and NASA's mission on the careers of its engineers was momentous. The design and execution of a successful project became the measure of success, and all of NASA's people were caught up in the annual need to market the agency's projects and programs to Congress in order to obtain the appropriations necessary to maintain themselves. For the last 20 years, insists Bill Cassirer, one of Langley Research Center's most accomplished research engineers, NASA has been caught up in "developing and engineering," not significant research. "When we decided to go with Apollo, we said ... everything else is just expanding the 'state of the art.' There were no more breakthroughs required for Apollo.... The main effort was monitoring, building, developing, and expanding the database so we could build a pump ... [so] we could guarantee success when we made the decision to 'Go.'" Overhead — facilities, advanced sustaining research, administrative support — corporate costs both mundane and noble, but not billable to a particular project, was harder to come by than appropriations for projects and programs. The tyranny of the project and program system over NASA's organizational life can also be explained by the fact that the project or program became the institutional and budgetary umbrella under which contracts were awarded to firms located around the country in the home districts and states of the members of Congress who voted on the agency's budget year after year.

Many engineers who have spent over a decade working for NASA have come to take for granted the project and program as a way of organizing the agency's work. At Ames Research Center, Thomas Swain supposes NASA has only followed a pattern found in private industry, where the emphasis is on projects, and manpower needs can be justified only in relation to them. Fred Hauser arrived at NASA's Marshall Space Flight Center in 1968, at the height of the "boom" times of Apollo. The son of a mechanical engineer for RCA, Hauser's great aspiration is to become a project manager because "if you had to pick one kind of job as being key to NASA ... it is the job of project manager." Langley Research Center, reminisces Richard Ashton, "used to be a big basic research center, but it's not anymore; it's projects, projects.... We are changed from worrying about contributing to man's knowledge of basic research ideas [and] principles to doing very big projects.... This thing is called being 'user friendly'; NASA is changing into a user friendly agency. That means we have to go out and sell ourselves like we have a product ... we have to get customers." The importance of projects and programs is equally evident in Ed Collins's frustration with Langley Research Center's preoccupation with its traditional mission of aeronautical research. Unlike Ashton, Collins thinks Langley did not move far or fast enough to capture projects. Langley's directors did not hustle for "a large chunk of Space Station like Marshall, Johnson, and Goddard [who] have big pieces of it." Langley got "what was left," and "our funding is hurt because of that. We're not on the cutting edge."

Some NASA engineers, however, believe that the added costs of the federal government's project and program system for national R & D are, if not measurable, nonetheless real and substantial. Lacking the promise of ongoing support for a government agency that produces widely appreciated items like national defense, public health, or social security, NASA has had repeatedly to market itself, and never more so than when the "boom" of the Apollo program was followed by the inevitable decline in popular interest that followed the return of Apollo 11. However the elaborate institutional machinery developed to carry out the Apollo program could not easily be disassembled, given the interlocking interests it created among NASA's installations, contractors, and geographic regions represented in Washington.

The Apollo project gave NASA a "job [that] was obviously much bigger than we had people to do. There was almost no limit.... Every center had plenty to do," recalls Werner Posen at Marshall Space Flight Center, "and ... when Apollo was done, we had to really fight for every dollar. It was not clear what NASA's role would be in the long run ... we were really recognizing that our territory [was] going to be restrained, and constrained." That, in Posen's view, was the origin of "the turf battles that are now raging between centers. Everybody wants to become essential; everybody wants to do something that [would cause] the agency [to] go under if they didn't have you." Michael Goldbloom, who has spent all of his NASA career at Headquarters in the Office of Space Sciences, echoes Posen's observation. During the 1960s, he remembers "relatively no intercenter rivalry because the problem there was for each center to get enough competent engineers to do the job, and there was more than enough work to go to every center." After Apollo 11, "several things happened: One was the temporary weakening of support for science and technology ... the product of the 1960s and the Vietnam war." With the "downturn of the NASA budget ... the centers were fighting for a smaller and smaller pie." Had a private corporation faced a comparable market loss, it might have closed a division. But "that is very difficult to do in a political sense for a government agency. What happened was that each of the centers tried to get a wider and wider charter so that they could retain the bulk of their people.... It wasn't a healthy kind of competition, because centers were fighting for their survival."

The consequences were probably natural. The newer space centers — Johnson, Marshall, and Kennedy — were born of space technology projects, especially for the manned space program (the only program, NASA management insisted, that could command sizable public enthusiasm and appropriations). But the older NACA centers struggled to adjust, their fate temporarily obscured by the largesse of Congress in the initial years of the Apollo project. Chances for good work at Lewis Research Center, where Robert Ostrand had worked since 1947, abounded in the early 1960s as the center's staff "doubled from 2500 to 5000 or so." But when Apollo 11 was over, "a thousand people were out of work." While during the 1970s and early 1980s barely 10 percent of the NASA budget went to aeronautical research, the old NACA centers took more than their share of the NASA budget cuts that set in after 1966 as they watched their 11 percent share of 1965 decline to the 7 percent of 1968.

It took a while for the lesson to sink in. The centers would have to capture portions of NASA's big projects, like Lewis's capture of the Space Station power system in 1984. And they would have to harness "the politicians ... so our politicians know who we are and know why they're our representatives." "What was going to save us in the short term," insists Ostrand, "was politics — nothing else would save us. But in the long term we might get ourselves postured [through projects] so that wouldn't happen again." Aeronautical research would have to be supported with funds diverted from major project assignments for sustaining engineering research. For Ronald Siemans, an engineer at Johnson Space Center, it is no revelation that politics is "a tremendous power," like the politics that accompanies a decision about where to locate a project office. "You've got Texas politicians and you've got Mississippi[12] politicians and you've got Ohio politicians and all that get [sic] into the game."

As public support for the civilian space program remained soft (at least, as measured by NASA appropriations, which have not recovered their 1965 level in constant dollars),[13] the number of government employees NASA was able to support continued its steady decline to about two-thirds (in 1988) of the almost 36,000 people on the NASA payroll in 1966. (NASA contractors' employees outnumbered civil servants 3 to 1 in the early 1960s, ballooned to 10 to 1 in 1966, and subsided to about 2 to 1 in the 1980s.[14]) Faced with deteriorating support, NASA executives had a legitimate desire to protect the centers whose most skilled technical employees were essential to the agency's ability to go about its work. One way to protect the agency's human resource was to use it more efficiently. By designating "roles and missions" for each of the centers, NASA attempted to avoid duplication and ensure that each installation had essential functions related to the particular project work assigned to it. Richard Ashton at Langley remembers that in 1976 "we had a reorganization.... Across NASA there was 'roles and missions' rather than all centers doing everything.... We're going to break the whole NASA stable up into various categories: 'Langley, you do aeronautics: the body, the wings, the fuselage, etc. Lewis, you will do the propulsion system for it.' They said, 'Marshall, you will do the rockets. Goddard, you will take care of the atmosphere around the Earth and interrogating and doing what have you with the satellites once they are launched. Houston, you are responsible for manned spaceflight, and Kennedy, you are responsible for [launching] the big rockets. Ames, you are doing environmental quality and deep space planetary stuff.' I used to work in aeronomy, the study of upper atmospheres of this planet and other planets — and that went to Ames.... We used to do helicopter research; that left here." (Ames Research Center took over most of NASA's helicopter research.) Part of the intent of the "roles and missions" concept may have been to reduce intercenter rivalry, but institutional specialization has apparently done little to relieve institutional particularism.

Another device was the "matrix" organization of technical work, so that scientists and engineers would be kept fully occupied in their specialties through the phases and transitions between individual projects. However efficient the "matrix" idea may have been from a management perspective, many engineers experienced it as a means of further splintering work that had already become fragmented by the growing complexity of engineering. Through NASA's matrix system (borrowed from industry), engineers are assigned to functional divisions from which they are detailed to particular projects as needed. Their time and work is charged to the projects in a lease-like arrangement that allows the institution to maintain its science and engineering divisions.

Few engineers seem to have welcomed the opportunity for variation in their work offered by the matrix system. Rather, what they experienced was further disintegration. Next to the need to leave engineering for management to "get ahead," the matrix system is Ernest Cohen's biggest complaint. "The matrix system is the system whereby ... instead of assigning you to a project for 40 hours, they say 'you're going to help this project 20 hours a week and this one 10 hours a week and this one 10 hours a week.' The problem comes in when they both want the 20 and 30 percent at the same time." Cohen would like his work better if, when "you wanted to build an instrument, you had a team report every day full time and [that] team works on it." "The way NASA works," observes Bettylou Sanders at Johnson Space Center, "you can't ever take credit for doing one thing because you always have [only] one piece." Perhaps Cohen's and Sanders's discontent comes from misplaced expectations: Paul Toussault at Goddard may accurately characterize work under the matrix system (and allude to its true origins) when he quips: "It's like somebody working in an automobile factory and they work on part of the thing and it goes on."

Hank Martin at Goddard explains the matrix system this way: "You've got a ... discipline like heat transfer: that's kind of like one column [of engineers] that you've got: heat transfer and power systems, electrical system structures.... And those people are supposed to be smart in those specific systems. Now, where do they apply their smartness? Along the different rows you've got the Space Station project, you've got the Space Telescope project, you've got these other [projects]. So that forms your matrix.... It's not the same thing as working on a focused project with the other people.... You pick up some information, but really appreciating what the other guy is doing ... and maybe giving up some of your design margin because that guy is in trouble ... there was some magic ... you've been involved since day one and when all is said and done, this thing is in orbit.... [There's] that sense of momentum, that sense of teaming with the other people.... I don't think it happens to all the troops involved because the pieces get broken down into such small parts." Martin thinks there is more behind the matrix system than efficiency. "A lot of the ... way we tend to fragment things," he speculates, "is based on lack of willingness to take risks. If you have that rigid structural breaking down of things, it makes everybody feel a lot more comfortable. It allows you to manage by committee, rather than an individual saying, 'Hey, is my neck on the line?'"

How the matrix system relates to the conservatism that inheres in a compulsive avoidance of risk is something of an imponderable. That kind of conservatism, if George Sieger at Johnson Space Center is right, comes not only from the diminished intimacy with a total project that any individual has; it also comes from a diminished intimacy with engineering that NASA's managers have. Engineers "are [making] constant trade-offs between gaining our objectives and risking the flight system. Management has to be willing to accept that same risk, and unless management recognizes what trade-offs we're making and why we're making them and how we're making them," management is ill equipped to make critical choices. Sieger "can't conceive" of a current NASA manager who has enough of an understanding of the technical issues about any one system to confidently affirm — or overrule — an engineering judgment.

David Strickland, who had a decade of experience building missiles for private industry before joining NASA, thinks the size, complexity, and costs of space projects are to blame for the agency's conservatism. "I blew up Atlases on my watch when I was 35. I use that somewhat figuratively. Atlases blew up, and the next day we went to work and we sat down and figured out why we blew that one up and three months later we tried again.... Nobody was looking down his throat because nobody expected perfection then.... The programs have gotten bigger; therefore, our mistakes get more expensive." That space projects should get "bigger," and thus more costly, is a virtual given in NASA's manned space flight program. NASA successfully argued at the end of the 1970s that the cost of relying on "throw-away" boosters to launch humans into space justified developing the Space Transportation System with its reusable Shuttle orbiter. Since then, the notion that NASA should aim for longer stays in space, which require more complex and costly hardware, has become the widely accepted requirement for any new space undertaking — most notably the Space Station Freedom program.[15]

Other engineers, like Toussault, who works in NASA's space science program, do challenge the need for size and complexity. Echoing one of NASA's most articulate outside critics,[16] Toussault speculates that "NASA usually doesn't like those things [inexpensive spacecraft]; they like big projects, really costly." Each project represents jobs to be protected and turf to be expanded: "projects — that's life and death to these centers." So long as the project and program system fosters large, multipurpose and expensive missions, there is little incentive for smaller, less complicated and thus more cost effective ones.[17] "Competition," claims Toussault, "is what makes the [space] program go. As soon as you start cooperating, you're going to have nothing. You're going to start squabbling and then, the next thing you know, nobody does anything. Everybody takes up their marbles and goes home."

———————

The accumulation of knowledge through basic research is at a disadvantage in a world of R & D projects and programs because basic research cannot guarantee a marketable product in the forseeable future. Nor does the matrix organization of engineering work promote basic research, for the intellectual command of a research problem requires continuity of involvement with that problem. Further militating against basic research in the U.S. government's approach to the acquisition of knowledge is its procurement system, which relies on the contract, which must be awarded for an identifiable product or service. Only the basic research grant, awarded to university researchers by NASA and other federal agencies with research as part of their missions, tolerates the spending of revenues for a process that may not lead to a useful outcome. Thus the constituency for federal grant programs has been largely confined to the universities that benefit from them, while the constituency for federal contracting — U.S. industries and the regions whose economic well-being depends on their profits — has remained a strong material supporter of an ideology that favors private over government enterprise generally.

The notion of contracting out was, of course, not novel with the Eisenhower administration. Since the early 19th century the military services had procured goods and services from private suppliers. What the military had *not* wholly relied on for commercial suppliers for was ordnance — hence the U.S. Army's scattered armories, or "arsenal system." The experience of World War II suggested that effective innovation in weapons technology can make the difference between victory and defeat. And in the 20th century innovation in weapons technology was no mere Edisonian enterprise; it required systematic, institutionalized research and development programs.

Ames Research Center's Thomas Swain, who has provided as thoughtful a retrospective on a NACA and NASA career as any of the engineers we interviewed, was able to have something of a global view of the shift to contracting that coincided with the transformation of NACA into NASA. After 1958 "it was obvious" to Swain "that the new organization … was a different animal. It was now part of a much bigger organization and it was suddenly a source of funds. NASA assumed the role of contractor [to the centers], of providing the motivation and the funding for research and development contracts outside of NASA. The NACA didn't work that way; NACA had very little on the outside; it was almost completely an in-house effort." When Ames was "part of NACA," the center had a certain amount of money which it "pretty much had control over [and] spent as they saw fit [in] in-house coordination with the other centers and NACA headquarters, and with the advice of the various … technical committees." Then "there was that shift to a different relationship between the centers and the industry. In the late '40s, the early '50s," recalls Swain, "the companies didn't engage in a lot of exploratory research work; they were pretty narrowly directed toward specific airplane projects." But after 1958 "it was not so much outside people coming in for answers, but coming in looking for contracts. Big aircraft companies, Lockheed or Rockwell, would be just as often approaching NASA with proposals for research work that they do, rather than proposing work that NASA do in-house."

Most NASA engineers' experience of the project and program system has been indirect; they have seen the broader institutional dynamics of the agency shaped by the politics of capturing projects and programs to survive, if not flourish. Reliance on contracting was a necessary accompaniment of the government's unprecedented need to harness talented and industrial capacity to carry out its weapons systems programs, for that capacity was located primarily in the private sector. Contracting, observes Bob Jones, who spent much of his NASA career at Marshall Space Flight Center, "goes clear back to the Army versus the Air Force concept, the in-house Army arsenal versus the Air Force contractor" approach to systems development. "I suspect that you have to do that in this country; a program of that magnitude — Apollo — you had to rely on industry to build those things. Marshall built some of the hardware in the old days themselves, as civil servants." But the hardware required for the manned space flight program "exceeded what Marshall Space Flight Center had done. Marshall even contracted the Redstones out."

Jones and others who have worked mostly at Johnson, Marshall, and Kennedy space centers, take contracting for granted as the only way the agency can go about its business and thus a necessary dimension of a NASA career. But virtually all of NASA's older engineers have seen the substance of their careers directly and immediately distorted by the contracting process, and none more so than those who came to NASA in the expectation of doing research. Robert McConnell, a chemist, came to Lewis Research Center in the early 1950s to do materials research. He remembers when he could "work on a thing [research problem] 3 to 5 years, and either you are [sic] successful or — generally you are successful in *some* degree; we were never unsuccessful…. Maybe you didn't get the answer you were after. You found out something else." Then, in the mid-1970s, he left the section for which he worked when he "saw the writing on the wall … we did less and less basic research…. We're practically devoid of actually looking into a basic research problem now." As McConnell experiences NASA, "people are more interested in — not a [research] finding — but programs. You know, that's the natural consequence of contracting." Lewis Research Center receives "money from NASA Headquarters just like a company receives it from [corporate] headquarters and, therefore, when you say you're going to do something, that's what you're going to do…. Maybe that's the best way … if that's what they want to do, that's fine; but that's not the environment I came into."

For John Songyin, who did research for the National Bureau of Standards before coming to Lewis in 1961, the 1970s was a period when contracting replaced basic research as the center's approach to engine development. The significance of the shift for him, and many others like him, was that instead of doing engineering work himself, he became a "contract monitor," overseeing the project-dedicated work of contractor industrial engineers. The shift to contracting, which at Lewis "really accelerated in the '80s," meant that there was "less and less real technical work that we'd be responsible for in-house. We ourselves would not be doing the hands-on kind of work, but overseeing and monitoring the work of contractors." Songyin's job likewise shifted from engineering to project management, which he's "not as thrilled about … as I was in the early days where I had more hands-on experience." Thomas Alvarin, also at Lewis, once "had a couple of technicians under me…. But at this point, this is just a project office, so mainly the work is contract monitoring." His experience is shared by his Lewis co-worker Matthew O'Day, whose version of what contracting has meant to him is simple: "I like doing the work myself more than giving it to somebody else to do."

The Lewis engineers' difficulty in adapting to contracting mirrors the response of engineers at Langley Research Center, another former NACA laboratory. One after another they complain of the deprivation of inherent interest and excitement of research that occurred as contracting usurped in-house work. "I think contracting is hellified … it's terrible," exclaims Richard Ashton. "There are a lot of new engineers and scientists coming out of school … joining the government, expecting to do great things, get hands-on experience. They can't do that because we're contracting the stuff out. Our computer facilities … we don't have a single NASA employee that works there." Ed Collins, who brought unusual experience for the time in integrated optics to Langley, had hoped to build a small laboratory at the center in the field, but he was told, "Ed, that is not the way we do things at Langley anymore. We're going contracts; all we want you to do is stay technical enough that you can monitor the contract efficiently. We don't want you in a lab."

Bill Cassirer also sees NASA following the Air Force pattern, and thinks the practice of contracting is ruining the agency's ability to do any good research. "At Wright Patterson Air Force Base," he alleges, "they used to do some real good research work early before World War II. And then they suddenly became nothing more than a bunch of contract monitors; they put out nothing of significance for years.[18] We have had some contract monitors here, and the poor guys, they just lose. First of all, you never really assign the sharpest people to the contract monitor [job] because you don't want to tie them down with the burden. The people that you do assign normally have some good ability; but after they have been contract monitors for a couple of years, they've lost that…. It's a great way to lose your research inertia." The transition to contracting sets in motion a cycle which makes it yet more difficult for the government to maintain its own engineering know-how. Engineers like Henry Blackwell at Langley, who tried to maintain their proficiency, found the going tough. Blackwell works in computerized data acquisiton at Langley and has watched a friend of his scooped in a research project. "About the time he'd gotten all of his ducks together to publish, here comes this article by a guy in one of the trade publications, the same stuff! The guy was consistently beating him to publication. Part of it was the procurement cycle: Because he was a glamour boy in the industry, all he had to do was say, 'I need this,' and 2 weeks later, he's got it." Blackwell's friend, on the other hand, "would say, 'I need this,' and then he'd have to draw up this [procurement request] and go out for bids, and evaluate the bids, and then we'd evaluate, and then we'd do this and that and so on … a lot of people got discouraged," and, as a consequence, thinks Blackwell, "we've gotten away from the forefront of innovation, development." His own section "in the last couple of years ... has become proposal and contract writers and monitors ... more or less an extension of procurement." Contracting out may "save the government money. But how about morale? Now industry is just outstripping us." Even if contracting out for engineering could be justified because "good people ... are smart enough to have gone outside to another company and are getting more money than we are," argues Ed Beckwith, the technical people left behind end up providing free training to the lower-level skilled personnel that industry hires. Beckwith claims, "I spend an awful lot of my time training contractors or working with them to do the same job over and over again ... because the contractor keeps pulling in new people [to replace] those people who left."

Marshall Space Flight Center, although not a former NACA center, was an in-house operation in its earlier incarnation as an Army installation. Like their fellow engineers at Langley, Ames, and Lewis, Marshall's engineers are restive with a system that relies on contractors for engineering as well as support services. Sam Browning began working for the Army Ballistic Missile Agency in 1956 after earning his degree in chemical engineering. By the mid-1960s Marshall had made the transition: "We didn't do a great deal in-house in those days ... which was sad.... I didn't really get to go into the laboratory and get hands-on type stuff, which I would have loved. I had to go visit a contractor's facility, who [sic] was having all the fun.... I came up with the ideas or picked them up from other people, and we secured funding from Headquarters to go fund the activity, and we'd award a contract to some propulsion company." Browning feels a personal loss from having been denied opportunities to accumulate his own experience with advanced propulsion systems — but the loss is not just his. He is currently working on a laser propulsion project that is "almost more research than technology, because we had to establish that you can, in fact, sustain a stable plasma in hydrogen supported by a high-powered laser." The work involves "an awful lot of high-temperature physics and computational flow dynamics, and a lot of other good stuff I don't know much about.... My frustration with that is that I don't understand enough about it to be able to intelligently guide the people who are working on the program."

Although NASA engineers who began their careers working for the NACA or who work in former NACA laboratories appear most sensitive to the loss of in-house research opportunities as a result of NASA's reliance on contracted work, engineers at post-1958 NASA centers (Johnson, Kennedy, and Goddard) are even more aware of the hidden costs of contracting. Paul Toussault and Frank Toscelli at Goddard both lament the loss of "in-house expertise," and do so especially because of NASA's increased reliance on contractors. "If you haven't really done some of the stuff once in your life and really gotten involved with it," insists Toussault, "then I don't see how you're going to be able to be a good monitor of these contracts."

Richard Williams at Kennedy likewise complains about NASA's reliance on contractors; for those who would argue that the nation does not suffer a loss of engineering know-how as a result — it only shifts it to the private sector — he has an answer: "Industry, on its own, is not going to be doing the type of things that we need to be doing." For example, in developing the Space Station, "we ought to be looking at new and innovative ways of manufacturing, putting this whole thing together. If we don't do it, it's not going to be done." Or there is the notion, a cornerstone of President Ronald Reagan's space policy issued in 1988, that the private sector should take over launch services, for which the government would be a buyer: "Every one of the contractors has come back and said 'it's not commercially, economically feasible.... Without government support [we won't do it]." In terms of "overall, long-range benefits, without government support, we're going to lose ground."

It could also be argued that a policy that builds aerospace engineering talent and know-how in the private sector is inherently sound public policy, since the federal government has always had to rely on the private sector to produce essential items during a national emergency. The Apollo program, which relied almost entirely on contracts to private industry, was certainly as much an industry as a government agency's triumph. But failures, such as the 1967 fire on the Apollo 204 spacecraft in which three astronauts perished, inevitably raise questions about the degree of vigilance the government can or will exercise over its contractors, especially if the technical expertise is weighted on the side of industry.[19]

The issue has persisted, especially at the manned spacecraft centers. The costs of missed opportunities in research are long term and difficult to assess in any event. But at Johnson Space Center and Kennedy Space Center, the two NASA installations with primary responsibility for NASA's largest program, human space flight, complex operations with low error tolerance are a fact of daily life; thus, the costs of failure can be immediate and severe. The tragedy of the Challenger accident in January 1986 was felt throughout NASA, but arguably most personally at Johnson and Kennedy Space Centers. Yet it did not take the Challenger accident for one of Johnson's most experienced flight operations engineers to become uneasy about the consequences of contracting for the reliability of space flight operations.

Managers at NASA Headquarters, observed George Sieger in the autumn of 1985, fail to recognize "the synergism that has always existed between operations and engineering; they tend to consider the operating element as a luxury [and thus] feel they can contract out the operating element." But, warned Sieger, "as they move further in that direction, we will find ourselves in the same position of impotence that I think the Nuclear Regulatory Commission ... as well as the Department of Transportation, as well as the military services [are in]." During the aftermath of a serious nuclear reactor fuel cooling misfunction at Three Mile Island in Pennsylvania in 1979, Sieger worked for 3 years on post-accident studies with the Nuclear Regulatory Commission and a variety of utility operators and contractors. He came away from that experience believing that "the healthiest nuclear plant operator" was Duke Power, because "they do their own design, they do their own engineering. They do not hire an integration contractor to build their facilities; they manage their contracts and then they operate the plant," as do many European utilities. At the heart of Sieger's concern is the belief that contracting out operations severs a vital communications link between managers, engineers, and operators that must be preserved if operations are to be effective and reliable. However, the weakening link between operations and engineering that disturbs Sieger is only part of his larger concern, which is (as he sees it) the hemorrhage of NASA's hard-won engineering skills to industry. During "the first 25 years of the space program," he argues, "NASA managed to grow a good percentage of the engineers that were necessary to manage the program, and they were good managers. Where they were deficient, they would go out to industry to bring [in] the strong corporate management philosophy." But since the end of the 1970s "we have moved ... away from that philosophy.... We are weakening our overall [technical] base to manage not only the Space Transportation System, but ... the Space Station program." For Philip Siebold at Johnson, NASA's increasing dependence on contractors has been accompanied by decreasing vigilance over their work. "When we started manned systems" in the early 1960s, he recalls "we were so concerned about the loss of a man that we very much did the whole field. We felt that two sets of eyes were better than one. In the Apollo program," for example, "we were very much in their program.... The reason we had so many inspectors is every time they had an inspection point, we had an inspection point." But "in the last few years we — government — are trying to get away with doing less in company plants.... Today we may only have one [inspector] for every four or five or so of theirs. We look at what they have done, rather than do it ourselves, in a lot of the detailed inspection functions; we do more of a verification and an overlook, [rather] than doing so much of the individual work ourselves."

In 1985 this trend did not particularly trouble Siebold. While he recognized that there was "not less criticality," he was confident that "we have learned to do things better. Our learning curve has gone up, and we have much more redundancy built into the system today." Another Johnson Space Center engineer, Ronald Siemans, was also comfortable with the shift of the critical mass of aerospace engineering expertise to industry through contracting: "We've got many more contractors now involved. They're all getting knowledgable about the systems, where just a year ago, we had nobody who knew anything.... Now you've got many contractors that know about the job; they may not know all the details, but two years from now they'll have had time to study, they'll have had time to get their experts, they'll have had time to hire college graduates out of college. That's what this was all about — to get industry up." But two years turned out to be too long.

That George Sieger had cause to worry was borne out by the Challenger accident that occurred a few months later. At Kennedy Space Center, whose engineers we interviewed after the Challenger accident, that event has heightened their concern about the use NASA makes of contractors — now not only for support service, engineering, and operations, but to essentially manage themselves. "The new contracts that we have," notes Hank Smith at Kennedy Space Center, "they [the contractors] have been given a mission. For example ... the base operations contract: [the contractor's] mission is base operations. They run the fire trucks, they have the cops. They paint the buildings, they fix the roofs. They do the air conditioning. We define the mission; they accept it. They are responsible for cost management and technical performance. If they don't do good, you downgrade them." Smith is refering to the "mission contract," a logical answer to the need to contract not only for particular end items or levels of effort, as in the case of ongoing services, but for functional areas like building construction and computer maintenance as well. The mission contract presents no problem for Smith "because there's not a whole lot of criticality to it. Mission contracts for space operations, however, are something else. "The business of Shuttle processing and launching — I think that's just too critical to turn over to a contractor. Management needs to be involved in that processing work. I don't think any one contractor can do the whole thing; it's too big a job."

Not only is the job too big, but accountability is spread too thin. "See," says Smith, the contractor is "responsible to check himself also. Now NASA's ultimately responsible, but I don't think [its responsibility goes] deep enough." He is keenly sensitive to the fact that NASA was held responsible by the media and post-accident inquiries for the Challenger accident. That being so, he thinks NASA must exercise more intensive oversight than what accompanies the mission contract. "In base operations, that's fine; we don't need to be responsible for the fire trucks," allows Smith. "But the intricate stuff — the critical stuff — I think NASA needs to be more involved. I just don't think you can say 'OK, Mr. Lockheed. Everything wonderful?' And he says, 'Oh yeah,' and you walk away. That's just too much."[20] But he is resigned: "Management has put down the edict that that's the way it will be." Smith's co-worker at Kennedy, Eleanor Finch, shares his reservations. "Contractors are in business to make money.... And they really don't care a lot of times whether the job gets done or not, nor do they even really know what the job is, sometimes. And NASA needs to remind them of what the job is. Day by day. And that is what the contract monitor role was." Finch says "was," because in the late 1970s the management consulting firm of Booz-Allen Hamilton recommended that Kennedy Space Center substantially reduce the number of contract monitors overseeing day-to-day contract activities. Booz-Allen argued that a great deal of money could be saved if NASA were willing to settle for periodic reports from contractors. NASA's euphemism for reduced supervision is "self-sufficiency," an attribute of Kennedy Space Center's comprehensive mission contracts. Self-sufficiency, explains Finch, "means that the contractor can make more decisions on his own without coming to NASA for guidance." She has managed contracts "both ways. You can't get much out of a report. You have to go down there and talk to those people and find out what the heck they're doing." And if you don't like what they're doing, "once you've turned the contract monitor [role] off, it's very hard to turn it around."

Discontent with contracting is by no means uniform among NASA's Apollo era engineers, nor is it apparently a consequence simply of the Challenger accident. There were engineers with whom we spoke, after as well as before the accident, and who had worked at NASA centers with earlier "in-house" traditions, who were content with the system. Both Fred Hauser and Dan O'Neill at Marshall Space Flight Center, for example, say their experience working with contractors has been positive. Hauser has "a lot of confidence in them," while O'Neill "can't think of a single bad experience" he's had with a contractor. Indeed, he finds that "the most fun is being involved with them.... We have, normally, pretty well structured contracts, so we know what they're supposed to do.... Working with the contractor on a problem that you have some interest in ... [on] the evolution of a solution ... can be very exciting." Marshall's Joseph Totten is also comfortable working with contractors, over whom, he feels, Marshall exercises close, reliable supervision.

In fact, Totten implies that the availability of contractors may be something of a Godsend, since NASA, a federal agency, would have difficulty putting any significant number of technical people on its civil service rolls. "The labor rates," he explains, "are quite a bit different, for one thing. Those people [contractors] can hire lower level journeymen than we can hire.... Our people here are almost of an age that all of them can retire, so that means they're probably at the top of whatever pay level they're at ... whereas a contractor can pay ten dollars an hour and beat us all to get out." Totten takes the global view: "What we have out here is a national facility ... a national asset. Right now, because of the lack of technicians, we cannot utilize it the way it should be utilized." But "eventually," with the help of contracting, "we're going to have to get around to providing that capability.... From the design and from the engineering side, I think we're going to retain that capability." At NASA Headquarters, Langley Research Center, and Ames Research Center, one can also find engineers who have turned into contract monitors and enjoy it. If their working relationship with their contractors is cooperative and productive, contracting, at least for engineering, may provide them access to a level and depth of professional work they might not otherwise have.

Whatever the merits of NASA engineers' views of the steady movement toward almost total agency reliance on contractors, that movement is likely to be sustained by the same rationales that led to government contracting in the first place. So also the other dimension of organizational life at NASA — the expansion of bureaucracy — which is no less likely to persist, inasmuch as it is endemic to any large organization carrying out a complicated enterprise. NASA's engineers complain bitterly of bureaucracy, its frequent absurdities, its incessant drain on one's time and energies, as do most employees struggling against paper barriers, hierarchical protocols, and the shackles of central administration everywhere. On this subject they are merely sections of a larger chorus and have little to add that is peculiar to NASA. But they are not wholly devoid of observations that suggest forces exacerbating the tendency toward bureaucratization in the nation's civilian space program.

One of those forces is procurement — contracting — which contributes its own special mound of paperwork and procedures to comply with the latest federal acquisitions regulations. At Langley Ed Beckwith ventilates vexation: "I'm right now in the throes of trying to get a purchase request through so I can get two contracts without going through a full and open competition." In Langley's procurement organization "they start talking to you about a JOFOC [Justification for Other Than Full and Open Competition]. I didn't know what that was. My memos should not have to go into detail to tell them how I ought to do this to get this contract out. My memo should say this is the reason for that.... Oh, Lord! You can see the frustration!" The reason for sluggishness in the procurement process, explains Henry Beacham at Goddard Space Flight Center, "is fear. Fear of getting a protest on a contract award. After you deal with a couple of them the system tells itself,

'We'll never let that happen again.'" And the way to prevent protests on a contract award is to cross every 't' and dot every 'i' in a complex procedure designed to ensure that every eligible individual or firm has been given a fair shake in the scramble for government funds.

On those rare and wonderful occasions when a courageous individual has used "the system" to get something done or, when that was impossible, has circumvented the system, it is because an individual has exercised independent judgment and exceptional powers of persuasion. The ability of an organization to nurture such individuals is an important element in its battle against bureaucratic ossification. But there are some NASA engineers who think their organization has failed to cultivate such individuals, even if they arrived at NASA well equipped to exercise independent judgment and to persuade. Robert McConnell at Lewis Research Center does not think they do. Newer and younger engineers may arrive at NASA with more advanced engineering skills, he concedes, but "in the area of liberal arts, sometimes I find it appalling — their inability to write." And "in some areas, like overall engineering judgment, there seems to be an inadequacy, but I guess you would expect that; it's something that comes with experience."

And then there's the passion for anonymity, the fabled virtue of the civil servant that appears too often as a refuge from accountability. If Hank Martin at Goddard could change anything, he "would change the cover your ass attitude.... It's making no one responsible: 'Well, this committee decided,' or 'it was the consensus of everybody,' so nobody's responsible." Always liable to intense public scrutiny, and with a mission that its critics claim is marginal and thus perpetually in danger of dissolution, NASA may be especially prone to facelessness. Derek Roebling and Bill Cassirer, at places as different as Kennedy Space Center and Langley Research Center, agree that the way NASA has adapted to its political circumstances and environment has much to do with the degree to which it is afflicted by the worst handicaps of a bureaucracy. Roebling sees, most of all, a "cultural change" as the "major" change to have occurred within the agency. With the massive organizational mobilization required to carry out the Apollo program, NASA "became very institutionalized," he asserts, and was soon transformed into a "corporate bureaucracy." More important, "the agency has matured from a small group without an agency culture into another federal agency. I imagine it's probably just as difficult to get things done in the Veterans Administration. We're no longer the laboratory; we're now the administrative kind of thing.... Bureaucratization was carried to extremes in many cases ... [with] increased complexity, less personal responsibility, and more organizational responsibilities achieved through division, multiple signatures, checks and balances, more reviews, more meetings, more formal systems to keep track of different items," and the replacement of "personal responsibility" by "organizational hierarchy."

If the worst excesses of bureaucracy are to be mitigated at all, they will be mitigated by those with the power to establish (or eliminate) administrative procedures, or at least mediate between externally imposed administrative procedures and the organization's own preferred ways of going about its business. This is a role that only NASA's senior management can play. However, NASA's engineers doubt that their own management are likely allies in the struggle against bureaucracy; perversely, they may be the flywheel in the engine of bureaucracy. Roebling suspects that the agency is increasingly held sway by managers who have distanced themselves from the actual business of working with hardware. NASA has changed "from the small NACA [of the] 1950s, X-series aircraft kind of operation, to this huge conglomeration where you have people who never go within three miles of flight hardware," leaving the organization enmeshed in "an enormous infrastructure of people who are not actively involved" in, and thus unlikely to have a genuine sympathy for, the agency's actual work. A veteran of many years in both the NACA and NASA, Robert Strong believes that if a project has been "well managed" at the start, "once a concept has jelled," it should "more or less flow evenly." Thus he suspects that there is a link between management's remoteness from engineering work and a proclivity to "micromanagement at high levels," which he finds as pronounced at NASA's research centers as at NASA Headquarters.

The association of status with managerial positions may encourage a clubbish self-isolation. Werner Posen compares the hierarchical distances in Marshall Space Flight Center's current organization to the 1950s, when, as branch head, he had regular conversations with Wernher von Braun. He observes: "I don't think that our center directors today talk to people of my level." Posen may also have benefited from a certain clubbishness among emigre Germans at Marshall. Be that as it may, Posen's co-worker at Marshall, Joseph Totten, echoes the view that much of the frustration of bureaucratization in NASA comes from excessive top-down micromanagement, from center managers as well as Headquarters. He concedes that NASA is "a government operation … public surveillance is always there, and we have to live with that." But he does not "believe we need this reporting in minute detail, [and] we do ourselves a disservice by our top management not letting us have a little more free reign in our activities."

The irony, of course, is that the managers of whom Totten and others complain were, once upon a time, NASA engineers. What happens when engineers become managers? Do they attempt to exercise the same vigilance over detail — a vigilance in which external forces conspire — over the human processes of organizational life as they once did when they were designing aircraft and engines? Ed Beckwith at Langley Research Center is convinced that NASA's management is incapable of resisting external pressures that produce a bureaucratic mentality. "Today," he complains, "even center directors say 'I'm sorry, I can't do anything about that. Headquarters says this or the Congress says this.' You would never hear those [earlier NACA] people say that; you would see smoke. In the management position now, we don't have anybody to respect.… They just sit back and count beans."

———————

The changes NASA's engineers perceive in the agency, its environment, and their careers reflect not only actual changes, but also the experiences and values they have shared during the most formative years of their careers. When talking with those scientists and engineers about "change," one learns, albeit indirectly, about a common culture that has been disturbed by events and the passage of time. As these men and women talk about change, they talk about computers, specialization, and fragmentation. And when they talk about NASA as a changing place, their talk often turns to loss: the loss of youthful creativity and energy in a maturing organization struggling with the stultifying forces of bureaucracy, the loss of an innovative research culture transformed by federal policy into a large procurement and contract management organization, and the loss of national purpose behind the peaceful mobilization which once played so great a role in the definition of their lives.

---

[1] For one view of the decade, see Allen J. Matusow, *The Unraveling of America: A History of Liberalism in the 1960s* (New York: Harper & Row, 1984).

[2] Robert A. Divine, Lyndon B. Johnson and the Politics of Space, in Robert A. Divine, ed., *The Johnson Years: Vietnam, the Environment, and Science*, Vol. II (University Press of Kansas, 1987), pp. 217-253.

[3] Computer-assisted design/computer-assisted manufacturing.

[4] A device which first appeared in 1960 and amplifies light through the stimulated emission of radiation. Whereas conventional light sources emit light that is diffuse or incoherent, the lazer produces a high-energy, coherent wave phase light used increasingly for micromachining and microsurgery as well "reading" minute measurements and other electromagnetically recorded information.

[5] See, for example, Sandra Jansen's account in chapter 3 of the transition from manual calculators to microcomputers used to gauge engine pressures at Lewis Research Center.

[6] Equations of motion for viscous fluids whose molecular viscosity is large enough to make the viscous forces a significant part of the total force field in the fluid. Derived from Stokes's Law of Bodies moving through viscous fluids, first formulated by Sir George Gabriel Stokes, British mathematician and physicist (1819-1903).

[7] There were three series of Pioneer spacecraft: the unsuccessful Pioneer lunar probes (1958-1960) NASA inherited from the Defense Department Advance Research Projects Agency; the four successful Pioneer interplanetary probes flown from 1960 through 1968; and the successful Pioneer-Jupiter, Pioneer-Saturn, and Pioneer-Venus solar system escape missions launched between 1972 and 1978.

[8] For an excellent and brief discussion of the NASA acquisition process, see Arnold S. Levine, *Managing NASA in the Apollo Era*, NASA SP-4102 (Washington, D.C.:U.S. Government Printing Office, 1982), chapter 4. For background, see Danhof, *Government Contracting*, and Peck and Scherer, *The Weapons Acquisitions Process*, loc. cit.

[9] See Richard P. Hallion, *On the Frontier: Flight Research at Dryden, 1946-1981*, NASA SP-4303 (Washington, D.C.: U.S. Government Printing Office, 1984) and Laurence K.

Loftin, Jr., *Quest for Performance: The Evolution of Modern Aircraft*, NASA SP-468 (Washington, D.C.: U.S. Government Printing Office, 1985), chapter 11.

[10] One of NACA's leading aeronautical researchers for transonic flight, Stack joined Langley Aeronautical Laboratory in 1928 and remained with the NACA to be transferred in 1958 with many of his colleagues to the new NASA.

[11] For classic discussions of popular American attitudes toward intellectual life, see Alexis de Tocqueville, *Democracy in America*, Francis Bowen, trans. (New York: Alfred A. Knopf, 1945) and Richard Hofstadter, *Anti-Intellectualism in American Life* (New York: Alfred A. Knopf, 1962).

[12] Location of NASA's Mississippi Test Facility, acquired in 1961 and renamed the National Space Technology Laboratories (NSTL) in 1974. Site of testing for the Saturn rocket stages and sea-level testing of the Space Shuttle's main engine, as well as environmental and resource work for other government agencies, the NSTL was renamed the John C. Stennis Space Center in 1988 after Stennis, a member of the U.S. Senate for over 40 years and Chairman of the Senate Appropriations Subcommittee. Stennis was responsible for the establishment of NSTL.

[13] "Towards A New Era in Space: Realigning Policies to New Realities," Committee on Space Policy, National Academy of Sciences and National Academy of Engineering (National Academy Press: Washington, D.C., 1988), Figure 1, p. 6.

[14] Jane Van Nimmen and Leonard C. Bruno with Robert L. Rosholt, *NASA Historical Data Book: NASA Resources, 1958-1968*, Vol. I, SP-4012 (Washington, DC: U.S. Government Printing Office, 1988), p. 118 and *NASA Pocket Statistics* (Washington, D.C.: U.S. Government Printing Office, 1986), p. C-27). Numbers of contractor employees can only be estimated.

[15] See Sylvia D. Fries, 20001 to 1994: Political Environment and the Design of NASA's Space Station System," *Technology and Culture*, Vol. 29, No. 3 (July 1988).

[16] Freeman Dyson, Science and Space, in *Infinite in All Directions* (New York: Harper & Row, 1988).

[17] For an entertaining and pithy account of the costing of government research and development programs, see Norman R. Augustine, *Augustine's Laws and Major System Development Programs* (New York: American Institute of Aeronautics and Astronautics, 1983).

[18] Needless to say, U.S. Air Force system program managers at Wright Patterson might have sound reasons to disagree with Cassirer.

[19] See Ivan D. Ertel and Roland W. Newkirk, with Courtney G. Brooks, *The Apollo Spacecraft: A Chronology*, Vol. IV, NASA SP-4009 (Washington, DC: U.S. Government Printing Office, 1978).

[20] NASA contracted with Lockheed Space Operations in 1983 to perform Space Shuttle launch and landing activities at the Kennedy Space Center and on behalf of

the U.S. Air Force at Vandenberg Air Force Base, including operation of related ground systems at both launch sites. Lockheed's Shuttle processing contract was the second comprehensive missions contract awarded by NASA; E G & G was awarded a comprehensive base operations contract at Kennedy in 1982.

Epilog

And so, they stayed. These engineers' tolerance for the changes that have enveloped them comes partly from the realization that the grass isn't always greener on the other side. Henry Beacham, who complains despairingly of bureaucratic impediments at Goddard Space Flight Center, recalls having worked for the Eastman Kodak Company after World War II. "I wasn't married," he remembers; "I didn't know the city, I was learning. So I used to like to stay at my desk. We had time cards. I had to punch out. All of a sudden I found out my boss was having me justify my overtime, so I learned that the thing to do was go punch out and come back to my desk." "I know a lot of young people make a lot more money when they go out into companies," concedes Marylyn Goode at Langley Research Center, "but I very often feel that the working atmosphere in companies is sometimes not as good as it is around here. And even the freedom — you know, we have things we have to work on, but there is a certain amount of freedom in how we do it."

With a doctorate in physics, now working on developing new programs for computational fluid dynamics at Ames Research Center, Richard Lockwood distinguishes between the relative latitude of working in "fundamental" and "applied" or project research; it is the engineers working in fundamental research who enjoy the greater freedom to do what interests them. "We're expected to just go out and try to push the frontiers back wherever we can," he explains, "and management tells us which parts of the frontier they'd like to see pushed back." Lockwood's own boss "isolates us pretty well, lets us do pretty much what we want. The freedom we get and the support, in terms of equipment and facilities that we get make the job fun enough that you can afford to give up the bigger salary" offered by industry. NASA — as experienced at Ames Research Center — "has got to be one of the better places for someone who wants to be a research person," thinks Abraham Bauer; the agency "does give freedom to people ... to work up to their maximum capability. And the problems are challenging."

Another "research person" at Ames, Thomas Swain, adds: "We have an opportunity which may not be appreciated by some of the young engineers as much as it should be, and that is [that] there are so many different things going on in the center, so many different disciplines — that [you have] the opportunity to look around, if ... the work that you're doing just isn't quite as exciting to you as what you see over in that other building [and] ... to follow your bent within the organization. I've seen a number of people do that with marvelous benefits to their careers, because they not only get to follow what they're interested in, but by the time they've made a few changes, they've broadened their background." Swain thinks that "there's a lot more individual work done within NASA" than in industry; the larger proportion of his own work is research he has chosen for himself.

Traces of the older culture of the in-house laboratory have also survived at Marshall Space Flight Center, where Fred Hauser appreciates a "flexibility" and "freedom" that he and others have experienced. "We have extremely talented, ambitious, diligent people that are allowed to exercise their diligence and ambition." If Sarah McDonald had her career to do over again, she would still work at Marshall, where she has relished "the sense of independence, ability to do the work, authority ... decision-making responsibilities, and freedom," all of which she doubts she would have had working in industry.

There are even engineers who question the notion of bureaucratization's baleful consequences. Willie Miller and Hank Smith at Kennedy Space Center deny that they have been plagued by an excess of bureaucratic procedure, while Smith points out, what has become increasingly true of much of the agency, that "NASA is really a technical management organization." Part of Miller's and Smith's tolerance of bureaucratic procedures may be due to the fact that they were interviewed after the Challenger accident, one effect of which was serious criticism of NASA's safety procedures. Thus does Derek Roebling even find merit in bureaucratization: "I think the good part was [that one] of those things that came out of [the post Challenger investigation] was the stronger emphasis [on] and formation of separate safety functions. I think those kinds of checks and balances are good."

The attributes of their NASA careers that have most inspired Philip Siebold and Michael Goldbloom are attributes that do not readily succumb to a single, dramatic failure. Still, Siebold's almost boisterous enthusiasm might have been somewhat dampened had he been interviewed after the Challenger accident, and not before. "I'm happy with NASA," declared Siebold from the vantage of pre-Challenger Johnson Space Center; "it's been good to me. I've enjoyed it. I like what I do. I guess the fact that we are the drivers, really, rather than the contractors. We're sitting at the top of the table. So, let's face it, we all like power. And you have a little more power if you're at NASA ... we probably work harder than anybody. We're more dedicated, hard driving. We never care how many hours we work, and what needs to be done, we go out and do it."

Goldbloom offers a somewhat more philosophical appreciation than Siebold, who exudes the "can do" attitude of NASA during the height of the Apollo program, when Siebold worked with launch operations at Kennedy Space Center. Notwithstanding a considerable loss of "esprit de corps" and bureaucratizaton, Goldbloom thinks that NASA's exploratory mission provides "intellectual content" to work that could not be found in industry, which, he thinks, is generally the better employer. Wherever engineers can still do hands-on work there is an "excitement" that comes from "working in the new frontier areas of technology." For Goldbloom, innovative engineering at NASA combines with "the sheer exploration ... that appeals to Americans — wanting to see what's on the other side of the hill, wanting to probe the unknown, expanding man's vista to new frontiers" that has made NASA, in Goldbloom's experience, a place "where for the most part it's a sheer joy to work."

Few of the engineers we interviewed allude to job security as a reason for staying with NASA; and, in any event, it is arguable whether jobs are ultimately more secure in the government, which has its own "reductions in force." On the other hand, many an engineer's job was lost in the early 1970s post-Apollo letdown in the aerospace industry. The only engineer who outright explained his choice of working for NASA as the desire for a secure, government job is also the only engineer we interviewed who remembers having been raised in a level of affluence that included servants, nannies, and private tutors. For most of the engineers of the Apollo era, establishing themselves in an engineering career was in itself an enormous achievement.

Beneficiaries of one of the great engines of social change — war — this generation succeeded in crossing the great American divide between the working class and the salaried middle class. Many did so consciously, purposefully choosing engineering as their vehicle. Having done so, they became ready recruits in another war, a war to preserve the bi-polar world that survived the conflagration of World War II. Footsoldiers in John F. Kennedy's "world-wide struggle ... to preserve and promote" American ideals against the "adversaries of freedom," these men and women made careers in the midst of a battle to exploit technology in the peaceful quest of American supremacy in the air and in outer space.

Before the end of that momentous decade in which the National Aeronautics and Space Administration and the armies of the U.S. aerospace industry succeeded in meeting Kennedy's challenge, the battleground had begun to shift under their feet. The idealism with which the 1960s opened turned sour before the decade was out. The era that began with the election of John F. Kennedy ended in the killing fields of Cambodia and Viet Nam, on the pavement at Kent State University, and in the corridors of Washington's Watergate hotel and office complex.[1] Success became as much a matter of survival as of achievement, whether in politics or in organizational life — both of which would have more to do with the nature of these engineers' careers than they could have imagined. The nation abandoned the battle for supremacy in space, partly because it was never wholly clear what — beyond Apollo — supremacy meant. Even though the Soviet Union began its virtually continuous occupation of its orbiting space station Salyut in 1971, as of 1989 the probability of a U.S. orbiting station being deployed in space by the mid-1990s was by no means certain. No policy existed for the demobilization of the troops who had fought in Kennedy's moral equivalent of war, men and women who were left stranded to cope with the vast machinery of institutional survival.

On the 20th anniversary of the Apollo landing, another president issued a call for another great adventure in space: a return to the Moon and a human expedition to Mars. But the magic of that earlier challenge is gone: the Challenger accident in January 1986, the intractability of federal budgetary politics, and the confusion surrounding the question of this country's future place in the world have produced a growing policy debate about the purpose and means of a continuing American role in space.[2] Skeptics demur, and believers take heart, urging the nation to ensure once again that a new generation of men and women well trained in science and engineering will be both ready and inspired to risk their personal aspirations and careers on another bold adventure beyond our planet.

----

[1] On April 30, 1970 U.S. and South Vietnamese forces invaded Cambodia to destroy North Vietnamese staging areas. Four days later violence erupted during an anti-war demonstration at Kent State University in Ohio, and National Guard troops opened fire on students; four were killed and eleven wounded. On June 17, 1972 five men were arrested for breaking into the offices of the Democratic National Committee in the Watergate complex in Washington, D.C. They turned out to have been working for the Committee to Reelect the President (Richard M. Nixon). In 1974 the House voted articles of impeachment against Nixon for White House efforts to "coverup" its role in the break-in. Nixon resigned from office August 9 in anticipation of the House action. The Viet Nam war nominally ended with the signing of the Paris Peace accords in January 27, 1973; the end of the U.S. military draft was announced that same day, and the last U.S. troops left at the end of March.

[2] See, for example, Radford Byerly, Jr., ed., *Space Policy Reconsidered* (Boulder: University of Colorado, 1989).

Appendixes

Appendix A

NASA Managers Solicited for Names of "Representative" NASA Engineers

In 1984, Dr. Hans Mark, NASA Deputy Administrator, asked the following present or former top NASA managers (letter of April 19, 1984) to provide the author with names of "individual members" of "NASA's pioneering generation of aerospace engineers" who, in their view, "reflect those characteristics which have typified NASA during its first quarter century." Ms. Josephine Dibella, who served as secretary to NASA's associate deputy administrator from 1959 to 1965, was also asked by Dr. Mark to suggest names. Of the 42 persons of whom Dr. Mark made this request, 25 responded, providing a total of 621 names. The named individuals constitute the "nominee" group referred to in Appendix B, Demographic Tables. In the following list, only the NASA management positions of highest rank are given for each person listed.

NAME	POSITION
Lew Allen	Director, Jet Propulsion Laboratory (in 1984)
Robert O. Aller	Associate Administrator, Office of Space Tracking and Data Systems (in 1984)
John F. Clark	Director, Goddard Space Flight Center, 1965-1976
Edgar M. Cortright	Director, Langley Research Center, 1968-1975
Philip E. Culbertson	Associate Deputy Administrator (in 1984)
Josephine Dibella	Secretary to the Associate Deputy Administrator, 1959-1965
William F. Ballhaus, Jr.	Director, Ames Research Center (in 1984)

John W. Boyd	Associate Administrator, Office of Management (in 1984)
June Gibbs Brown	Inspector General (in 1984)
Burton I. Edelson	Associate Administrator, Office of Space Science and Applications (in 1984)
Stuart J. Evans	Assistant Administrator for Procurement (in 1984)
Robert R. Gilruth	Director, Manned Spacecraft Center, 1961-1972
Robert H. Gray	Deputy Director of Launch Operations, Kennedy Space Center (in 1984)
Donald P. Hearth	Director, Langley Research Center (in 1984)
Noel W. Hinners	Director, Goddard Space Flight Center (in 1984)
I. Jerry Hlass	Director, National Space Technology Laboratories (in 1984; in 1988 the NSTL was renamed the John C. Stennis Space Center
S. Neil Hosenball	General Counsel (in 1984)
Roy P. Jackson	Associate Administrator, Office of Advanced Research and Technology, 1970-1973
Harriet G. Jenkins	Assistant Administrator, Office of Equal Opportunity Programs (in 1984)
E.C. Kilgore	Associate Administrator, NASA Management Operations, 1980-1981
Robert L. Krieger	Director, Wallops Flight Research Center, 1948–1981
William R. Lucas	Director, Marshall Space Flight Center (in 1984)
Frank B. McDonald	Chief Scientist (in 1984)
John J. Martin	Associate Administrator, Office of Aeronautics and Space Technology (in 1984)
Jesse W. Moore	Associate Administrator, Office of Space Flight (in 1984)
John E. Naugle	Associate Administrator, 1975-1977
C. Thomas Newman	Comptroller (in 1984)
William H. Pickering	Director, Jet Propulsion Laboratory, 1954-1976
Eugene D. Rosen	Director, Office of Small and Disadvantaged Business Utilization (in 1984)
Robert C. Seamans, Jr.	Deputy Administrator, 1965-1968

Willis H. Shapley	Associate Deputy Administrator, 1965-1974
Milton A. Silveira	Chief Engineer (in 1984)
Abe Silverstein	Director, Lewis Research Center, 1961-1969
Richard G. Smith	Director, John F. Kennedy Space Center (in 1984)
Andrew J. Stofan	Director, Lewis Research Center (in 1984)
Ernst Stuhlinger	Associate Director for Science, Marshall Space Flight Center, 1960-1975
C. A. Syvertson	Director, Ames Research Center, 1978-1984
Norman Terrell	Associate Administrator, Office of Policy (in 1984)
Patrick A. Templeton	Associate Administrator, Office of External Relations (in 1984)
Walter C. Williams	Associate Director, Space Task Group, 1959-1962 (NASA Chief Engineer, 1975-1982)

Appendix B

Demographic Tables

The following tables provide statistical summaries of the number of scientists and engineers in NASA (in comparison to other categories of NASA employees from 1958-1970 (table 1), NASA Apollo era engineers' fields of specialization by training (table 2) and NASA occupation (table 3), their ascent through civil service ranks through 1980 (table 4), their educational levels (table 5), their average ages (table 6), the number of years they have worked in NASA, and their ethnic and gender distribution.

Table 1 is drawn from information in the *NASA Historical Data Book, 1958-1968: Vol. I: NASA Resources*, NASA SP-4012 (Washington, D.C.) and "NASA Pocket Statistics" for January 1971 (NASA History Office). Tables 2-8 were prepared from data generated and analyzed in 1985 by the Personnel Analysis and Evaluation Office at NASA Headquarters in Washington, D.C.

Individuals represented by the category "Nominees" are the 446 verified cases of the 621 names submitted by NASA senior managers in 1984 as those persons of "NASA's pioneering generation of aerospace engineers" who most "reflect those characteristics which have typified NASA during its first quarter century" (see Appendix A).

Table 1. NASA Scientists and Engineers (S & Es) and Total NASA Personnel, 1958 – 1970 [a]

	Fiscal Year												
	1958	1959	1960	1961	1962	1963	1964	1965	1966	1967	1968	1969	1970
Total Personnel	7,966	9,235	10,232	17,471	23,686	29,934	32,499	34,049	35,708	35,860	33,641	31,733	31,223
Percent rate increase over previous FY	—	15.9	10.7	70.7	35.5	26.3	8.5	4.7	4.8	0.4	-3.3	-8.3	-1.6
Accessions	375	2,115	1,793	3,634	7,044	8,706	6,316	5,014	5,361	4,742	1,948	1,278	1,070
Separations	226	850	842	1,621	2,153	3,241	3,945	4,079	4,891	4,597	3,458	2,015	1,672
Net accessions	149	1,265	951	2,013	4,891	5,465	2,371	935	470	145	1,510	-737	-602
Annual turnover rate (separations as percent total annual personnel)	2.8	9.2	8.2	9.2	9.0	10.8	12.1	11.9	13.6	12.8	9.9	6.3	5.3
Scientists and engineers [b]	2,648	3,194	3,509	5,765	8,161	10,978	12,427	13,265	14,060	14,455	14,221	13,839	13,837
Percent rate increase S & Es over previous FY	—	20.6	9.8	64.2	41.5	34.5	13.1	6.7	5.9	2.8	-1.6	-2.6	0.0
S & Es as percent total personnel	33.2	34.5	34.2	32.9	34.4	36.6	38.2	38.9	39.3	40.3	41.0	43.6	44.3
Apollo generation S & E accessions still in NASA as of 1980		←——— 2,477 ——→				←——— 5,310 ——→				←——— 2,088 ——→			
Contract employees (estimated)	N/A	N/A	36,500	57,500	115,500	218,400	347,100	376,700	360,000	272,900	211,200	200,000	170,000

a   Permanent civil service employees only. Sources: NASA Historical Data Book, 1958-1968. Vol. I: NASA Resources. NASA SP-4012. Washington, D.C., 1976; NASA Pocket Statistics, Washington, D.C., January, 1971; Personnel Analysis and Evaluation Office, NASA Headquarters, Washington, D.C., May 1986. Until 1976, the fiscal year ended June 30.

b   Includes NASA Occupational Codes 200, 700, and 900: general and aerospace scientists and engineers, and "primarily life sciences."

Table 2. Apollo Generation: Percent of Highest Degree Field, Total Population and Nominees

Field	Group 1 (to 1960)	Group 2 (1961-1965)	Group 3 (1966-1970)	Total/average	Nominees
Electrical engineering	17.0	24.0	22.0	21.0	23.8
Mechanical engineering	22.5	19.0	12.0	17.8	17.9
Aeronautical engineering	16.0	10.0	9.5	10.8	–
Aerospace engineering	–	–	–	–	9.9
Other engineering fields [a]	8.6	13.4	9.1	10.4	12.8
Total engineering	64.1	66.4	52.6	60.0	64.4
Other technical fields [b]	5.9	1.8	0.5	2.7	2.6
Mathematics and science [c]	25.2	24.6	35.5	28.4	18.8
Social sciences [d]	3.9	5.2	6.2	5.1	11.1
Arts, humanities, law, and theology	0.6	0.9	0.7	0.7	0.4
No degree field	2.0	0.5	0.3	0.9	0.0

a   Civil, industrial, chemical, general, nuclear, agricultural, architectural, mineral, biomedical, petroleum, geological, geophysical, environmental, material, metalurgical, ceramic, and textile engineering.

b   Agriculture, naval engineering or architecture, engineering technology, engineering mechanics, statistics, computer sciences, information sciences, systems analysis.

c   Mathematics, physics, chemistry, biology, biochemistry, physiology, zoology, astronomy, geophysics, earth sciences, other science.

d   Education, business management, psychology, social sciences, communications, military science, naval science, interdisciplinary studies, public affairs, health professions.

Source: Personnel Evaluation and Analysis Office, NASA Headquarters, Washington, D.C., June 1985.

Table 3. Apollo Generation: Percent in Occupational Categories, Total Population and Nominees

Occupation	Group 1 (to 1960)	Group 2 (1961-1965)	Group 3 (1966-1970)	Total/average	Nominees
Research and development	–	–	–	–	16.0
Design	–	–	–	–	22.1
Testing and evaluation	–	–	–	–	9.0
Fluid flight mechanics	17.7	9.4	10.3	12.5	–
Flight systems	14.8	19.0	13.5	15.8	–
Piloting	0.3	0.2	0.7	0.4	–
Materials and structures	8.0	4.9	5.9	6.3	–
Propulsion and power	6.0	4.6	4.1	4.9	–
Measurement and instrumentation	10.9	11.0	11.2	11.0	–
Data systems	10.1	10.5	15.4	12.0	–
Data analysis	–	–	–	–	5.0
Facilities and operations	10.0	13.1	12.6	11.9	–
Construction	–	–	–	–	0.5
Operations and maintenance	–	–	–	–	7.7
Total	77.8	72.7	73.7	74.8	60.3
Technical assistance	–	–	–	–	0.5
Technical information	–	–	–	–	0.9
Non-aerospace science and engineering	3.0	3.5	2.0	2.8	–
Unclassified	3.7	3.0	3.3	3.3	–
Total	6.7	6.5	5.3	6.1	1.4
Space science	2.6	2.2	6.5	3.8	–
Life science	0.5	2.7	2.3	1.8	–
Total	3.1	4.9	8.8	5.6	–
Management	11.5	14.3	9.8	11.9	–
Administrative professional	1.0	1.5	1.6	1.4	–
Management	–	–	–	–	36.5
Planning	–	–	–	–	1.1
Regulatory	–	–	–	–	0.2
Total	12.5	13.8	9.4	13.3	37.8

Source: Personnel Evaluation and Analysis Office, NASA Headquarters, Washington, D.C., June 1985. Because of changes in occupational codes between 1960 and 1985, uniform codes for both the total population and the nominee group are unavailable. Table represents a merging of occupational codes.

Table 4. Apollo Generation: Percent Grade Achieved as of 1980, Total Population and Nominees

Grade [a]	Group 1 (to 1960)	Group 2 (1961-1965)	Group 3 (1966-1970)	Total/average	Nominees
GS 7	0.0	0.0	0.1	0.0	–
GS 8	–	–	0.0	0.0	0.2
GS 9	0.2	0.2	0.9	0.4	–
GS 11	1.3	0.9	3.0	1.7	1.4
GS 12	7.0	9.4	26.0	14.1	11.0
GS 13	32.0	47.9	48.4	42.7	29.1
GS 14	30.4	26.5	14.0	23.5	23.0
GS 15	22.2	12.4	5.9	13.5	16.4
GS 16	0.3	–	–	0.3	4.3
GS 17/SES	6.5	2.7	1.6	3.6	14.6

a   GS, government service; SES, Senior executive service.

Source: Personnel Evaluation and Analysis Office, NASA Headquarters, Washington, D.C., June 1985.

Table 5. Apollo Generation: Percent Highest Degree, Total Population and Nominees

Degree	Group 1 (to 1960)	Group 2 (1961-1965)	Group 3 (1966-1970)	Total/average	Nominees
No degree	1.5	0.5	0.4	0.8	0.0
Associate	0.2	0.1	0.3	0.2	0.2
Bachelor	68.0	68.0	60.0	65.3	69.0
Masters	23.0	25.0	27.0	25.0	26.5
Doctorate	7.0	7.0	14.0	9.3	4.3

442 valid cases out of 621 nominees. Source: Personnel Evaluation and Analysis Office, NASA Headquarters, Washington, D.C., June 1985.

Table 6. Apollo Generation: Average Age in 1980, Total Population and Nominees

Age (years)	Group 1 (to 1960)	Group 2 (1961-1965)	Group 3 (1966-1970)	Total/average	Nominees
25 – 29	–	–	0.2	0.2	–
30 – 34	–	0.3	11.8	4.0	0.6
35 – 39	0.1	9.8	31.5	13.8	7.7
40 – 44	10.8	27.7	23.2	20.6	17.2
45 – 49	28.9	28.3	14.8	24.0	28.0
50 – 54	27.8	17.8	8.6	18.1	22.9
55 – 59	24.7	11.3	6.5	14.2	17.1
60 – 64	6.5	4.0	2.8	4.4	5.4
65 – 69	1.1	0.7	0.5	0.8	} 0.6
70 +	0.2	0.0	0.0	0.1	

Source: Personnel Evaluation and Analysis Office, NASA Headquarters, Washington, D.C., June 1985.

446 valid cases out of 621 nominees.

Table 7. Average Years of NASA Service in 1984 for Apollo Generation: Total Population [a] and Nominees

	Average [b] years	Standard Deviation	No.	%	% (Nominees)
			Total Population		Nominees
20+ years	21.0	0.9	2477	25	28.3
15 - 19 years	17.2	1.2	5310	54	57.4
10 - 14 years	12.8	1.3	2088	21	14.3

a   Total cases = 9875.

b   Mean average.

Table 8. Ethnic and Gender Distribution, Total Population and Nominees

	Total population [a]			Nominees [b]	Total (%)
	Group 1	Group 2	Group 3		
Male	97.0	98.0	96.0	96.2	97.0
Female	3.0	2.0	4.0	3.8	3.0
American Indian	0.1	0.2	0.1	0.7	0.3
Asian	1.0	1.0	1.0	0.9	1.0
Black	1.5	1.5	3.0	4.5	2.0
Hispanic	0.4	1.0	1.0	3.8	0.8
White	97.0	96.0	95.0	90.1	96.0

a   Group 1 = 20+ years; arrived NASA up to 1960.
     Group 2 = 15 - 19 years; arrived NASA 1961 - 1964.
     Group 3 = 10 - 14 years; arrived NASA 1965 - 1970.

b   446 valid cases out of 621 nominees.

Source: Personnel Analysis and Evaluation Division, NASA Headquarters, Washington, D.C., June 1985.

Appendix C

Education and Military Service of NASA Apollo Era Engineers Interviewed

Institution and Highest Degree	Year entered NACA/NASA	Military service
Massachusetts Institute of Technology (BSAE)	1938	No
Stanford University (MSE)	1944	No
University of California, Berkeley (BSME)	1945	Yes (USN)
University of Montana (BSCE)	1948	No
Ohio State University (BSEd)	1948	No
Cornell University (MSE)	1949	Yes (USAAF)
Techniche Hochshule Berlin (Ph.D.)	1952	Yes (German Army)
University of Virginia (MAE)	1952	Yes (USA)
Virginia Polytechnic Institute and State University (BS)	1953	?

Institution and Highest Degree	Year entered NACA/NASA	Military service
Purdue University (Ph.D.)	1953	No
Case Western Reserve University (Ph.D.)	1957	No
University of Kansas (MSAE)	1957	Yes (USA)
Stanford University (MSE)	1958	Yes (USAF)
Parks College (BS)	1958	Yes (USAF)
University of Alabama in Huntsville (MBA)	1958	Yes (USA)
Florida State University (MBA)	1958	Yes (USA)
University of Rochester (MME)	1959	Yes (USN)
California Institute of Technology (Ph.D)	1959	(Peace Corps)
University of Alabama (BSE)	1960	No
Cornell University (MSPhyCh)	1960	Yes (USA)
University of Alabama (MSEd)	1960	Yes (USAF)
City College of New York (BSME)	1961	Yes (USA)
Auburn University (Ph.D., Management)	1961	No
Auburn University (BSCE)	1962	Yes (USAF)
University of Illinois at Urbana-Champaign (BSCE)	1962	Yes (USA)
Massachusetts Institute of Technology (BSE)	1962	Yes (USN)
Prairie View A&M University (BSE)	1962	No

Institution and Highest Degree	Year entered NACA/NASA	Military service
College of William and Mary (MSPhys)	1962	No
University of Texas at El Paso (BSEE)	1963	Yes (USA)
Emory University (BA, Mathematics)	1963	No
University of Florida (BSE)	1964	Yes (USN)
University of Naples (Ph.D)	1964	Yes (Italian Army)
North Carolina State University (MA, Mathematics)	1964	No
Stanford University (Ph.D)	1964	No
The Johns Hopkins University (BSE)	1964	Yes (USA)
University of Michigan (MSAE)	1965	Yes (USN)
Clemson University (BSME)	1966	No
University of Virginia (MSEPhys)	1966	No
St. Joseph's College (BS)	1966	Yes (USAF)
Catholic University of America (BS)	1966	No
Louisiana State University (MSME)	1967	Yes (USAF)
George Washington University (Ph.D)	1967	No
Cleveland State University (BSEE)	1967	No
University of Houston (Ph.D)	1968	No
Notre Dame College (BSAE)	1968	No

Institution and Highest Degree	Year entered NACA/NASA	Military service
Texas Women's University (BS, Mathematics)	1968	No
New York University (BSAE)	1968	Yes (USA)
Stanford University (Ph.D)	1969	Yes (USA)
Brooklyn College, City University of New York (MSE)	1970	Yes (USN)
Case Western Reserve University (MAE)	1972	Yes (USN)
Rice University (BSE)	1972	No

Index

NASA History Publications

REFERENCE WORKS, NASA SP-4000:

Grimwood, James M. *Project Mercury: A Chronology,* (NASA SP-4001, 1963)

Grimwood, James M., and Hacker, Barton C., with Vorzimmer, Peter J. *Project Gemini Technology and Operations: A Chronology.* (NASA SP-4002, 1969)

Link, Mae Mills. *Space Medicine in Project Mercury.* (NASA SP-4003, 1965)

Astronautics and Aeronautics: A Chronology of Science, Technology and Policy. (NASA SP-4004 to SP-4025, a series of annual volumes continuing from 1961 to 1985, with an earlier summary volume, *Aeronautics and Astronautics, 1915–1960.*

Ertel, Ivan D., and Morse, Mary Louise. *The Apollo Spacecraft: A Chronology, Volume I, Through November 7, 1962.* (NASA SP-4009, 1969).

Morse, Mary Louise, and Bays, Jean Kernahan. *The Apollo Spacecraft: A Chronology, Volume II, November 8, 1962–September 30, 1964.* (NASA SP-4009, 1973).

Brooks, Courtney G., and Ertel, Ivan D. *The Apollo Spacecraft: A Chronology, Volume III, October 1, 1964–January 20, 1966.* (NASA SP-4009, 1973)

Van Nimmen, Jane, and Bruno, Leonard C., with Rosholt, Robert L. *NASA Historical Data Book, Vol. I: NASA Resources, 1958–1968.* (NASA SP-4102, 1976, rep. ed. 1988).

Newkirk, Roland W., and Ertel, Ivan D., with Brooks, Courtney G. *Skylab: A Chronology.* (NASA SP-4011, 1977).

Ertel, Ivan D., and Newkirk, Roland W., with Brooks, Courtney G. *The Apollo Spacecraft: A Chronology, Volume IV, January 21, 1966–July 13, 1974.* (NASA SP-4009, 1978).

Ezell, Linda Neuman. *NASA Historical Data Book, Vol. II: Programs and Projects, 1958–1968.* (NASA SP-4012, 1988).

Ezell, Linda Neuman. *NASA Historical Data Book, Vol. III: Programs and Projects, 1969–1978.* (NASA SP-4012, 1988).

MANAGEMENT HISTORIES, NASA SP-4100:

Rosholt, Robert L. *An Administrative History of NASA, 1958–1963.* (NASA SP-4101, 1966).

Levine, Arnold S. *Managing NASA in the Apollo Era.* (NASA SP-4102, 1982).

Roland, Alex. *Model Research: The National Advisory Committee for Aeronautics, 1915–1958.* (NASA SP-4103, 1985).

PROJECT HISTORIES, NASA SP-4200:

Manned Space Programs:

Swenson, Loyd S., Jr., Grimwood, James M., and Alexander, Charles C. *This New Ocean: A History of Project Mercury.* (NASA SP-4201, 1966).

Hacker, Barton C., and Grimwood, James M. *On Shoulders of Titans: A History of Project Gemini.* (NASA SP-4203, 1977).

Benson, Charles D., and Faherty, William Barnaby. *Moonport: A History of Apollo Launch Facilities and Operations.* (NASA SP-4204, 1978).

Ezell, Edward Clinton, and Ezell, Linda Neuman. *The Partnership: A History of Apollo-Soyuz Test Project.* (NASA SP-4209, 1978).

Brooks, Courtney G., Grimwood, James M., and Swenson, Loyd S., Jr. *Chariots for Apollo: A History of Manned Lunar Spacecraft.* (NASA SP-4205, 1979).

Bilstein, Roger E. *Stages to Saturn: A Technological History of the Apollo/Saturn Launch Vehicles.* (NASA SP-4206, 1980).

Compton, W. David, and Benson, Charles D. *Living and Working in Space: A History of Skylab.* (NASA SP-4208, 1983).

Compton, W. David. *Where No Man Has Gone Before: A History of Apollo Lunar Exploration Missions.* (NASA SP-4214, 1989).

Unmanned Space Programs:

Green, Constance McL., and Lomask, Milton. *Vanguard: A History.* (NASA SP-4202, 1970; rep. ed. Smithsonian Institution Press, 1971).

Hall, R. Cargill. *Lunar Impact: A History of Project Ranger.* (NASA SP-4210, 1977).

Ezell, Edward Clinton, and Ezell, Linda Neuman. *On Mars: Exploration of the Red Planet, 1958–1978.* (NASA SP-4212, 1984).

Scientific Programs:

Newell, Homer E. *Beyond the Atmosphere: Early Years of Space Science.* (NASA SP-4211, 1980).

Pitts, John A. *The Human Factor: Biomedicine in the Manned Space Program to 1980.* (NASA SP-4213, 1985).

Naugle, John E. *First Among Equals: The Selection of NASA Space Science Experiments* (NASA SP-4215, 1991).

CENTER HISTORIES, NASA SP-4300:

Hartman, Edwin, P. *Adventures in Research: A History of Ames Research Center, 1940–1965.* (NASA SP-4302, 1970).

Hallion, Richard P. *On the Frontier: Flight Research at Dryden, 1946–1981.* (NASA SP-4303, 1984).

Muenger, Elizabeth A. *Searching the Horizon: A History of Ames Research Center, 1940–1976.* (NASA SP-4304, 1985).

Rosenthal, Alfred. *Venture into Space: Early Years of Goddard Space Flight Center.* (NASA SP-4301, 1985).

Hansen, James R. *Engineer in Charge: A History of the Langley Aeronautical Laboratory, 1917–1958.* (NASA SP-4305, 1987).

Dawson, Virginia P. *Engines and Innovation: Lewis Laboratory and American Propulsion Technology.* (NASA SP-4306, 1991).

GENERAL HISTORIES, NASA SP-4400:

Corliss, William R. *NASA Sounding Rockets, 1958–1968: A Historical Summary.* (NASA SP-4401, 1971).

Wells, Helen T., Whiteley, Susan H., and Karegeannes, Carrie. *Origins of NASA Names.* (NASA SP-4402, 1976).

Anderson, Frank W., Jr., *Orders of Magnitude: A History of NACA and NASA, 1915–1980.* (NASA SP-4403, 1981).

Sloop, John L. *Liquid Hydrogen as a Propulsion Fuel, 1945–1959.* (NASA SP-4404, 1978).

Roland, Alex. *A Spacefaring People: Perspectives on Early Spaceflight.* (NASA SP-4405, 1985).

Bilstein, Roger E. *Orders of Magnitude: A History of the NACA and NASA, 1915–1990.* (NASA SP-4406, 1989).

NEW SERIES IN NASA HISTORY, PUBLISHED BY THE JOHNS HOPKINS UNIVERSITY PRESS:

Cooper, Henry S. F., Jr. *Before Lift-Off: The Making of a Space Shuttle Crew.* (1987).

McCurdy, Howard E. *The Space Station Decision: Incremental Politics and Technological Choice.* (1990).

Hufbauer, Karl. *Exploring the Sun: Solar Science Since Galileo.* (1991).

Sylvia Doughty Fries

Sylvia Doughty Fries is Director of the Office of Special Studies in the Office of the Administrator of the National Aeronautics and Space Administration (NASA). The Office of Special Studies provides executive staff and research support to the NASA Advisory Council, NASA's most senior continuous external advisory body. She had been a member of the NASA Advisory Council from 1981–1983, when she came to NASA to direct the history program, which has been in continuous existence since the agency was first established. From 1983 to 1990 Dr. Fries was NASA's Chief Historian and director of the History Division.

A native of Germany, Dr. Fries was raised and educated in Washington D.C. She received her bachelor's degree in English from Hollins College and her doctorate in the history of ideas from The Johns Hopkins University in 1969. She then pursued an academic career, teaching European and American cultural history at Vassar College, Southern Methodist University, and the University of Maine at Brono.

Meanwhile the focus of her research and writing evolved from 18th century ideas of urban life to the ideological origins of federal science and technology policy during the late 1960s. It was the later interest which led to her involvement with NASA, which began in 1978 when she was asked to serve on the NASA History Advisory Committee, a standing committee of the NASA Advisory Council. Her publications include *The Urban Idea in Colonial America* (1977) and "2001 to 1994: Political Environment and the Design of NASA's Space Station Systems," *Technology and Culture* (July 1988), winner of the James Madison Prize of the Society for History in the Federal Government. Dr. Fries has prepared numerous historical background papers for the agency's management.